Bristol
Aircraft

since 1910

This Blenheim IV, painted as *V6026* of No. 105 Squadron, was rebuilt from a derelict Bolingbroke airframe recovered from a field near Winnepeg. Reconstructed over 12 years by a team at the British Aerial Museum at Duxford near Cambridge, it flew again on 23 May 1987 but was damaged beyond repair a month later during an air display at Denham on 21 June.

The same team has since been working to restore another ex-*RCAF* Blenheim to flying condition. This aircraft came from the Strathallan Collection in Scotland. Further details of these rebuilds are given on page 280. (*Courtesy British Aerial Museum of Flying Military Aircraft*)

Bristol
Aircraft

since 1910

C H Barnes

PUTNAM

BY THE SAME AUTHOR
Shorts Aircraft since 1900
Handley Page Aircraft since 1907

ISBN 0 85177 823 2
Copyright © C. H. Barnes 1964
Printed in Great Britain for
Putnam, an imprint of
Conway Maritime Press Ltd,
24 Bride Lane, Fleet Street,
London EC4Y 8DR
by Richard Clay Ltd, Chichester
First published 1964
Second edition 1970
Third edition 1988

IN MEMORIAM
SIR G. STANLEY WHITE, Bt.

Founding Director, February 1910
Managing Director, 1911–1955
Deputy Chairman, 1955–1964

whose wise counsels guided his Company
throughout the events recorded in this book.

" There be of them that have left a name behind them ".

ECCLESIASTICUS XLIV, 8.

Contents

Acknowledgements

The author acknowledges with gratitude the very generous contributions, advice and encouragement given by his colleagues throughout the Company; particularly he thanks the Chairman and Directors of the Bristol Aeroplane Company Ltd. for so readily granting him permission to prepare this work for publication and allowing him unrestricted access to the Company's voluminous photographic and documentary archives. The original draft was begun in 1946, with the approval of the late Herbert J. Thomas, who made many valuable comments on the history of the first ten years. Others no longer with us who contributed first-hand reminiscences included the brothers Frank and Arthur Coles, George Clephane and Gilbert Williams, while among those now living in retirement who have helped are Charles Briginshaw, Arnold Clinton, Frank Davey, Sir Roy Fedden, Jack Gommo, Reg Hearder, Cy Holmes, Ernie Knight, Fred Mayer, Bill Morgan, Harold Soloman and Clifford Tinson. Of those still with the Company, special thanks are due to Cyril F. Uwins, O.B.E., A.F.C., Chief Test Pilot for thirty years and later Deputy Chairman, who has read and approved the present text, which he has enriched by many detailed accounts of events not otherwise on record. For advice on commercial aspects the author is very grateful to A. W. Barr, C. S. Cowles and W. Slatter. Over the past twenty years nearly everybody in the firm with any material to contribute has either given it gladly or been browbeaten by the author into doing so; it is impossible to name all who have helped and invidious to attempt any further selection from among so many. Their contributions could not, however, have been welded into a balanced and coherent whole without the good offices of various members of the Contracts, Sales and Service, Flight Test, Full-scale Layout, Secretarial, Public Relations, Printing and Photographic Departments.

Outside the Company, the author owes much to the editors and staffs of *Flight*, *The Aeroplane* and *Air Pictorial*, and the librarians and staffs of the Royal Aeronautical Society, the Royal Aero Club, the Science Museum, the Imperial War Museum and the Royal Aircraft Establishment. Assistance has been generously given from time to time by Bristol-Siddeley Engines Ltd., Canadair Ltd., D. Napier and Sons Ltd., Rolls-Royce Ltd., Vickers-Armstrongs (Aircraft) Ltd. and Westland Aircraft Ltd.; by B.O.A.C. and El Al Israel Airlines and by many serving and former members of the Royal Navy and Royal Air Force. Special thanks are due, too, for the valuable help received over many years from C. F. Andrews, L. L. Bridgman, P. W. Brooks, J. M. Bruce, C. W. Cain, H. F. Cowley, C. H. Gibbs-Smith, A. J. Jackson, Hans Kofoed, L. E. Opdycke, E. A. Ritaranta, F. G. Swanborough, J. W. R. Taylor and G. Wansbrough-White, all of whom share the author's enthusiasm for elucidating aeronautical history.

Finally there are those 'but for whom . . .': the author's wife, who unfailingly supplied criticism, consolation and coffee, as required; his colleagues Ellen Summers, John Jupe and Ken Winkley, whose excellent drawings enhance the text; and Jacqueline Welch, who undertook the burden of typing out the manuscript; in this connection must also be remembered Miss M. G. I. Morgan, who performed a similar service in 1948 for the unpublished Company History.

C. H. B.

Kendleshire, Bristol.
May, 1964.

Note to Third Edition. This edition incorporates minor changes, corrections and additions to update the second edition of Chris Barnes' classic book. They cover the Bristol aircraft which remained in service after 1970 and references to rebuilds of old aircraft and the construction of replicas.

J. R. C.

Repton, Derby.
April, 1988.

For assistance in updating this work thanks are due to: Paul Elkin, Bristol City Museum; John Romain, British Aerial Museum, Duxford; Howard Berry, Ellis Johns, George Lambe, Duncan Greenman, Sir Robert Wall, all present or past members of British Aerospace; Michael Rule, Instone Air Line; Kenneth Munson; Jim Oughton, formerly Bristol Aeroplane Co; Ray Funnell and Andrew Cormack, RAF Museum; John Heaven, Martin Brodie, Ernie Brook, Tom Frost, Ken Skuse, Rolls-Royce; Librarian, Royal Aeronautical Society; and Tim Moore, Skysport Engineering.

History of the Company

FORMATION OF THE COMPANY

No magic is claimed for the famous name of Bristol, nor indeed has the Board of Trade ever allowed it to be registered as a trade mark. It was probably with such registration in mind that Sir George White formed, on 19 February 1910, not one but four companies:—

The Bristol Aeroplane Company Limited;

The Bristol Aviation Company Limited;

The British and Colonial Aeroplane Company Limited; and

The British and Colonial Aviation Company Limited.

Well versed in company law, he regarded the making of aeroplanes as one object and the flying of them as quite another. He also recognised that premature adoption of the name 'Bristol' in a company's title might well prejudice a later application for its registration as a trade mark. So he chose to begin trading with the third of the four new companies, the others being provided with only a nominal capital of £100 each. The British and Colonial Aeroplane Company, however, began operations with no less than £25,000; all the money was subscribed by Sir George White, his brother Samuel and his son G. Stanley White, so that all the risks were taken by the family alone; indeed it would have been useless to appeal for public subscriptions, for, although the local press welcomed the new enterprise, Sir George's colleagues on Bristol Stock Exchange quite frankly called him mad. Sir George, his brother and his son were named as Directors, with himself as Chairman. At their first meeting, at the registered office at Clare Street, Bristol, on 28 February, Sir George's nephews Henry White Smith and Sydney Smith were appointed Secretary and Manager of the new Company; Émile Stern was appointed the Company's agent in Paris, and an agreement licensing the Company to manufacture aeroplanes designed by the Société Zodiac was formally signed.

Factory premises were made available by leasing from the Bristol Tramways Company their omnibus depot and repair shop, comprising two iron sheds, at their northern terminus at Filton, some four miles from the city centre. Filton House, in private occupation until August 1911, was then acquired by the Tramways Company and merged with the factory and leased to the Aeroplane Company as general offices. The two sheds which comprised the whole original factory were still in use sixty years later as part of the main machine shop, and can be seen near the right-hand edge of the illustration on p. 44.

Sydney Smith, accompanied by Sir George's youngest nephew Herbert J. Thomas, went to Paris to examine the designs and methods of the Société Zodiac, and arranged for a Zodiac biplane to be exhibited at the Olympia Aero Show in March. This was received at Filton by the newly appointed Engineer and Works Manager George H. Challenger (son of the General Manager of the Tramways Company) and his assistant Collyns Pizey (a former Tramways apprentice later in charge at the generating station at the Counterslip, Bristol). It had been hoped also to obtain a Zodiac monoplane for the Show, but this was never sent from Paris.

After the Show the Zodiac was sent to Brooklands, where the Company had leased a shed on the flying ground. Unfortunately it refused to leave the ground, and Edmond, the French pilot engaged to fly it, recommended its abandonment in favour of an improved version of the Henri Farman type. Five more Zodiacs had already been started at Filton, but the Directors took the decision to discard them as part of the price to be paid for experience. Nevertheless, they claimed damages against the Société Zodiac for failing to make good their warranty to fly, and the licence was cancelled on payment by Zodiac of 15,000 francs in compensation. Prior to this, however, the Zodiac trade mark had been adopted as that of the British and Colonial Company and for a time appeared on the Company's letterhead.

About this time the French 50 h.p. Gnome engine had just become available for export, and Émile Stern secured one of the first for installation in Challenger's Farman-type biplane, also the Company's sole agency in the British Empire for the Gnome engine. Although the Farman brothers complained that the Company had infringed their patents, no court action was taken; no doubt they recognised that the success of the Bristol biplane could do nothing but enhance their own reputation, and they always remained most friendly with the Directors.

There was plenty of confidence in the new biplane, and one was offered to Capt. R. F. Scott for his Antarctic Expedition; Scott wisely declined, for no aeroplane was at that time anywhere near reliable enough for such a task. In the same imaginative spirit Sir George White wrote to Mr. Haldane, Secretary of State for War, offering to place the Company's entire resources at the disposal of the War Office and to abstain from all business with foreign powers. The Minister declined the offer and preferred the Company to develop business abroad without restriction; nevertheless, the War Office agreed to lease to the Company a site and flying rights over 2,284 acres of land at Larkhill on Salisbury Plain, where in June the Company erected three iron sheds.

The Directors realised that sound manufacture was not enough and prospective purchasers of aeroplanes would need to be taught to fly. The Brooklands and Larkhill sheds were ideal nuclei for flying schools, and from Larkhill on 30 July 1910 Edmond flew the Boxkite for the first time. The use of Larkhill as a flying school was opposed because of alleged loss of amenities at Stonehenge, and an undertaking was given to site buildings so as not to obscure the rising sun on Midsummer Day. As more hangars came to be built they were arranged in two groups, the space between, 'Sun Gap', often proving invaluable to a pupil compelled to land while approaching the sheds. Although Brooklands attracted many pupils from London, Larkhill had some advantage in being near Bulford and Tidworth camps, thus bringing aviation to the notice of the War Office from within the Army, for subalterns and senior officers alike quickly took an interest in the new activity overhead.

Only two Army officers, Lts. J. W. Dunne and Lancelot D. L. Gibbs, had so far been officially authorised to take part in flying trials (at Blair Atholl), and when these were abandoned Gibbs had been permitted to continue at his own expense, which he did at Châlons, where he met Capt. Bertram Dickson, on furlough from arduous consular service in Persia. Dickson took to flying like a duck to water and was soon challenging the French premier pilots over their own flying grounds. At the Bournemouth meeting in July he carried off many first prizes on his Farman and also met Sir George White, whose views on building up British aviation were the same as his own. When the War

Pioneers in conference:

Sir George White and
Col. S. F. Cody at
Larkhill in August 1912.

Office, forced at last by public opinion to take official notice of aviation, invited four pilots, including Dickson, to co-operate in the Autumn Manœuvres, he chose a Bristol biplane, his example being by followed Lt. Robert Loraine (later to become famous as an actor-manager). Their exploits were vividly reported by the late Harry Harper, but the occasion also marked the first use in this country (though just antedated by McCurdy in America) of air to ground radio communication, using a spark and coherer apparatus designed by T. Thorne Baker of Cricklewood.

After this demonstration of the value of aerial reconnaissance, the War Office grudgingly extended permission for officers to fly, and Lt. H. M. Maitland and Capt. H. F. Wood enrolled on 21 September as the first pupils of the 'Bristol' school at Brooklands, where Archibald R. Low was manager. The first pupil to gain a Royal Aero Club certificate at Brooklands was Bristol-born Leslie Macdonald on 12 November, who received no. 28. Low and Sydney Smith quickly followed with certificates nos. 33 and 34, and Capt. Wood gained no. 37, while at Larkhill Edmond's first pupil to qualify was Joseph Hammond, a New Zealander, who received certificate no. 32. Meanwhile Dickson, fulfilling a long-standing engagement to fly at Milan, was all but fatally injured in the first recorded mid-air collision, from which he made a miraculous but never complete recovery, to become the Company's technical adviser and London and Continental representative in January 1911. For two more years he contributed much to the Company's success, although not as a pilot, but his health began to fail in the summer of 1913 and he died in Scotland on 28 September.

Pioneers in the field: Edmond in Boxkite No. 8 at Lanark in August 1910, with (l. to r.) Crisp, Frank Coles, Leslie Macdonald, Collyns Pizey, G. H. Challenger, Bendall and Briginshaw.

By November 1910, Boxkites were being built at Filton at the rate of two a week, and two well-known French pilots, Henri Jullerot and Maurice Tétard, had been engaged to test them. On 14 November a spectacular public demonstration was given from a temporary tent hangar on Durdham Down, Bristol, whence Tétard took Stanley White and other privileged passengers over Clifton and the Suspension Bridge. This was a rehearsal for more ambitious demonstrations overseas, and in December two missions, each with two biplanes, were dispatched to India and Australia, respectively, the former in charge of Farnall Thurstan, with Jullerot as pilot, and the latter in charge of Sydney Smith, with Hammond and Macdonald as pilots. These missions aroused the greatest interest, although few sales resulted, their outstanding achievement being the introduction to flying of Capt. Sefton Brancker, who was to become such a dynamic figure in both military and civil aviation.

On 15 November Henry White Smith reported to his Directors that Émile Stern had successfully negotiated the sale to the Russian Government of eight Boxkites, but this news was not made public until four months later.

By the end of 1910 seven pupils had earned their brevets at the Bristol

16

schools, including Herbert Thomas, aged only 18, the youngest qualified aviator in the country. Sixteen biplanes had been built, and by using the prime 10% of the Tramways Company's timber stocks, leaving the remainder for the coachbuilders, they could incorporate the finest materials and still be sold for £1,100 apiece, of which the Gnome engine accounted for £600. Such excellent value earned a special tribute from the Belgian aviator Christiaens, who chose two Boxkites in preference to Farmans for a tour of Malaya and South Africa. He later sold one to John Weston of Pretoria, who, being already a qualified balloonist, became the first holder of both the aeronaut's and aviator's certificates of the Royal Aero Club.

In spite of Christiaens' approval, however, the War Office ordered its first two aeroplanes from Henri Farman and Louis Paulhan, and it was not until 14 March 1911, after the Russian contract had been made public, that Mr. Haldane announced the purchase of four Boxkites, the first British aeroplanes for the Army Air Battalion. Late in 1910, Capt. H. F. Wood had demonstrated a Boxkite at the Royal Aero Club's ground at Eastchurch in the hope of starting a third Bristol school adjacent to Chatham and Sheerness, but the Admiralty accepted an offer by George Cockburn to instruct Naval officers at Eastchurch, using biplanes supplied by Short Brothers.

Eastchurch in January 1911 suffered the loss of Cecil Grace in his attempt to win the de Forest Prize; bad weather also caused the discomfiture of several other competitors, including the popular hero Claude Grahame-White, who quickly disposed, in minor crashes, of two Boxkites lent to him for the attempt. In spite of these misfortunes the Company's progress continued, and on 18 January 1911 Stanley White was appointed Managing Director and the

Henri Jullerot and Stanley White at Durdham Down, 14 November 1910.

17

Larkhill Flying School photographed from a Boxkite by Stanley White in 1911.

Company's capital was increased to £50,000. The Filton factory by then employed 80 men and had been enlarged to provide floor space to allow five aircraft at a time to be laid down.

Both Brooklands and Larkhill attracted many pupils, and Maurice Tabuteau, who had recently flown across the Pyrenees and had gone on to win the Coupe Michelin de France, was engaged, together with Versepuy and Robert Grandseigne, to augment the flying staff. A few weeks later Douglas Graham Gilmour joined the Company as demonstration pilot, having already been lent a Boxkite in which to install a borrowed E.N.V. engine to compete for the British Michelin Cup of 1910, won that year by S. F. Cody. Gilmour was the most daring and skilful British pilot of the day, and his manœuvres were the envy and delight of the whole Brooklands fraternity, but his disregard for petty restrictions later brought him into conflict with the law and at the end of 1911 the Directors terminated his agreement; a few weeks later he fell victim to the structural failure of a monoplane, in which he was killed during one of his least ostentatious flights. Nevertheless, during his short career with the Company, he clearly showed what a Bristol Boxkite could achieve when used regularly as a cross-country vehicle.

Though successful, the Boxkite was soon eclipsed by faster, lighter and handier monoplanes of equal power, and the Directors were fully aware of the advantages of speed both in transport and in warfare. To investigate the possibility of alternative designs, Challenger and Pizey were charged with forming an experimental department, and their first step was to learn to fly at Larkhill, under Tétard's instruction. Pizey showed such aptitude that he remained as an instructor and took charge of the Larkhill school when Tétard returned to France. Meanwhile Low's ability as a mathematician had been recognised and he joined Challenger at Filton in place of Pizey; at the same time Gabriel Voisin was retained as technical consultant, and Grandseigne also collaborated. A monoplane and a small biplane were designed and built at Filton and shown at the 1911 Olympia Aero Show, but no real progress was made until Pierre Prier, an outstanding Blériot pilot and engineer, came to Filton in the spring of 1911 to design a fast monoplane for entry in the Gordon Bennett Cup Race. From this single-seater sprang a family of two-seaters which were built and sold abroad in numbers until they were superseded by the Coanda monoplanes of 1912. Both Capt. Dickson and Farnall Thurstan helped to improve the Prier monoplanes, by arranging demonstrations for overseas customers and suggesting new features to meet customers' special problems and preferences.

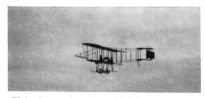 

Flying instruction, 1911: (l.) Solo on a Boxkite at Brooklands; (r.) Dual on a Prier monoplane at Larkhill.

The Bristol flying schools, using Boxkites for primary instruction and Prier monoplanes for advanced work, had been so successful during 1911 that on 30 December the Company's capital was again doubled, to £100,000, to cope with the demand for new aeroplanes. In October 1911 the Directors had written to both the War Office and the Admiralty offering to undertake and complete within six months the tuition of 250 army officers and 250 naval officers at specially low and advantageous rates; both services had declined the offer but the War Office granted the meagre sum of £75 to volunteers suitable for posting to the Army Air Battalion, to be paid after they had gained their Royal Aero Club certificates at their own expense. Even without official support, the Bristol schools had trained 53 out of the 109 pilots who qualified in Britain in 1911, five times as many as the output of the next most successful schools, those of Grahame-White and Hewlett & Blondeau at Hendon.

Greater interest in aviation meant that more attention was being paid to it in the older-established branches of engineering, and late in 1910 Vickers Sons and Maxim Limited had acquired a licence to manufacture Esnault-Pelterie monoplanes and had appointed Capt. H. F. Wood as their aviation manager. He immediately set about recruiting technical staff, among them George Challenger, Archibald Low and Leslie Macdonald. Tétard and Versepuy had decided to return to France when their original contracts expired, and were followed later in 1911 by Tabuteau and Prier, so there were several vacancies at Filton for both pilots and designers by the end of the year.

Collyns Pizey on T-type biplane in Circuit of Britain Race, July 1911.

They were quickly filled, the new pilots including James Valentine, Harry Busteed, Eric Gordon England, Howard Pixton and H. R. Fleming. Of these, Gordon England showed aptitude as a designer, and was allowed his head.

Meanwhile, Sir George White, always with a keen eye for talent, had been impressed by a highly original design by a Rumanian engineer, Henri Coanda; this aeroplane employed a ducted fan instead of an airscrew and had many other ingenious features. Coanda was invited to Filton, and in January 1912 was appointed 'chef technique' to develop and improve the Prier monoplanes which had been so successful. He worked independently of Gordon England, who was engaged on biplane design, and neither Coanda nor England had any contact with a third highly secret design office, set up in December 1911, whose sole staff at first consisted of Frank Barnwell, a marine engineer trained on Clydeside, and his assistant Clifford Tinson. Their duties were to collaborate with Lt. Charles Burney, R.N., in the development of his ideas for sea-going naval aircraft of original design, for which patents were taken out jointly by Burney and the Company.

Introduction

Like most successful enterprises, the Bristol Aeroplane Company grew from small beginnings. It was not the first to manufacture aeroplanes in Britain, being antedated by both Short Brothers and Handley Page Limited, but was distinguished by the very ample financial and commercial footing on which it was placed at its inception by its founder and first Chairman, Sir George White, Bt., the millionaire Bristol-born pioneer of electric tramways. While other firms began as syndicates of sportsmen and engineers, having a common interest in flying but little idea of business organisation, and were often on the verge of bankruptcy, Sir George formed his company with the express intention of developing reliable aeroplanes capable of useful and profitable operation in both peace and war.

The manner in which he announced the enterprise, and the consternation he caused among his less imaginative business colleagues, have been well described by John Pudney in *Bristol Fashion*, which admirably conveys the atmosphere of that heroic age in which the first 'Bristol' aeroplanes began flying. It is the purpose of this book to record the design philosophy, manufacture, performance and achievements of the multitude of Bristol aeroplanes which have spanned the half-century since then. Indeed a book of this size cannot contain more than the bare facts of the record, even if the manufacture of aeroplanes were the whole of the story. But although aeroplanes have been the continuing product, they have not always been the only one or even the most important one; nor has manufacture been the Company's sole activity.

From the first year of its existence the Company set up flying schools at Brooklands and Larkhill which provided a standard of tuition unmatched between 1910 and 1914. In 1923 the Bristol flying school was restarted at Filton to train R.A.F. Reserve pilots, and this developed into management by the Company of both Elementary and Instructors' Flying Training Schools, which remained active until 1953. Experimental work also began at an early date, and one of the most interesting projects of those days was the collaboration between the Company and Lt. Charles Burney, R.N., whose novel ideas on sea-going naval aircraft led to a series of hydrofoil experiments. Even more imaginative was Burney's proposal for an aerial torpedo to be fired from large-calibre smooth-bore naval guns, and a great deal of pioneer work was done by the Company on this project also.

During the 1914–1918 War the Company's output was enormously expanded, and when hostilities ceased the Directors courageously decided to diversify the products, while continuing aircraft development; they undertook a large and successful coach-building programme for both Bristol Tramways and Armstrong Siddeley Motors, also the design of a small light car and a 'skimmer' or air-propelled hydroplane vessel for use in shallow water. These tentative ventures were abandoned when in 1920 the Company took over the defunct Cosmos Engineering Company, whose technical director, Roy Fedden, had designed and begun manufacturing the air-cooled radial Jupiter and Lucifer aero-engines. From that point the Bristol Aero-Engine Department became the major production unit in the Company, winning world markets first from the Napier Lion and then from the Armstrong-Siddeley Jaguar, finally in 1959 to merge with its former rival, Armstrong Siddeley Motors Ltd., to become Bristol Siddeley Engines Limited, which itself in 1968 became the Bristol Engine Division of Rolls-Royce Limited.

Another of the Company's activities was the Armament Department, formed in 1935, from which, when war ended in 1945, emerged two further products—motor cars and plastics. Then there were prefabricated houses, developing into the export of complete schools, churches and hospitals; but the stories of all these enterprises would fill several volumes of this size, so this book must be about Bristol aircraft only, for space will permit no more.

Anglo-French co-operation at Filton began with the Zodiac biplane in March 1910; sixty years later this same building still contributed its quota of numerically-controlled machined parts to the Anglo-French Concorde assembly lines.

Filton Works in October 1910.

George Dacre, Frank Barnwell and Lt. C. D. Burney with X.2 at Filton, 1912.

Coanda remained in charge of general design policy until he returned to Rumania in October 1914 and took over biplane design after Gordon England resigned in the spring of 1913. Barnwell concentrated solely on Burney's projects until the end of 1913, when he and Busteed collaborated in the creation of the first Bristol Scout—a classic design which marked him as one of the world's foremost aeronautical engineers and set the pattern for the long line of Bristol prototypes which stemmed from his drawing board until his untimely death in 1938. Barnwell was a contemporary of Gordon England and was appointed to his specialised post before Coanda joined the Company.

At first the schools at Brooklands and Larkhill were filled by private pupils of many nationalities, but soon their reports brought purchasing commissions to view the Company's products and facilities, and by 1912 Bristol pilots were regularly demonstrating their mounts at the military centres of France, Spain, Italy, Germany and Rumania, with such success that not only were Bristol aeroplanes ordered in quantity but schools of military aviation were established on the Bristol pattern. Thus, in February 1912, schools were formed simultaneously at Madrid and at Halberstadt in Germany. Bristol monoplanes were in use at Malpensa in Italy in April, and a new school on Bristol lines was opened at Mirafiore in August. At home Mr. Haldane had received a peerage and his successor Col. Seely expanded the Army Air Battalion into the Royal Flying Corps with its own Central Flying School. The Corps was commanded by Col. Sir Alexander Bannerman, who had learned to fly at the Company's Brooklands school in April, when the Corps had 81 certificated officers, 50 of them from Bristol schools.

Although the Spanish school at Cuatros Vientos was organised by the army and commanded by Capt. Barron, it was intended to equip it entirely with Bristol aeroplanes, and Eric Harrison, who had come to Bristol from Australia with Harry Busteed in 1911, was appointed Chief Instructor. In Germany a different arrangement was made, and on 28 February the Deutsche Bristol-

Werke, with a capital of 200,000 Marks (half subscribed by the Bristol Directors), was formed to manufacture Bristol aeroplanes under licence and to operate a flying school at Halberstadt, supervised by Bristol instructors. The Deutsche Bristol-Werke later came under pressure from the German Government to produce aeroplanes of new design rather than Bristol types, so the licensing agreement fell into abeyance and was formally cancelled on 23 June 1914.

Howard Pixton and Bertram Dickson at Mirafiore in January 1913.

A Rumanian army contingent, headed by Prince Cantacuzene, was trained at Larkhill during 1912, and subsequently he organised a military flying school at Bucharest. Of the 211 pupils who qualified in the sixteen British schools, 98 were Bristol-trained and of these 63 had passed through the hands of Hotchkiss and Merriam at Brooklands. Edward Hotchkiss had qualified for Royal Aero Club certificate no. 87 on 16 May 1911 at Larkhill; his assistant, F. Warren Merriam, graduated at Brooklands on 6 February 1912 with certificate no. 179. In July the Larkhill school was transferred to Brooklands because of the military aeroplane competitions in August, and the combined Bristol school at Brooklands became busier than ever. Hotchkiss and Merriam beat all records for early rising and working round the clock; in one week of fine weather they passed out seven pupils in the course of 300 instructional flights totalling 1,600 miles. The Larkhill school returned to Salisbury Plain in September, and Hotchkiss then went into training as a volunteer pilot in the R.F.C. Special Reserve, which had just been formed, only to be killed, with his passenger, Lt. C. A. Bettington, in one of the prize-winning Coanda military monoplanes when it crashed near the Trout Inn at Wolvercote,

Oxford. Merriam then became chief instructor at Brooklands until he himself met with an accident early in 1914, from which he never fully recovered, although he went on to a distinguished career as a pilot in the R.N.A.S. and later civil flying activities.

The accident in which Hotchkiss died was one of a spate which alarmed the War Office and led to a temporary ban on monoplanes, although the Admiralty took no similar action. Thus the Company, which, after winning the third prize in the military competitions, had looked forward to substantial interest at home in the Coanda monoplane (having already received many foreign orders and granted a licence to Caproni in Italy), found itself compelled to accept a contract to build B.E.2a biplanes instead. Experience with the official drawings soon brought discrepancies to light, but in spite of such exasperations the Filton-built B.E.s were of high quality and the Company received a succession of further contracts, but always in disappointingly small batches, with many minor modifications which prevented profitable production. Profitable or not, these contracts represented increased turnover and more space became urgently needed. To cope with this expansion, the Company's capital was again increased, from £100,000 to £250,000 on 10 February 1913.

During 1913 and 1914 new designs of biplane were brought out, and after a few early set-backs success was achieved by converting Coanda monoplanes into biplanes and in some cases substituting floats for wheels. The T.B.8

Harry Busteed on T.B.8 seaplane at Dale in September 1913.

23

biplane was so far in advance of its French contemporaries at the 1913 Paris Salon that Breguet obtained a licence to make it in France. But the real breakthrough occurred when Frank Barnwell, released from specialisation on Burney's flying boat project, sketched out the brilliant Baby Biplane, first of the Bristol Scouts. Even the official command to produce nothing but the B.E.2c after the outbreak of war in 1914 could not strangle the infant Scout, and for the next two years it became the major product of the Bristol Tramways works at Brislington, after their resources were combined with those of Filton.

B.E.2d and Scout D biplanes ready for dispatch from Filton in 1916.

On the outbreak of war the Bristol schools were taken over by the military, Larkhill having been closed on 2 June 1914 by the mobilisation of the R.F.C. for manœuvres based on Netheravon. All its machines and pupils were transferred to the Brooklands school, which was in turn transferred to the War Office on 17 August, although tuition to existing pupils did not cease until 30 September. Altogether the Brooklands school trained 178 pilots and Larkhill 129 up till 4 August 1914, so that 308 out of all the 664 Royal Aero Club certificates issued to that date had been gained at the Company's schools. The next most prolific of the other 27 British schools was Vickers' (also at Brooklands), which trained 77 pilots and had itself been staffed, from its earliest days, by Bristol-trained veterans headed by Capt. H. F. Wood.

The popularity of the first Scouts with the few Service pilots who had had an opportunity to fly them led to orders, for 12 in November 1914 from the War Office and for 24 in December from the Admiralty. The Company's acceptance of the latter order displeased Col. Brancker, who reprimanded Henry White Smith for not having consulted the War Office first and asked the Company to arrange for the Admiralty to transfer the contract to the War Office. White Smith called on Capt. Murray Sueter to discuss the matter, and it was finally agreed that the dispute lay entirely between the two Services and was no concern of the Company. Such petty jealousies in official quarters, combined with recurring errors in the official drawings for the ever-increasing B.E. contracts and the impossibility of persuading the War Office to consider original designs and projects, soon frustrated the more talented members of the Filton staff and they began to disperse, some to the Admiralty Air Department or their contractors, others to join the fighting forces. Tinson was among the former, going to join Harris Booth above the Admiralty Arch, while Barnwell joined the Royal Flying Corps as a Second Lieutenant. Coanda had left on 21 October 1914 to return to Rumania, and Busteed, Merriam, Dacre and Sippe had all joined the R.N.A.S. in August. Farnall Thurstan, already a Naval Reservist, took charge of R.N.A.S. equipment and supplies in Paris, while Sydney Smith, a Territorial officer, eventually organised the vast R.F.C. repair depots in Normandy.

Throughout the first year of the war Herbert Thomas, by then Works Manager, faced a severe problem in stepping up production because of the difficulty of replacing skilled men who had enlisted. Slowly the payroll rose from 200 at the outbreak of war to 520 a year later. A bonus scheme introduced in June 1915 did something to attract and retain skilled employees until in August 1916 the Company's facilities were declared 'a controlled establishment', concurrently with the introduction of conscription. Production of later versions of the B.E.2 continued through 1916 and 1917, and in September 1916 a large new erecting hall, with associated fabric and dope shops, was brought into use, the War Office having contributed £30,000 towards the cost of this extension and given an assurance of full employment until the end of the year. A new canteen was also built, together with a rest-room for the many women who were taken into employment from July 1916 onwards.

Although production of the outmoded B.E. had been pressed so vigorously by the War Office, experience in the field during 1915 had proved it woefully inadequate in self-defence and manœuvre, and insistent demands for more aggressive aircraft at length forced the War Office to invite tenders for competitive new designs. Fighters to combat the Zeppelin airships and the Fokker monoplane were the first priority and in August 1915, Frank Barnwell, by then a Captain, was sent back to Filton 'on indefinite leave without pay' to resume his post as Chief Designer. After making minor but effective improvements in the Scout, he went on to design a series of fighting biplanes, first the twin-engined T.T.A., then its single-engined equivalent the F.3A, followed by the S.2A two-seater variant of the Scout, none of which was successful enough to attract production contracts. Then came a tentative reconnaissance two-seater, R.2A, and a monoplane Scout, M.1A, both of which temporarily hung fire until, with the introduction of the new Rolls-Royce Falcon engine, the two-seater blossomed out into the F.2A and F.2B, the famous Bristol Fighter. The spectre of the monoplane ban still lingered in spite of the M.1A's top speed of 132 m.p.h., and, although it achieved limited production as M.1C, it was never matched against the Fokker but relegated to service in the Middle East, where its superior performance was wasted on the desert air. The Bristol Fighter, by contrast, became a legend almost as soon as it flew. The first order for 50 in August 1916 had been increased to 600 by July 1917,

F. P. Raynham in M.1A after first flight at Filton, June 1916.

followed by a further order for 800 in September 1917 and in March 1918 by two more orders for 500 and 700. The works were again greatly enlarged, at a cost of £88,000, and it became necessary to engage a full-time test pilot instead of relying on the C.O. of the Filton Aircraft Acceptance Park, R.F.C., Capt. Hooper, or on free-lance test pilots such as Fred Raynham. The new post was filled by Joseph Hammond, the first pilot ever to qualify at the Larkhill school, who was now a Captain, R.F.C.; he joined the Company as Test Pilot on 19 January 1917.

But the Company's success with the Bristol Fighter was overshadowed by the sudden death, in his 63rd year, of Sir George White, on 22 November 1916. Thirty years later his name was fittingly honoured by the endowment of the Sir George White Chair of Aeronautics at the University of Bristol. His brother Samuel White was elected Chairman on 23 January 1917, and at the same time Henry White Smith and Herbert Thomas were appointed Directors, still retaining their respective duties of Secretary and Works Manager. In the previous year Henry White Smith had also been elected first President of the Society of British Aircraft Constructors, which he had helped to found.

In July 1917 the War Office decided to re-equip all fighter-reconnaissance and corps-reconnaissance squadrons of the R.F.C. with Bristol Fighters. This needed rapid production on an unprecedented scale. Although general control was exercised by the Ministry of Munitions, it could never have worked so effectively without the whole-hearted co-operation and initiative of the manufacturers. A major bottleneck was the supply of metal fittings, which were to be made up by some thirty to forty sub-contractors, most of whom were newcomers to aircraft work, with mainly unskilled labour. Hopeless delays would have ensued had not the Company, and in particular

John Daniel and Frank Davey, gone to immense trouble to provide simple but effective jigs ensuring foolproof and rapid assembly and guaranteed interchangeability even in the hands of novices. In September 1917 it was decided to expand the programme still further by placing contracts for complete aircraft, as well as parts, in the motor car and general engineering industries. Here the Company followed the precedent of its own licensing practice as extended to Deutsche Bristol-Werke, Caproni and Breguet and supplied a complete skeleton airframe to each sub-contractor as a sample, together with templates for all ribs and photographs and detail drawings of all jigs and tools required.

Before long airframe production began to outstrip the supply of Rolls-Royce Falcon engines, and alternatives were sought, leading to further modications in design and generally unsatisfactory results from engines released to production without having been fully developed. When the United States joined the Allies in 1917 the Bristol Fighter was one of the types selected for mass production in America. Contracts for 2,000 were placed initially, but American political insistence on the use of the big Liberty engine led to a series of accidents for which the aircraft rather than the choice of engine was blamed. Capt. Barnwell went out to America at Lord Weir's urgent request to advise on improvements where possible, and eventually a successful installation of the Wright-Hispano-Suiza engine resulted in an unofficial world altitude record in November 1918; but before then Capt. Hammond had been amongst the several test pilots killed on American aeroplanes that year.

Frank S. Barnwell,
Experimental Designer 1911–1914,
Chief Designer 1915–1921, 1923–1936,
Chief Engineer 1936–1938.

Cyril F. Uwins, Chief Test Pilot 1918–1947,
Asst. Managing Director 1947–1957,
Deputy Chairman 1957–1964.

His successor was Flight-Lt. Cyril Uwins, who was seconded from the R.A.F. to the Company's staff as Test Pilot on 25 October 1918, being finally demobilised on 1 May 1919.

During 1917 and 1918 the Company's efforts were by no means confined to the prodigious Bristol Fighter programme. When the last of the B.E.2e contracts had been completed it was asked to undertake the production of large Porte flying boats of the F.3 type, manufacturing the wing and tail components and assembling them on to hulls supplied by other contractors. This proposal was first discussed with Sir William Weir on 31 May 1917, and on 19 June the Directors visited Felixstowe to see the prototype. The proposed programme to build 50 flying boats would have required further large extensions to the works and the dismantling of the completed aircraft for transport to the coast, so the project was abandoned. But the Company's interest in large multi-engined aeroplanes had been excited and continued after the war.

Very large bombers were needed for long range offensives into Germany, and in November 1917 Capt. Barnwell drafted a proposal to meet this requirement; this eventually matured as the Braemar triplane, of which three prototypes were ordered. Other concurrent projects were the single-seater Scout F, and the two-seater F.2C fighter, which became the Badger; prototypes were built, but no production orders were obtained. There was also the M.R.1, a metal-framed variant of the Bristol Fighter, of which two examples were built for evaluation. But the product which made the name of Bristol aeroplanes a household word was the Rolls-Royce engined Fighter, which King George V and Queen Mary came to Filton to see in production, on 8 November 1917.

In the year that followed, over 2,000 aircraft were turned out from the Filton and Brislington works, and there were over 3,000 on the payroll when the Armistice was declared on 11 November 1918. The works immediately closed for three days' holiday and all overtime ceased as from 14 November; on 26 November the Company received formal notice from the Ministry of Munitions terminating all existing contracts for Bristol Fighters and spares. There had been remarkably few disputes and only four short strikes, involving a loss of a total of 13 days' work throughout the whole period of the war.

PROBLEMS OF PEACETIME

Like other well-established aircraft manufacturers, with experience of pre-war conditions, the Company was determined to stay in the aviation business, yet the Directors were under no illusions about the smallness of the civil market and the penalties of imprudent optimism. There could be practically no demand for new types of aircraft while vast surplus stocks of unused machines were available at scrap prices; on the other hand military aircraft were unattractive to passengers and military engines notoriously expensive to run and far from reliable. Nevertheless, the Company owned the best-equipped factory in the country, covering 8 acres of floor space, and had the pick of 3,000 operatives, including an exceptionally skilled toolroom staff. Fortunately the Air Board reconsidered the application of the break clause to Bristol Fighter contracts and agreed to accept most of the aircraft already in progress, totalling 788 at Filton and 192 at Brislington. The Company also took over from Parnall and Sons, Ltd., a contract for 150 Parnall Panthers, and there was no curtailment of the existing experimental contracts covering three Braemars and three Badgers. Thus there was just enough work in hand to occupy the factory for a further year, and during this breathing space it was hoped to explore the market and design a winner to capture it.

On 3 February 1919 the Directors met to discuss future design policy with Capt. Barnwell, and Sir Stanley White emphasised that "they wished to proceed as fast as possible with new machines which would be in advance of anything yet produced and that out-of-date designs should be discarded as soon as possible". Barnwell insisted that a wind-tunnel was essential for success, and this was built in June 1919 and equipped with a balance bought from Parnall's. This tunnel (No. 1) remained in service until destroyed by a German bomb in 1942.

The projects discussed centred round the Royal Mail Steam Packet Company's interest in flying boats to speed up mail delivery along the South American eastern seaboard. At first the Directors considered buying and refitting F.5 flying boats, but it transpired that these suffered from too rapid deterioration in service, if moored out; that only F.3 boats would be released for sale, and that their hold capacity was too small to carry the required payload of 1 ton of mail. In considering a larger boat, the R.M.S.P. expressed a strong preference for steam turbine propulsion, which all their engineers understood and which, it was hoped, could be made both quieter and safer than petrol engines. This requirement gave rise to a succession of designs with central engine rooms, culminating in the Tramp, which never flew because of power transmission difficulties. It was developed from the Pullman, which was the third Braemar completed with a new large fuselage containing a cabin for 14 passengers and would have enjoyed reasonable success had it been put to work in revenue service, instead of being held at Martlesham for official tests.

Barnwell also outlined a series of general purpose load-carriers generically named 'Grampus', but these never reached maturity, although followed by the Ten-seaters a year or two later. Among the smaller projects were the Badger X, the Babe and the Tourer, all of which are described later in this book. The Tourer, which was a fairly simple adaptation of the Bristol Fighter, built from the existing details and jigs, seemed likely to be a best-seller in America in spite of the memory of the Liberty affair, and in re-appointing agents all over the world the Directors took the risk of opening an office in New York; fifteen Tourers and a reconditioned M.1C monoplane were laid down for export to America and several were delivered against orders accompanied by small cash deposits. The American market, so promising at first, vanished in 1920 when Congress raised tariffs on certain imports including aircraft, which absorbed the small profit margin; and the New York office was closed at the end of that year with the aircraft already delivered still unpaid for. However, most were still at the works and these were resold to buyers in Canada, Spain and Australia as well as at home.

On 20 September 1919 all outstanding Bristol Fighter contracts were cancelled and over 12 months were to elapse before the adoption of the type as the R.A.F.'s standard army co-operation aeroplane resulted in new orders being placed. In the interval, while aircraft production was at its lowest ebb, the unremitting efforts of Herbert Thomas to obtain non-aeronautical work proved of the greatest value in keeping together the firm's nucleus of skilled employees. Throughout 1919 he was very active in seeking coach-building contracts from the motor-car industry, and eventually set up a production line of bus and coach bodies for the Bristol Tramways Company and saloon bodies for Armstrong Siddeley cars which lasted through the worst of the lean years. A different project in the sphere of motoring was a single-seat light car designed by W. T. Reid, called the Monocar. Six prototypes, with Henderson motor-cycle engines, were laid down for test and demonstration, and Reid was also authorised to build a high-efficiency three-cylinder two-stroke 15 b.h.p. engine of his own design; this was to replace the Henderson in production Monocars and also formed the basis of a proposed domestic electric lighting plant called the 'Bristolite'. Two Monocars and one Reid engine were completed, but after various mishaps, including the disintegration of the first Henderson engine, the project was abandoned. In any case, this tentative essay into engine manufacture was negligible by comparison with developments which were soon to take place.

Close technical liaison existed between Barnwell and Roy Fedden, chief engineer of the Cosmos Engineering Company of Fishponds, Bristol, who had designed first the Cosmos Mercury and then the Jupiter and Lucifer engines, all air-cooled radials. Barnwell designed an aerobatic single-seater, the Bullet, specifically for the testing and demonstration of the Jupiter, and later one of the M.1B monoplanes was modified to take the Lucifer for the same purpose. Both engines promised a combination of low installed weight, fuel economy and ease of maintenance hitherto unattained in any wartime engine, and it was therefore a severe blow to the Cosmos organisation when its proprietors, having struck a bad bargain in a shipping deal, found it necessary to recoup their losses by withdrawing capital from all their aviation interests.

The Cosmos Engineering Company went into liquidation early in February 1920, but Fedden obtained the Official Receiver's consent to keep the design team together and the work in progress intact, while he attempted to find a new proprietor willing to back the Jupiter development programme. His offer to go in with the Siddeley organisation, whose Jaguar engine was the Jupiter's chief rival, was declined and at first the Bristol Directors also were unwilling to risk so speculative a venture. After some encouragement from the Air Ministry, the Company agreed to take over the Cosmos organisation as the nucleus of its new Aero-Engine Department, and the deal was completed just in time for Jupiter and Lucifer engines to be shown on the Bristol stand at the Aero Show at Olympia in August 1920.

Before this date, the British and Colonial Aeroplane Company itself had gone into voluntary liquidation, but for a very different reason. Many applications had been made over the years for the registration of the name 'Bristol' in association with aircraft products as a trade mark, but all had been rejected. After Sir George White's death the matter had begun to seem less important because the Bristol Fighter had by then become world famous. Also the Excess Profits Duty, for which the Treasury claimed payment in 1920 and which was to put many aircraft firms out of business, was found to be less punitive if an existing business was discontinued and its fixed assets were transferred to a new trading company. So on 9 February 1920 the shareholders of the Bristol Aeroplane Company Limited adopted new Articles of Association which on 6 March 1920 created 999,900 new shares of £1, raising the authorised share capital of The Bristol Aeroplane Company Limited from £100 to £1,000,000, of which £553,000 were fully secured by the assets of The British and Colonial Aeroplane Company Limited, whose business was transferred without interruption and at a cost of only about £300, mainly in re-registration of patents. The old Company, having served its purpose, was formally wound up on 23 March 1920, after ten years of almost explosive evolution.

At the end of the war a period of retrenchment and re-appraisal began, not only of the aircraft industry but of the entire outlook for aviation in peacetime. Important political decisions had to be taken on the future status and equipment of the R.A.F. before any promise of peacetime orders could be given to the industry. An important aspect of this problem was the desirability of making the best use of German innovations in aeronautics which had only become known to the Allies after the Armistice, such as the use of thick aerofoils derived from airscrew blade-sections, which permitted wing spars to be made deep enough to carry all flying loads without external bracing, or at least with such bracing reduced to a few streamlined struts. Successful cantilever wings had been made and proved in wood by Fokker and in metal by Junkers and Dornier.

In face of drastic Treasury economies, arguments for metal construction on one hand and maximum versatility of equipment on the other became more cogent than ever, since time was no longer the essence of military contracts and ease of production was sought as a means of reducing cost rather than of speeding output. These considerations crystallised into official insistence on a general purpose aeroplane, capable of serving in all single-engined roles— even of being convertible from single-seater to two-seater—of all-metal construction for long life in any climate, easily transported by rail or road, quickly erected and requiring the minimum of maintenance in the field or in store. Evidently this was a case for an all-metal cantilever monoplane, fitted with the Company's own Jupiter engine, convertible from single-seater to two-seater by means of a self-contained second cockpit section; in fact a logical extension of Barnwell's original M.R.1 philosophy. Thus the Bullfinch was hatched, a most ingenious design, into which Barnwell put all his customary skill and energy. But too little money was available from official sources and too many unused wartime aircraft were still held in store for any real enthusiasm to be shown for new projects by the politicians of the Air Ministry; when it became clear that only three prototypes of the Bullfinch and none of several other tendered designs would be ordered, Barnwell lost heart and decided to take up a technical commission in the Royal Australian Air Force in order to work with Squadron Leader L. J. Wackett, who was about to establish an experimental department at Randwick. Lawrence Wackett had been the seventeenth pupil of the original Australian Flying School at Point Cook and had qualified for his pilot's certificate on the last surviving Bristol Boxkite (No. 133) on 20 October 1915. At the end of September 1921, Barnwell resigned from the Company, in spite of the Directors' efforts to dissuade him, and his departure on 1 October was much regretted by his colleagues. His successor as Chief Designer was Wilfred T. Reid, who had already been responsible for most of the work on the Ten-seater, of which the first prototype, with a Napier Lion engine, had flown successfully in May.

Reid and Fedden worked together to get the Jupiter accepted as the logical successor to the universally established Napier Lion, and their first step, after the Jupiter's Type Test had been passed in September 1921, was to produce a Jupiter-engined Ten-seater which in due course went into airline service as a freight carrier, a development of it for ambulance duties being purchased by the Air Council as the Brandon.

Other joint projects by Reid and Fedden with Jupiter engines were the Racer, with totally submerged engine and retractable undercarriage; the Jupiter-Fighter and its trainer derivative; the Fighter 'C' project which developed into the Bloodhound two-seater fighter; and a number of unbuilt projects to official specifications. Smaller designs using the Lucifer engine were the M.1D racing monoplane, the Taxiplane and the Lucifer Trainer; the last-named equipped the Reserve Training School set up at Filton under an Air Ministry scheme for training reserve pilots in 1923. Advanced training at this school was carried out on Puma-engined Trainers derived from the Tourer, which in due course were superseded by similar machines with Jupiters. The Aero-Engine Department was by no means dependent on Bristol airframes to carry its engines, for Jupiters were in use all over the world particularly since the Société des Moteurs Gnome et le Rhône had acquired the European manufacturing licence; Lucifers, too, were in demand and among the first few exported were four to Soviet Russia, via their London agency, Arcos Ltd.

Although the Company was more prosperous than many others during the lean years, it needed every bit of income to develop manufacturing facilities both for engines and for aircraft, particularly for improved methods of metal airframe construction. Fortunately the Bristol Fighter, revised to suit the Army Co-operation role, remained on active service in India and the Middle East, and there was a steady intake of these aircraft for reconditioning to

Rigging a 300 hp Hispano-Suiza engined Bristol Fighter for Spain, Filton 1924.

provide the Company's bread-and-butter; for some time this was supplemented by production of new bus and coach bodies for the Bristol Tramways Company.

Capt. Barnwell soon realised that his hopes of making a new career in Australia were ill-founded, and in 1923 returned to Filton to resume his old position as Chief Designer, Reid having been invited to join Canadian Vickers Ltd. Before this, Barnwell's former assistant, Clifford Tinson, had returned. Since leaving Filton in 1915 to join the Air Department of the Admiralty, he had been successively Chief Designer to Frederick Sage and Co. at Peterborough and assistant to Roy Chadwick at A. V. Roe and Co. at Hamble. Some months before Tinson's return there had also arrived at Filton Harry Pollard, a specialist in a new form of high-tensile steel rolled-strip construction developed by J. D. North of Boulton and Paul Ltd. Barnwell, Frise, Pollard and Tinson formed a very strong team, and their method of using high tensile steel proved very successful for over ten years, until it was superseded by the improved stressed skin construction made possible by the American invention of Alclad, coupled with more adequate experience of heat treatment of aluminium alloys.

Barnwell's first new design after his return, the Berkeley bomber, was the last to employ drawn tubes and sockets as the major part of the primary structure; it was also the last for ten years to use a 'foreign' engine. Throughout that period Bristol airframes were built up from high tensile steel strip rolled into various sections and powered by Bristol engines exclusively. The Brownie, Boarhound, Beaver, Bagshot, Bulldog, Bullpup, 109, 110A, 118 and 120 all followed this formula; only the Badminton and 101 were of wooden construction, and even the latter had steel wings. All were biplanes except the Brownie and the Bagshot, and experience with the latter showed the low torsional stiffness of a fabric-covered two-spar cantilever wing of orthodox design. The Company's last biplane, the 123 fighter, had cantilever wings with stressed-skin light alloy torsion-box leading edges; it was also the first since the Berkeley to have a Rolls-Royce engine and the combination was a somewhat unhappy one. Thereafter all Bristol aeroplanes have been monoplanes with stressed-skin primary structure, and the use of Bristol engines

33

has been the rule from which the only deviations have been those of necessity rather than choice.

Few Bristol aeroplanes of the 'all-steel' period got beyond prototype status, the famous exception being the Bulldog of which nearly 450 were produced for the R.A.F. and eight other national air forces. Before the Bulldog was ordered in quantity in 1929, the Company had also built under sub-contract a batch of 84 Armstrong Whitworth Siskin IIIA fighters, when this was the only all-metal fighter approved for squadron service in the R.A.F. Bulldog production came to an end in 1934, and since by this date the Bristol Fighter had at last become obsolete so that no more needed reconditioning, the aircraft works at Filton were almost at a standstill, although the Company's output of engines was higher than ever before. Then the tide turned in May 1935, when the Government abandoned appeasement and disarmament and decided at last to build up the R.A.F. with modern equipment. In spite of having just lost a promising private venture single-seat monoplane fighter, the Bristol 133, the Company was ready with another brilliant contribution—a twin-engined high-speed transport monoplane, 50 miles an hour faster than the R.A.F.'s latest biplane fighters. Built as a private order for Lord Rothermere, it became world famous as *Britain First*, and from it was derived the Blenheim bomber, for which a large production contract was placed later in the year. To meet the challenge of the new era, the Bristol Aeroplane Company Ltd. was reorganised on 15 June 1935 as a public limited liability company with a share capital of £1,200,000. On that date there were 4,200 employees on the pay-roll, mostly in the engine factory, and the aircraft and engine works together occupied 13 acres. The lean years had ended at last.

EXPANSION

Few industries have ever experienced such a sudden boom as that which began for the aircraft manufacturers of Great Britain in the summer of 1935. The Government had suddenly called for new equipment in quantities which staggered the imagination of even the most fervent advocates of military preparedness. To some extent the delay in re-arming was fortunate, for 1935 was a critical year technically as well as politically; it marked the emergence of a new race of aeroplanes—clean, efficient monoplanes, with cantilever wings, retractable undercarriages and metal monocoque bodies, powered by supercharged engines driving variable pitch airscrews and giving enormously increased power by virtue of high-octane fuel, which was available in quantity for the first time. Had rearmament begun two years earlier, the R.A.F. might well have been equipped with large numbers of biplanes and braced monoplanes, which indeed proved a handicap to the French and Italian air forces when war eventually broke out.

The Air Ministry's first proposal was for the Company to produce 271 biplanes—Audax, Fury and Gauntlet—before the end of 1937. Two batches of Audax, numbering 56 and 85 respectively, were in fact built and delivered during the autumn of 1935 and enabled the Filton labour force to be expanded and trained, while the factory was being retooled and extended for production of the Blenheim bomber, of which 150 had been ordered in September. From 4,200 in June the payroll rose to 8,233 by Christmas. Extensions were made necessary by the larger size of the Blenheim, and also by the changes in workshop practice and layout enforced by the introduction of monocoque light alloy construction. The erecting shop, unaltered since 1916, was doubled in floor area by an extension on the south side, the new bay having full span folding doors opening on to a new internal road leading direct to the airfield. Large extensions were also made to the tool room and machine shop; a new wing assembly shop was built, also new metal stores for Alclad sheets and very extensive anodising and cadmium plating plant, which took the place of the former stove-enamelling baths. The floor space required for fabric work and doping was much reduced, but a new spraying shop had to be built for cellulose painting of components and later for applying camouflage to the complete aircraft. An important extension was the building of a new head office block fronting the Gloucester Road and adjoining Filton House, which was occupied in April 1936 and was a notable achievement for its architect, Austin Hall, F.R.I.B.A.

The productive capacity for aero-engines had to be expanded even more than for aircraft, since the existing works could only produce a small proportion of the Mercuries and Pegasus required by the whole industry and virtually none of the later sleeve-valve Perseus, Taurus and Hercules. A large new engine factory of 200,000 sq. ft. was built early in 1936 east of the Gloucester Road, opposite the existing works, together with additional test plant; space was reserved for three later extensions, each of similar size. A separate single-storey factory was also built to specialise in cowlings and exhaust systems and was named Rodney Works. Although engine development and production are not the province of this book, it would be unrealistic not to mention the premises which, together with Filton Works, made the Bristol Aeroplane Company the largest single aircraft manufacturing unit in the world, before war broke out in 1939; at that date the Company's buildings covered 2,688,324 sq. ft. and the total area of land occupied was 732 acres.

Early in 1936, it became clear that, even after expansion to meet the 1935 programme, the existing aircraft industry could not produce all the aircraft needed to achieve parity with Germany, so plans were made to bring in the automobile industry by means of a 'shadow' scheme. By way of a start, the motor industry was invited to manufacture a basic aero-engine, and on 7 April 1936 the Bristol Mercury was selected for the project. No. 2 Shadow Factory was built next to the East Works at Patchway and was managed by the Company on behalf of the Air Ministry; the other five were all in the Birmingham and Coventry districts. After experience had been gained with the Mercury the scheme was extended to the Pegasus also, and in 1937 was further enlarged to cover complete aircraft. The first such contracts were for 50 Bombays with Short and Harland Ltd. at Belfast and 250 Blenheims with A. V. Roe and Co. Ltd. at Chadderton; a similar contract for Blenheims was placed with Rootes Securities Ltd. at Speke; Rootes were the first firm outside the aircraft industry proper to built complete aircraft since 1918 and the only such firm in Great Britain to build Blenheims and Beaufighters.

The prototype Blenheim I made its first flight at Filton on 25 June 1936 and after completing service trials was cleared for production in December. Deliveries to the R.A.F. began in March 1937, and Filton production rose from 6 per month in January 1937 to 24 in January 1938. During this period large factory and drawing office extensions were continued, and the associated administrative and recreational facilities included new canteens and a large new sports field and pavilion.

An important innovation was the Armament Section, set up to specialise mainly in the design and development of power-operated turrets, also controlling general hydraulic engineering components, such as undercarriage retraction gear and engine-driven pumps. Hitherto these components had been regarded as a normal part of aircraft design, but the many initial difficulties encountered emphasised the need for specialist attention. The multi-stage gear-type hydraulic pump evolved for the Blenheim had to be developed because no suitable unit could be obtained elsewhere, and the design was put into large-scale production by the Integral Engineering Co. for use on many other aircraft beside Bristol types. The Bristol B.I Mark I dorsal turret for the Blenheim was the first power-operated turret to obtain Air Ministry clearance and led to many successful and ingenious designs produced to cope with successive problems of high speed defensive gunnery, culminating in the B.17 dorsal turret for the Lincoln and Shackleton bombers ten years later. Turret production in war-time was sub-contracted, mainly to the Daimler and Brockhouse companies.

The detail design of the Blenheim posed many problems, because the only available draughtsmen were accustomed to frame structures and all had to be instructed in the new monocoque system at a time when the urgency of the work rendered mistakes more likely to occur. Much closer liaison than hitherto was necessary between draughtsmen and stressmen, to prevent liberties being taken with the primary structure in the design of stowages, access doors and other cut-outs in the shell. The problem was further aggravated because much of the specified armament and service equipment had been designed before internal installation was thought of and little attempt had been made to keep it small enough. Officials were pessimistic because of the mid-wing layout, which entailed cutting into a large section of the body at its most highly stressed part, but the Company's confidence in its accumulated theoretical and practical knowledge was confirmed by the final test results, which showed all the stiffness and weight calculations to be correct. The value of the mid-wing arrangement became even more evident in later developments of the Blenheim, which could carry long bombs internally with relatively few restrictions.

Two of these developments were proposed in November 1935 to meet official specifications for a land-based torpedo-bomber and a general recon-

Blenheims in production at Filton, September 1938.

naissance and coastal bomber. Both featured separate navigating and radio stations, and after some discussion it was decided to combine them, and the Company tendered Type 152, which was accepted and put into production as the Beaufort. As an interim aircraft until the Beaufort could become available in squadron service, Type 149, a lengthened version of the Blenheim with a navigation station forward and increased fuel tankage, was also accepted for production, under the name Bolingbroke I, which was later amended to Blenheim IV because so many Blenheim components were incorporated; this helped the changeover on the production lines not only at Filton but also at Chadderton and Speke.

In 1937 both the Australian and Canadian governments were considering building British types of aircraft from local resources, and were interested in the Bolingbroke and Beaufort. The former was chosen for production in Canada under a licence granted to Fairchild Aircraft Limited of Longueuil, Quebec. The Australian home aircraft industry was much less experienced in metal aircraft construction than the Canadian and therefore had to spend more time developing local resources. This factor, together with the desire for a better tropical performance, led to the eventual choice of the Beaufort instead of the Bolingbroke for production in Australia. In detailing the Beaufort, transport joints were carefully provided, so that components could be completely fitted out before final assembly; this simplified manufacture by groups of sub-contractors in Australia, mainly in railway and industrial workshops.

Although Blenheim, Bolingbroke and Beaufort detailing and modification occupied most of the Filton drawing office capacity, a small project section was kept active on new tenders, and between 1936 and 1938 designs were submitted in response to Specifications nos. 35/35, F.37/35, B.12/36, P.13/36, F.11/37, F.18/37, S.24/37 and 15/38; none of these tenders gained a prototype contract, but the last, a temporary relaxation from emphasis on military re-equipment, was for a four-engined low-wing airliner with Taurus engines and a tricycle landing gear, recommended by the Cadman Committee in March 1938. Concurrently, the Civil Air Guard scheme to promote public air-mindedness had been launched and Capt. Barnwell was anxious to design a light single-seater for C.A.G. use. He was no longer permitted to fly the Company's aircraft, as he was considered to be uninsurable as a pilot, so he arranged for a syndicate of aircraft workers at Bristol Airport (Whitchurch) to build him a small wooden monoplane for his private use; he designed this in his spare time, fitted it with a 25 h.p. two-stroke Scott Squirrel engine and flew it at the end of July 1938. After adjustments, he took off on a second flight on 2 August, but crashed and was killed instantly. His death robbed the Company and the country of a Chief Engineer of whom a contemporary wrote: "He was beyond question one of the best aeroplane designers in this country or in the world. No other designer has turned out so many first-class aeroplanes which have become historic."

Frank Barnwell's colleagues had little time to mourn before the Munich crisis startled the aircraft industry into still greater activity. The Luftwaffe's numerical superiority continued to rise, and the R.A.F.'s deficiency in long-range cannon-armed fighters became increasingly serious, as the officially

Beauforts and Beaufighters in production at Filton, September 1940.

chosen Westland F.37/35 and Gloster F.9/37 twin-engined prototypes made slow progress towards approval for squadron use. In October 1938, with the Beaufort beginning to replace the Blenheim IV on the Filton production line, Fedden and Frise put forward a proposal for a fighter version of the Beaufort, combining existing wings, tail unit and landing gear with a new smaller fuselage carrying four 20 mm. Hispano cannons, with Hercules instead of Taurus engines, giving 50% more power. This project, named Beaufighter, went on like those earlier private venture stop-gaps, the Bulldog and Blenheim, to win undying fame in squadron service all over the world. Although the Beaufort continued in production until 1944, it was soon totally eclipsed as a front line torpedo-carrying strike aircraft by the coastal Beaufighter, which succeeded the earlier night fighter version. The Beaufighter prototype came on the scene just in time to save the Company from being brought into an Air Ministry group of sub-contractors for manufacture of Stirling bombers.

The Beaufighter's inherent versatility enabled it to perform most offensive and defensive roles with little modification, but official interest in a bomber derivative led in 1941 to orders for the heavily-armed Buckingham bomber; this was too late for the European theatre of war, but would have seen active service in the Far East had 'Tiger Force' gone into action against Japan in 1945 as planned. After VJ-Day, Buckingham production was cut back and existing aircraft were completed either as transports or as Buckmaster trainers. The possibility of producing a large-capacity transport, having Buckingham wings, power plants, landing gear and tail unit assembled to a cargo-carrying fuselage, was investigated, but found less attractive than a simple freighter design derived from the Bombay. This project, Type 170, was to provide the Company with an immediate peacetime product, which made the transition from war to peace in 1945 less drastic than in 1919.

Concurrently with the 170, limited production was undertaken of the Brigand, a strike aircraft replacing the coastal Beaufighter and having many

Freighters in production at Filton in 1953.

features in common with the Buckingham. Brigands did valuable work in the Far East, where they were well suited to extremes of tropical environment; they remained in service at home also as radar trainers for some years.

As soon as war ended, the Directors considered every possible activity for their factories and workpeople, and embarked on such diverse projects as the manufacture of high-quality motor cars, prefabricated houses and other buildings, plastics and marine craft. They also set up a helicopter department under Raoul Hafner, and this grew into an important activity, which eventually achieved the status of a separate Division at Weston-super-Mare, occupying the Old Mixon Shadow Factory originally built in 1940 for Beaufighter production. The Helicopter Division was finally taken over by the Westland Aircraft group early in 1960.

By far the most ambitious aeroplane project undertaken by the Company till then began tentatively in 1943, with an investigation into post-war civil transport requirements by the first Brabazon Committee, which recommended, as one of five types, a long-range transatlantic airliner. The Company submitted a design for an eight-engined 100-ton aeroplane and was awarded a prototype contract in 1945. Although the Brabazon I never went into revenue-earning service, the research and manufacturing experience gained from building and flying so large a pressurised prototype established the Company in an unassailable technical position in the field of structural design. The lessons learned were applied with brilliant success to the smaller but commercially more acceptable Britannia airliner, of which 85 were built between 1948 and 1960.

Britannics in production at Filton in 1957.

Although many new projects and design tenders were studied after 1945, only two other Bristol aeroplane designs reached the stage of prototype flight. One was the stainless-steel Bristol 188 research monoplane designed to fly at speeds over Mach 2. Its design, construction and operation were not merely novel, but posed problems requiring a new outlook for their solution, a technical advance of inestimable value in the practical approach to supersonic transport operation; the other was the gothic-winged Type 221.

Other design studies and research programmes, including tests at rocket-ranges both at home and in Australia, culminated in the perfection and adoption by the R.A.F. and foreign air forces of the supersonic ramjet-powered Bristol Bloodhound ground-to-air defence missile; apart from the exacting problems of weapon reliability to be solved, research into stratospheric environmental effects and improved electronic techniques yielded a vast store of knowledge, which can be applied to the problems of supersonic civil aviation. Both the short-range subsonic BAC One-Eleven and the Anglo-French Concorde supersonic transport contain major contributions from Filton experience, although they were destined not to bear the name of Bristol.

The long tradition of Bristol flying schools continued until 1953; the former Filton reserve flying school was completely re-equipped with Tiger Moths in 1933 and, after a further four years' operation, was reorganised as No. 2 E.F.T.S., continuing at Filton until 3 August 1940, when it moved to

Staverton because of the establishment of the Filton balloon barrage, moving on again to Worcester in September 1941, and becoming No. 6 Flying Instructors' School until August 1942, when it reverted to its former function and title of No. 2 E.F.T.S.; it moved back from Worcester to Yatesbury in August 1945. A second school, No. 10 E.F.T.S., which began operations at Yatesbury under the Company's management in January 1936, moved to Weston-super-Mare in September 1940 and again to Stoke Orchard in October 1941, being then doubled in establishment. It was closed in July 1942, after flying some 104,000 hours on Tiger Moths and training 2,100 pilots *ab initio*. The Bristol Wireless Flight started at Yatesbury in October 1939, and flew Dominies for the pupils of No. 2 Radio School, R.A.F. In 1942 it was re-equipped with Proctors, and the Company's flying staff were replaced by R.A.F. instructors; but the Company continued to maintain the fleet, which rose to 104 before the school closed in July 1945, when 18,500 wireless operators had been trained in 224,000 flying hours. The Company's premises at Yatesbury were presented to the R.A.F. Malcolm Clubs when No. 2 E.F.T.S. closed in September 1947. A new reserve school contract was negotiated in 1948 and No. 12 R.F.S. was opened at Filton on 1 April, using Tiger Moths and Ansons; it closed finally on 31 March 1953.

In gaining acceptance in world markets, military and commercial, design integrity and constructional quality are only the minimum essentials; equally important are reliability and economy, which in turn demand the best possible after-sales service from the manufacturer. This has always been a feature of Bristol philosophy, and in particular the Aircraft Service Department proved its merit when suddenly expanded in 1940 to meet the R.A.F.'s demand for repaired aircraft to supplement new production. Aircraft requiring factory repair were sent to 'fringe firms' in Scotland, Lancashire, Surrey and Wales; those beyond economic repair came back to the Company's salvage depot near Avonmouth. Here, too, was established a training school to give short intensive courses on Bristol airframe maintenance and repair to hundreds of R.A.F. personnel, a corresponding engine school being operated at the Bristol Blind School at Henleaze. Mobile working parties were sent to airfields all over Great Britain and Northern Ireland to repair aircraft on site; out of 6,578 Bristol-designed aeroplanes repaired and returned to service during the war years, over 1,200 were repaired on site by the Company's working parties, no fewer than 142 such repairs being completed in October 1940, when R.A.F. resources were stretched to the limit. The repair parties drew spare compenents and materials from strategically placed depots at St. Columb, Barnstaple, Bicester, St. Ives (Hunts.), Oswestry, Goole and Leuchars, which were kept stocked by a fleet of regularly scheduled lorries.

The experience thus gained in liaison between factory and operating personnel was crystallised in the post-war service department, whose representatives accompanied Bristol aeroplanes and helicopters all over the world, wherever operators needed their assistance. The training and support facilities given to Britannia operators equalled those of the most experienced American manufacturers and were an essential ingredient in the world-wide acceptance of the Britannia as a sophisticated airliner.

The activities of the Aircraft Service Department during the war occupied only a very small proportion of the premises into which the Company was forced to disperse after enemy bombing began in earnest in the summer of 1940. The first night raid on Bristol did not occur until 24 June 1940, and the works were by then protected by a formidable balloon barrage, backed-up by light and heavy anti-aircraft batteries; in addition the Company had trained an efficient A.R.P. contingent and had expanded the existing fire and ambulance services, including a comprehensively-equipped underground emergency hospital.

On 4 July a single enemy bomber penetrated the balloon barrage in daylight and dropped two bombs on a balloon winch opposite Rodney Works. No damage was done to the factory, and on 14 August three Ju 88 bombers, which attacked at 5 p.m., were driven off by anti-aircraft gunfire, two being shot down later by fighters. The following night minor damage was done to the East Works at Patchway, and night raids were also made on 17 and 22 August, causing some damage and a few casualties. During the height of the Battle of Britain, work at Filton was interrupted on most days by air raid warnings, and the Company introduced a private warning system based on information direct from observer posts, so that workers went to shelter only when the factory, as distinct from the city of Bristol, appeared to be threatened. On 25 September 1940 one such warning was given at 11.30 a.m., and all employees had taken cover when enemy bombers dropped their entire load right across the factory from south-west to north-east, in the space of a few minutes. Over 100 bombs fell on the works and airfield, many of them with delay fuses, but the material damage was less then it might have been, although direct hits demolished shelters at both Filton and Rodney Works, killing 72 employees outright and injuring 166, of whom 19 subsequently died. Only three raiders were shot down by the local defences, although more were accounted for by fighters before reaching the coast. Next day No. 504 Fighter Squadron's Hurricanes were sent to Filton, and on 27 September a second daylight raid by bombers and fighters was driven off by the Hurricanes; no damage was done.

Immediately after this raid all departments whose presence at Filton was not absolutely necessary were dispersed. Head Office staff moved to houses on Durdham Down and part of the aircraft drawing office to various premises at Clifton and Clevedon. A proposed move of the rest of the aircraft drawing office on 24 November to Lennard's Buildings, Clifton, was postponed for some trivial reason, and by this lucky chance the entire stock of production drawings escaped destruction the same night, when Lennard's Buildings were gutted in one of the first intensive night raids on the city. By this time the Beaufighter Shadow Factory at Old Mixon, near Weston-super-Mare, was in production, although output was restricted for a time by the effects of the raids on Coventry where many of the component suppliers were located. In their last major night attack on Bristol on 11 April 1942, the Luftwaffe dropped the only bomb to fall on a main building in the Aircraft Works; this demolished the original wind tunnel and an adjacent office building.

In 1942 the Company recorded its peak employment of 52,095 personnel, including the Shadow Factories at Weston-super-Mare and Accrington, which it directly controlled, and occupied over 100 dispersal premises, including such unlikely places as Wells Prison, Highbridge Cheese Stores, part of Loxton Rectory and a railway arch at Worcester. There were drawing offices in hotel bedrooms, engine repair shops in a tobacco bonded store, spar assembly in a bus garage, turret manufacture in a chocolate factory and component stores in a cider factory. On 1 July 1944 separate Divisional Boards came into being to control the activities of the Aircraft, Aero-Engine and Armament Divisions which had by then acquired informal status; after the war ended, the Armament Division became the Light Engineering Division, which evolved into the Car Division and a separately registered Plastics Company.

Most of the requisitioned premises were given up soon after hostilities ended, but many large extensions were then built, in addition to the new Design Office which rose in 1945 on the site of the blitzed No. 1 Wind Tunnel. These included that very prominent feature of the Filton landscape, the 8 acre Assembly Hall built in 1947, originally for the Brabazon and subsequently put to full use for final assembly of Britannias and other large aircraft. Another major extension of this period was the specially strong and wide runway, which extended the airfield boundary westwards into the village of Charlton.

In January 1956 the manufacturing and sales activities of the Aircraft, Aero-Engine and Car Divisions were further reorganised into three separate companies: Bristol Aircraft Ltd., Bristol Aero-Engines Ltd., and Bristol Cars Ltd., each being wholly owned by the Bristol Aeroplane Company Ltd. The facilities belonging to Bristol Aircraft Ltd., including more recently built special laboratories and test plant, were the main Bristol contribution to the British Aircraft Corporation, formed in June 1960 to pool the aviation interests and resources of the Company with those of Vickers Ltd. and the English Electric Company; soon afterwards the Corporation acquired Hunting Aircraft Ltd. All the aircraft and missile projects were thereafter developed under the new Corporation's auspices and consequently the Bristol 221 was the last aeroplane to be built under the familiar name. In the final step in rationalisation, on 28 December 1963, the four constituent operating companies were merged into a single unit, British Aircraft Corporation (Operating) Limited, of which Bristol Aircraft Ltd. then became the Filton Division. Between February 1910 and June 1960 some 15,750 aircraft of 85 different designs had been built in the Company's own works and in shadow factories under its direct management; only about 10% of these (1,600 aircraft of nine types) were not of Bristol design, but by contrast some 8,320

43

aircraft of Bristol design had been manufactured by licensees and other contractors at home and overseas, giving a total world production of 22,470 Bristol aeroplanes in fifty years.

Similar changes took place in the Company's engine organisation, for in April 1959 Bristol Aero-Engines Ltd. amalgamated with Armstrong Siddeley Motors Ltd. to form Bristol Siddeley Engines Ltd., jointly owned by the Bristol Aeroplane Company and the Hawker Siddeley Group; subsequently Bristol Siddeley Engines Ltd. absorbed the de Havilland Engine Co. Ltd. and Blackburn Engines Ltd. after their respective parent companies had joined the Hawker Siddeley Group. Finally in January 1968 the latter sold its share of Bristol Siddeley Engines Ltd. to Rolls-Royce Ltd. who had already acquired the Bristol Aeroplane Company itself. Thereafter the aero-engine plant at Filton became the Bristol Engine Division of Rolls-Royce Limited, while the Bristol Aircraft Corporation perpetuated the familiar initials B.A.C. until 1977 when it became part of British Aerospace.

The restored Bulldog, formerly *G-ABBB*, flying over Filton Works after its presentation to the Shuttleworth Trust in July 1961.

44

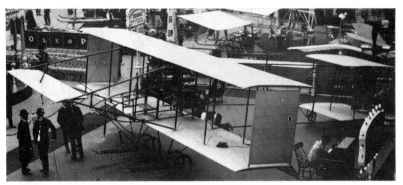

The Zodiac biplane at Olympia in March 1910.

The Bristol Zodiac

The Société Zodiac of Paris was formed in the late nineteenth century to make balloons, and in due course extended its activities to include small dirigible airships. By 1907 the brothers Gabriel and Charles Voisin had developed their 'boxkite' type of biplane to the point where, on 13 January 1908, Henri Farman was able to fly one round a closed course of 1 kilometre, thereby winning the prize of 50,000 francs offered for this feat by Ernest Archdeacon and Henri Deutsch de la Meurthe. This achievement brought the Voisins into the ranks of the leading aeroplane designers of the day, and the Société Zodiac extended its interests to include manufacture of biplanes and monoplanes designed by Gabriel Voisin. These had been placed on the market by the end of 1909, and were offered with a guarantee of flight. Sir George White, having consulted Émile Stern on the choice of a suitable aeroplane to begin manufacturing at Filton, was advised to consider the Zodiac models and in due course arranged to acquire the British manufacturing rights for them. Meanwhile, Henri Farman, having introduced improvements in a new Voisin biplane which he had ordered but never received, set up his own workshop and brought out replicas of the Farman III, which set the pattern for simplicity and performance for some years to come. Farman and his brothers were not much concerned with high-grade finish, although their materials were sound and their methods of construction safe enough for competition flying. Gabriel Voisin, having lost a good customer in Henri Farman, was anxious to advertise the superior workmanship of his products, and so the Zodiac biplane, though of outmoded design, was strongly recommended to Sir George White and chosen because of the excellence of its finish. Having decided that the newly formed British and Colonial Aeroplane Company should take a stand at the Aero Show at Olympia in March 1910,

45

the Directors speedly authorised the importation of a Zodiac biplane, to be exhibited as a sample of the type to be built by the firm, and this was delivered in crates to Filton just in time to be prepared for the Exhibition. This preparation was no mere formality, for it was found that the 50 h.p. four-cylinder upright Darracq engine, purchased with the biplane, had no mounting lugs or other means of attachment to the airframe, so Charles Briginshaw, the fitter deputed to install the engine, had to make clamps to fit round the crank-case.

Like most of the Voisin biplanes, the Zodiac had a single elevator in front and a biplane tail carried on four booms, the engine being mounted on the lower wing and driving a propeller behind the trailing edge. A single vertical rudder was provided between the tailplanes, and vertical surfaces were also fixed to the outer pairs of interplane struts; these were intended to resist any tendency to sideslip in a turn, but had been discarded by the Farmans and others after Wilbur Wright had demonstrated the safe and natural technique of banking on turns. The camber of the mainplanes and tailplanes was unusually flat, but both upper and lower surfaces were fabric-covered. Ailerons were fitted to the lower wing only and were linked to the rudder, which was controlled by rotating a handwheel which also moved fore-and-aft to control the elevator. Ailerons had not been a feature of earlier Voisin designs but were among the improvements introduced by Henri Farman. The undercarriage comprised a pair of skids each pivoted at the rear end to an inverted pyramid of steel tubes attached under the wing; a pair of wheels was mounted behind the pivot point so that, when landing, the front of the skid was pulled down against a rubber shock absorber into contact with the ground. Two small castoring wheels supported the tail. Unfortunately the excellent workmanship was not matched by aerodynamic knowledge, and many of the refinements served only to increase weight without any corresponding gain in lift.

After the Aero Show, the Zodiac was returned to Filton to be tuned for flight tests for which a Belgian pilot, Arthur Duray, had been engaged. Tests should have begun on 30 April, but the biplane was then still at Filton; meanwhile, Duray met with an accident in France and another pilot had to be sought. The Zodiac arrived at Brooklands on 10 May and was forthwith erected in the 'Bristol' shed by Sydney Smith and his assistants Leslie Macdonald, Charles Briginshaw and Henri Labouchère. From the first it proved to be very underpowered and all efforts to coax it off the ground failed. New wings with increased camber were assembled and eventually, on 28 May, it made a single brief hop in the hands of Edmond, who had taken Duray's place. Edmond thought little of its prospects and, after a final attempt to fly it on 15 June, when the landing gear was damaged, he persuaded Sydney Smith to abandon it in favour of the successful Henri Farman. The five Bristol-Zodiacs already started at Filton were scrapped and the Zodiac licence was cancelled soon afterwards.

Type:	Zodiac 52B
Manufacturers:	The British and Colonial Aeroplane Co., Ltd., Filton, Bristol, under licence from Société Zodiac, Paris
Power Plant:	One 50 hp Darracq
Span:	33 ft 3 in
Length:	39 ft 3 in
Height:	10 ft 2 in
Wing Area:	525 sq ft
Empty Weight:	1,000 lb
Speed:	35 mph
Accommodation:	Pilot and Passenger
Production:	1 assembled, 5 abandoned
Sequence Nos:	1 to 6 inclusive

Edmond on Boxkite No. 7 at Larkhill on 30 July 1910.

The Bristol Boxkite

The Bristol biplane of 1910, familiarly but inaccurately dubbed 'the Boxkite', was an unashamed copy of the Henri Farman, using the same dimensions and scantlings, but introducing the more refined metal fittings, such as steel clips and cast aluminium strut sockets, of Zodiac practice. The quality of French-built Farmans was somewhat variable, but the Bristol biplane, though similar in general appearance, was equivalent to or better than the best that France had produced at that time. Indeed, when the solicitors for Farman Frères proposed to sue the 'Bristol' Directors for infringement of patents, the Directors immediately entered a defence claiming substantial improvements, and no court proceedings ensued. The first two Boxkites were constructed at Filton to drawings made by George Challenger in June 1910, immediately after the abandonment of the Zodiac. They differed from all later Boxkites in having rear elevators with straight trailing edges and in having two, instead of one, intermediate vertical struts between each pair of upper and lower front booms. No. 7 was at first fitted with a 50 h.p. Grégoire four-cylinder engine and No. 8 with a 50 h.p. eight-cylinder E.N.V., both being watercooled. A further point of difference was that No. 8 had double-surfaced wings whereas No. 7 had a single fabric covering with pockets enclosing the ribs; the latter was standard Farman practice and was adopted on all later Bristol Boxkites, mainly to save weight. The Grégoire was unreliable and deficient in power, so Émile Stern's success in obtaining one of the first 50 h.p. Gnome rotaries released for export was particularly valuable. Fitted with this engine, No. 7 was taken to Larkhill on 29 July 1910, assembled overnight, and flown the next day to a height of 150 ft. at the first attempt by Edmond, to the astonishment of beholders who had taken up prone positions on the ground in order to detect the first glimmer of daylight between the grass and the wheels.

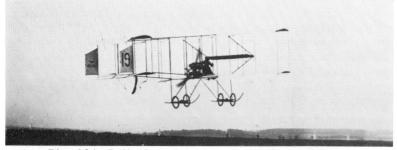

Edmond flying Boxkite No. 7 at Lanark in August 1910. (*Photo H. G. Adams.*)

With the efficiency of the design thus spectacularly confirmed, the two Boxkites were crated and dispatched to Lanark, where a six-day aviation meeting opened on 6 August at the race course. Only No. 7 took part in any events, which Edmond completed without incident but with only one award, the second prize for the slowest lap, in which his speed was 45 m.p.h. Meanwhile, more Boxkites were laid down at Filton and Nos. 7 and 8 were allocated as initial equipment of the flying schools at Brooklands and Larkhill, respectively; No. 8 retained the Lanark competition number 19 on its rudders for some months. As new aircraft were completed, the schools' complement was doubled, Larkhill receiving No. 9 in September and Brooklands No. 11 in November. Captain Dickson flew No. 9 in the army autumn manœuvres in September and Lt. Loraine accompanied him on No. 8, which had been equipped with a Thorne-Baker wireless transmitter. Nos. 10 and 12 were specially prepared for the Missions to Australia and India, respectively, the latter being the first to have upper wing extensions. The next two, Nos. 12A and 14 (No. 13 being unacceptable to any pilot of that date!) were flown from Durdham Down in the first public demonstration of the Company's activities;

48

Boxkite No. 8 (50 hp E.N.V.) at Larkhill in November 1910.

when these ended No. 12A was lent to Oscar Morison, who flew it in various demonstrations and competitions; No. 14 went on to Larkhill as a school aircraft, releasing No. 9 for duty as the spare for the Indian Mission. Two further new Boxkites, Nos. 15 and 16, went to Brooklands, whence No. 11 was brought back for overhaul and packing as the spare for the Australian Mission. No. 16 was fitted with extended wings and a 60 h.p. E.N.V. water-cooled engine; the latter made it technically an 'All British' aeroplane for competition purposes, and thus it became the mount on which Howard Pixton, with Charles Briginshaw as mechanic, won the Manville Prize of £500 for the highest aggregate time flown on nine specified days in 1911.

Both the Australian and Indian Missions arrived at their destinations in December, and on 6 January 1911 Jullerot demonstrated No. 12 before a Vice-regal party and a large crowd of spectators at the Calcutta Maidan. Invited to participate in the Deccan cavalry manœuvres, Jullerot made several flights from Aurangabad, from 16 January onwards, carrying Capt. Sefton Brancker as army observer, and later took part in the Northern Manœuvres at Karghpur. Here conditions were very severe and both No. 12 and No. 9 came to grief on the rock-strewn terrain, with a ground temperature of 100°F, but many flights were made and repairs kept pace with damage. When all the spares were used up, No. 9 was cannibalised to keep No. 12 flying and the latter survived to return to Larkhill as a school machine, being flown by many notable pupils, including Robert Smith-Barry, who was charged £15 in October 1911 for repairs after a heavy landing on it.

In Australia, Hammond began flying on No. 10 at Perth late in December, going on to Melbourne, where 32 flights, many with passengers, were made. The Mission then moved to Sydney, whence Hammond went home to New Zealand leaving Macdonald as sole pilot. By 19 May 1911, 72 flights totalling 765 miles had been completed without having had to replace a single bolt or wire on No. 10. The spare machine, No. 11, still in its packing case, was sold to W. E. Hart, of Penrith, N.S.W., together with the unused spares, when the Mission left to return to England. Although this was the only direct sale made by both Missions, the Boxkite had by now begun to attract foreign buyers. The outcome of negotiations with the Russian Attaché in Paris, William

Rebikoff, was the first Government contract in the world for British aeroplanes, signed on 15 November 1910 for the supply of eight improved Boxkites having enlarged tanks and three rudders, which were called the Military model. The first three of these, Nos. 17, 18 and 19, were at first flown with 50 h.p. Gnomes, although 70 h.p. Gnomes had been specified for delivery in April 1911, when they were to become available. Meanwhile, No. 16, brought up to Military standard with three rudders but retaining its E.N.V. engine, was lent to Claude Grahame-White for an attempt to win the prize of £4,000 offered by Baron de Forest for a flight from England to the most distant point along the Continental coast. No. 16 was damaged by a storm while waiting to take off from Swingate Downs, Dover, but was repaired in time for a second attempt on 18 December 1910, when Grahame-White was caught by a down-gust at the cliff-edge and crashed. No. 17, which was at Brooklands, was at once dispatched as a replacement, but caught fire soon after arrival at Dover, and Grahame-White then retired from the contest on his doctor's advice. Lt. Loraine had also entered the competition, flying No. 8, but this too was badly damaged in the storm; No. 16 was eventually rebuilt and flown again at Brooklands. In April Nos. 18 and 19 were shipped to St. Petersburg together with Nos. 20 to 25 inclusive, after installation of 70 h.p. Gnome engines, but were later exchanged for two new machines, Nos. 26 and 30, in July 1911. No. 18 was damaged in transit back to Filton and written off, but No. 19 survived at Larkhill until May 1913, when it was dismantled and reconstructed as No. 134, which in turn was crashed at the Brooklands school in November 1913.

Still no contract came from the British War Office, and the next two Boxkites, Nos. 27 and 28, were standard school machines bought by the Belgian pilot Joseph Christiaens, who chose them for his flying displays in Malaya and South Africa. He took delivery of them on 19 January 1911, and after successful flights at Singapore on No. 27 went on to Cape Town and Pretoria, where he sold No. 28 to John Weston, who became the Company's agent in South Africa. A further school machine, No. 29, was sent to Brooklands in February 1911 and then two special exhibition models were built, having 70 h.p. Gnome engines, enclosed nacelles and increased span. The first, No. 31, was exhibited at Olympia in March 1911, and the second, No. 32, at St. Petersburg in April. The latter was inspected by the Czar and so impressed his military advisers that a gold medal and certificate of merit were awarded to the Company; and No. 32 was purchased in addition to the eight already ordered.

The War Office at last placed a contract, on 14 March 1911, for four Military Boxkites with 50 h.p. Gnomes as described in a specification submitted on 20 October 1910. Meanwhile Oscar Morison had damaged No. 12A while giving exhibition flights at Brighton, and No. 34 was taken from the production line to replace it. The first two War Office machines, Nos. 37 and 38, were delivered at Larkhill on 18 and 25 May, respectively, but then the War Office asked for the other two to be supplied with 60 h.p. Renault engines for comparison. This required a redesign of the engine mounting and carlingue, which resulted in a substantial nacelle structure in front of the pilot. No. 39, thus modified, was delivered at Larkhill on 9 July, by which time four more had been ordered, two with 50 h.p. Gnomes and two as spare airframes without engines. The latter (Nos. 40 and 41) were dispatched on 31 July, the second Renault machine (No. 42) on 2 August and the remaining Gnome machines (Nos. 48 and 49) during the subsequent fortnight. Nos. 43 and 47 were standard school Boxkites, the first being supplied to

Jullerot on No. 39 (60 hp Renault) at Larkhill, July 1911.

Larkhill while the second was taken to France by Versepuy when he returned in September 1911; he demonstrated it at Issy-les-Moulineaux and Vichy, where his mechanic was George Little; subsequently he sold it to the Bulgarian Government, to be flown by Lt. Loultchieff.

By this time the Boxkite production line had become well established and continued, mainly to supply wastage at the various schools, until 1914. In the standard models the wing extensions were retained but the third rudder was deleted. Strict interchangeability of components was maintained, and many later school machines incorporated serviceable parts from earlier aircraft. The 50 h.p. Gnome remained as the standard power unit except for No. 60 and No. 139, which had 70 h.p. Gnomes. The latter machine was supplied to R.N.A.S. Eastchurch in April 1913, receiving Naval serial no. 35, and was standard except for the engine, but No. 60 was similar to Nos. 31 and 32 with an enclosed nacelle, also incorporating longitudinal tanks and a push-pull handwheel control instead of the simple control-stick; this was demonstrated at Cuatros Vientos by Busteed in November 1911 and purchased soon afterwards by the Spanish Government, who ordered a similar spare airframe (No. 79) in which they fitted one of their own 70 h.p. Gnomes. Including rebuilds which received new sequence numbers, the total number of Boxkites built was 76, all at Filton except for the final six (Nos. 394–399), which were the first aeroplanes constructed at the Tramways Company's Brislington works. Although underpowered and out-dated at the end of their career, they survived mishandling often to the point of demolition, but the pupils emerged more or less unscathed and the mechanics performed daily miracles of reconstruction, so that school machines were constantly reappearing Phoenix-like from their own wreckage. Apart from the nine exported to Russia, three were sold to South Africa, two each to Australia, Germany and Spain, and one each to Bulgaria, India, Rumania and Sweden.

In addition to the Boxkite proper, there were two variants, both for competition work. The first of these was No. 44, which had wings of much reduced span and a small single-seat nacelle. This was for Maurice Tétard in the Circuit de l'Europe (racing no. 3) and was first flown on 30 May 1911; in the race it developed engine trouble and Tétard retired at Rheims, half-way through the first stage. The other was No. 69 and was a redesign in November 1911 by Gabriel Voisin using standard wings, but with the gap reduced and the front elevator and booms deleted; a single large tail plane and a single rudder replaced the normal biplane tail unit. It was sent to Larkhill for tests in February 1912. No photograph of this machine has survived and it was apparently soon rebuilt as a standard school Boxkite, in which form it was crashed at Larkhill by Major Forman on 3 November 1912.

Three Boxkite replicas were constructed in 1964 for the film *The*

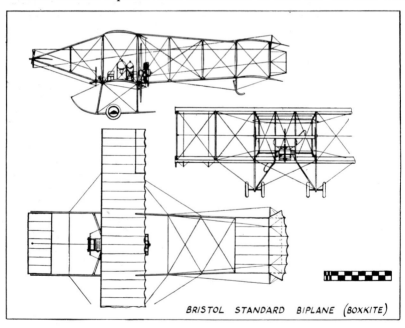

BRISTOL STANDARD BIPLANE (BOXKITE)

Magnificent Men in their Flying Machines. The specification called for historical accuracy apart from using a modern powerplant adequately disguised to give the impression of being an original engine.

A Rolls-Royce Continental flat-four engine of 65 h.p. was initially installed, but flight testing showed that more power was needed and it was replaced by a 90 h.p. Continental. The change was made because the modern engine provided thrust at high engine rpm using a small-diameter propeller which was not as efficient at Boxkite airspeeds as the old Gnome propeller of larger diameter which ran at half the rpm. After flight testing the Boxkites were used with success for both flying and ground scenes in the film—and also undertook a number of cross-country flights between filming locations.

Air Cdre Alan Wheeler, who was responsible for the replica aircraft used in the film, said that the detailed design of the Boxkite was up to the highest standard of engineering practice for 1910, as would be expected from a first-class engineering concern in a city which had made the phrase 'shipshape and Bristol fashion' accepted worldwide as denoting good workmanship. This reputation was further enhanced when on stressing the Boxkite it was found that the structure compared well with the current British Civil Airworthiness Requirements.

Two of the replica Boxkites made for the film are still in existence. One is in the Bristol City Museum; it now has a Gnome engine provided through the Rolls-Royce Bristol Engine Division. The other is with the Shuttleworth Collection at Old Warden airfield in Bedfordshire, where it takes part in occasional flying displays.

SPECIFICATION AND DATA

Type: Bristol Biplane (Boxkite)

Manufacturers: The British & Colonial Aeroplane Co. Ltd., Filton and Brislington, Bristol

Power Plant: One 50 hp Grégoire, 50/60 hp E.N.V., 50 hp Gnome, 60 hp Renault, or 70 hp Gnome

Model	Standard	Extended (Military)	Racer No. 44	Voisin No. 69
Span	34 ft 6 in	47 ft 8 in or 46 ft 6 in	35 ft	32 ft 8 in
Length	38 ft 6 in	38 ft 6 in	38 ft	30 ft 9 in
Height	11 ft 10 in	11 ft 10 in	11 ft 10 in	9 ft 6 in
Wing Area	457 sq ft	517 sq ft	350 sq ft	420 sq ft
Empty Weight	800 lb	900 lb	800 lb	800 lb
All-up Weight	1,050 lb	1,150 lb	1,000 lb	1,000 lb
Speed	40 mph	40 mph	50 mph	50 mph
Accommodation	2	2		2
Production	16	60	1	1
Sequence Nos.	7–11 12A 14 34 43 49 55 61– 63 65 66	12 15–32 37–42 47 48 60 67 79 93 99 119 124–129 133–139 179 180 203 204 207 222 226 347 394–399	44	69

The Bristol Glider, October 1910.

The Bristol Glider

The Bristol Glider was a biplane designed by George Challenger for presentation by Sir George White to the Bristol and West of England Aero Club, of which Sir George was elected President in October 1910; this was a thriving organisation boasting over 75 members. The Glider was designed to carry two persons and was intended to take an engine of 30 h.p. at a later stage. It was sturdily constructed, with double-surfaced mainplanes and tailplane; ailerons were fitted to the upper wing only and the forward and aft elevators were coupled. Two very small rudders were mounted between the upper and lower tail-booms forward of the aft elevator and a conventional control system was used. The Glider was first flown at the Club's flying ground near Keynsham, Somerset, on 17 December 1910, with Challenger at the controls; it was hand-towed down a slope by ropes attached to the lower wing-tips, and a two-wheeled dolly was used for uphill retrieval. On 27 February 1911 it was damaged and was repaired by the Company for the nominal cost of 12s. 6d., but on 4 September 1911 it was more severely crashed and the repairs then cost £30. No engine was ever installed, but the Glider appears to have survived at least until 1912; as it was constructed to Sir George's private order, it had no Bristol sequence number.

SPECIFICATION AND DATA

Type:	Glider
Manufacturers:	The British & Colonial Aeroplane Co. Ltd., Filton, Bristol
Power Plant:	Nil (provision for 30 hp later)
Span:	32 ft 4 in
Length:	33 ft 10 in
Height:	6 ft 8 in

Biplane No. 33, March 1911.

The Bristol Racing Biplane (1911)

The Bristol biplane No. 33 (dubbed 'The Racer'), a single-seater designed by Grandseigne and Versepuy under the supervision of George Challenger in the winter of 1910–11, was an attempt to combine a monoplane's performance with a biplane's structural advantages. It had double-surfaced wings of unequal span, the upper being inversely tapered. The wings, built round single steel-tube spars, were designed to warp for lateral control and to be readily folded for storage. A large fixed tailplane carried divided elevators, with an unbalanced rudder mounted above with no fin. The fuselage was rectangular in section, of composite steel-tube and wood construction and fabric-covered throughout its length. The engine, a 50 h.p. Gnome mounted on double bearers, was enclosed in an aluminium cowl. The sturdy twin-skid steel-tube chassis was attached to the lower longerons, carrying two wheels on a rubber-sprung cross-axle stabilised by telescopic struts attached to the upper longerons. The main skids extended back to act as brakes when landing, a flexible tail skid being also fitted. The Racer deserved better success than to be wrecked by overturning on its first attempted flight at Larkhill in April 1911, soon after being shown on the Bristol stand at Olympia.

SPECIFICATION AND DATA

Type: Racing Biplane (1911)
Manufacturers: The British & Colonial Aeroplane Co. Ltd., Filton, Bristol
Power Plant: One 50 hp Gnome
Span: 27 ft
Length: 25 ft
Wing Area: 210 sq ft

Empty Weight:	570 lb
All-up Weight:	750 lb
Speed:	55 mph (estimated)
Accommodation:	Pilot only
Production:	1 only
Sequence No.:	33

Monoplane No. 35, March 1911.

The Bristol Monoplane (1911)

The first Bristol monoplane was designed by George Challenger and Archibald Low in January 1911 and was a single-seater incorporating both Blériot and Antoinette features, having the warping wing of the former and the slim, triangular-section fuselage of the latter. The 50 h.p. Gnome engine was mounted in a steel frame, and the undercarriage was a simple arrangement of two wheels and a central skid anticipating that of the famous Avro 504 biplane. Two of these monoplanes (Nos. 35 and 36) were constructed in February 1911, and the first was sent to Larkhill for preliminary testing before returning to Filton to be prepared for the Olympia Exhibition in March. It attracted great interest there and the second monoplane was similarly shown at St. Petersburg from 23 to 30 April. When flight tests of No. 35 were attempted by Versepuy at Larkhill, the monoplane failed to take-off and was damaged, and no attempt was made to repair it, in view of Pierre Prier's impending arrival as a monoplane designer.

SPECIFICATION AND DATA

Type:	Tractor Monoplane (1911)			
Manufacturers:	The British & Colonial Aeroplane Co. Ltd., Filton, Bristol			
Power Plant:	One 50 hp Gnome			
Span:	33 ft 6 in			
Length:	31 ft 6 in	*Speed:*	55 mph (estimated)
Wing Area:	215 sq ft	*Accommodation:*	Pilot only
Empty Weight:	580 lb	*Production:*	2
All-up Weight:	760 lb	*Sequence Nos.:*	35, 36

Maurice Tabuteau starting from Vincennes on No. 45 in Circuit de l'Europe Race, June 1911.

The Bristol Biplane Type T

The racing Boxkite No. 44, flown by Tétard in the Circuit de l'Europe, has already been described. Contemporary with it was a single-seat biplane designed by George Challenger for Maurice Tabuteau. It was not a Boxkite variant, although it incorporated details based on Boxkite experience and also owed much to the practical advice of Capt. Dickson, for which reason it was often called the Challenger-Dickson biplane. The first of the type, No. 45, had long upswept skids similar to those of the Farman Longhorn, but was a more compact design. The engine, a 70 h.p. Gnome, was mounted at the back of a rectangular nacelle containing fuel and oil tanks arranged longitudinally behind the cockpit. A push-pull handwheel control was installed, as in the Zodiac, and the forward elevator was carried at the apex of the front booms and the chassis skids. A single tailplane, with the rear elevator hinged to it, had a pair of narrow chord balanced rudders mounted close together below, in the slipstream. The T-type biplane, its official designation, was intended for cross-country racing and Tabuteau was one of nine entrants who completed the Circuit de l'Europe course out of the 38 starters. The route of 1,025 miles was from Paris via Liège, Spa, Liège, Venlo, Utrecht, Breda, Brussels, Roubaix, Calais, Dover, Shoreham, Hendon, Dover, Calais back to Paris.

The vantage points which attracted most spectators were Calais and Dover, where there was the prospect of witnessing a mass crossing of the Channel for the first time, only seven crossings, including Blériot's first in 1909, having been previously accomplished. The 11 pilots who arrived at Dover did in fact all cross within 45 minutes of each other. Tabuteau lost his way to Hendon and landed at Northwood to ask his way; for such an emergency he carried a placard inscribed: "Hold back the aeroplane. Do not let it go only when I am in and raise the hands. Do not frighten if the motor makes noise and smoke and wind and above all do not let it go."

Four more T-type biplanes (Nos. 51–54) were built for entry in the Circuit of Britain race, for which the *Daily Mail* offered prize money totalling £10,000. They were to have been flown, respectively, by Graham Gilmour, Collyns Pizey, Gordon England and Howard Pixton, with Tabuteau also competing on No. 45. However, Tabuteau was unable to take part and Gilmour had had his aviator's certificate suspended by the Royal Aero Club for alleged dangerous flying over Henley Regatta on 7 July, so only Pizey, England and Pixton started. The new biplanes differed slightly from No. 45, having modified nacelles with normal control sticks and the rudders were set as far apart as possible, out of the middle of the slipstream. Nos. 52 and 53 had 70 h.p. Gnome engines, but No. 54 had a 60 h.p. Renault. The team was unlucky, for England had engine trouble and could not take-off, Pizey broke his undercarriage in landing near Melton Mowbray and Pixton was slightly injured in landing near Harrogate. After the race, Gilmour's machine, No. 51,

Collyns Pizey on No. 52 at Larkhill, June 1911.

was fitted with a 50 h.p. Gnome and sold on 22 July to Gerald Napier, a newly qualified pilot trained at the Brooklands school. On 1 August he made several practice flights, with somewhat erratic landings, and then he took-off again with a passenger, although the machine was only a single-seater. He stalled on a gliding turn and crashed, being killed, but his passenger was thrown clear and received only minor injuries. No further flying was done with T-type biplanes after this, although one of them was handed over to Gordon England for experimental work and he converted it into a tractor biplane with a 60 h.p. E.N.V. engine. This machine, No. 59, was called the Challenger-England and was delivered to Larkhill in November 1911. It was not very successful, and is notable chiefly because it had a fuel system comprising main tanks in the fuselage from which fuel was transferred by air pressure to a small gravity tank under the upper wing, thus preventing air bubbles from reaching the carburettor as so often happened with a direct feed from a pressurised tank. No. 59 was flown from time to time by advanced pupils (including Robert Smith-Barry) at Larkhill and, on 19 May 1912, was taxied into a crowd of spectators and overturned, one person being killed; after this it was dismantled. One further T-type biplane, No. 78, was never completed, but was to have had a 100 h.p. Gnome.

SPECIFICATION AND DATA

Type:	Biplane Type T
Manufacturers:	The British & Colonial Aeroplane Co. Ltd., Filton, Bristol
Power Plants:	One 70 hp Gnome
	One 60 hp Renault
	One 100 hp Gnome
Span:	35 ft
Length:	24 ft 6 in
Wing Area:	350 sq ft
Empty Weight:	800 lb
All-up Weight:	1,000 lb
Speed:	58 mph
Accommodation:	Pilot only
Production:	6
Sequence Nos.	45 51–54 78

Challenger-England No. 59 at Larkhill, December 1911.

SPECIFICATION AND DATA

Type:	Challenger-England
Manufacturers:	The British & Colonial Aeroplane Co. Ltd., Filton, Bristol
Power Plant:	One 50/60 hp E.N.V.
Span:	35 ft
Length:	23 ft
Wing Area:	350 sq ft
Accommodation:	Pilot only
Production:	One only
Sequence No.:	59

Pierre Prier with P-1, No. 46, at Larkhill, July 1911.

The Bristol-Prier Monoplanes

Pierre Prier was an experienced Blériot pilot and a qualified engineer, who made the first non-stop flight from London to Paris on 12 April, 1911, while he was chief instructor of the Blériot school at Hendon. He was keen to design aeroplanes to his own ideas and found the opportunity to do so when invited to join the British and Colonial Aeroplane Company's staff in June. He at once undertook the design of a fast single-seat monoplane to compete in the annual Gordon Bennett Cup race, at Eastchurch on 1 July, when it was to be flown by Graham Gilmour. In spite of all efforts, this monoplane, Type P-1, No. 46, could not be completed in time for the race, but two more (Nos. 56 and 57), of almost identical design but with overhung engine mountings, were put in hand for the Circuit of Britain competition, in which they were to be flown, respectively, by Prier himself and Oscar Morison. Unfortunately Prier crashed No. 56 on the morning of the race and meanwhile Morison injured his eye, so the Prier monoplane's debut had again to be postponed. The P-1 had a 50 h.p. Gnome engine and Blériot-type warping wings; its undercarriage had sprung skids, and the tail unit comprised a balanced

Sir George White inspects No. 56 at Larkhill, August 1911.

60

rudder and a single balanced elevator without any fixed surfaces. The designed top speed of 70 m.p.h. was achieved without difficulty, and the next development was to produce a useful two-seater version. The first of these, No. 58, was the prototype of a successful series of military and training monoplanes, which were produced in some numbers during 1912 and followed the Boxkite into service in military flying schools in Spain, Italy and Germany as well as at Larkhill, Brooklands and the Central Flying School. The single-seat version was also developed as a low-powered runabout for advanced solo pupils, for which purpose it was fitted with a three-cylinder Anzani radial engine of 35 h.p. Nos. 46 and 57 were the first to be so converted, and one new single-seater, No. 68, was built to the same standard. It was intended to install a 40 h.p. Clément Bayard flat-twin engine in No. 57 at a later date, but this engine shed its airscrew while being run on test, causing severe head injuries to Herbert Thomas which nearly proved fatal. No. 56 retained its Gnome engine, and was acquired, after repairs, by James Valentine, who flew it on a cross-country flight to qualify for one of the first Superior Certificates granted by the Royal Aero Club. In November 1911 he fitted it with a 40 h.p. Isaacson radial engine for entry in the British Michelin Cup no. 2 competition, which was restricted to all-British aircraft and pilots.

No. 56 re-engined with 40 hp Isaacson for James Valentine, 1911.

Prier and Valentine flew the two-seater, No. 58, extensively during September and October 1911 and satisfied the Directors that it was suitable for quantity production with a good prospect in foreign markets. A batch of six, Nos. 71–76, was laid down and the first was specially finished for exhibition at the Paris Salon de l'Aéronautique in December 1911, where it was the sole British representative. All steel parts were burnished and 'blued' to resist rust, aluminium panels were polished to mirror finish and the decking round the cockpits and the wing tread-plates were panelled in plywood. The seats were suspended on wires and, like the cockpit rims, were upholstered in pigskin. A cellulose acetate window was fitted in the sloping front bulkhead to give the passenger a downward view and a sketching board, map case and stowages for binoculars and vacuum flask were also provided. Each cockpit had a Clift compass and the cowling was extended well over the engine to prevent oil being thrown back. A speed of 65 m.p.h. was guaranteed and the price quoted was Fr. 23,750 (about £950). No. 71 was dispatched from Filton to Paris on 10 December 1911 and No. 72 was shipped to Cuatros Vientos for demonstration to the Spanish Army on 19 December. No. 73 had been sent incomplete to Larkhill in November as a replacement for No. 58 which had crashed on 30 October and No. 74 was rushed out to Issy-les-Moulineaux on 22 December, just before the Filton works closed for Christmas. So when the Paris Salon opened, visitors who had been impressed by the appearance of No. 71 were further delighted by seeing Valentine flying No. 74 round the Eiffel Tower. Valentine was in constant demand for further demonstrations, and on 2 January 1912 made a spectacular arrival with a passenger at St. Cyr in appalling weather just before dusk. A few days later, flying with Capt. Agostini of the Italian Army as passenger, Valentine found his landing baulked by troops, after a long glide with engine off. Unable to restart, he had to swerve through the top of a tree to find a clear space for landing, but, although a branch was carried away, only minor damage resulted. Capt. Agostini was so impressed by this evidence of sturdy construction that an order for two monoplanes arrived from the Italian Government before the end of the week.

Howard Pixton, who had gone to Madrid to demonstrate No. 72, was faced with a more formidable task than Valentine, for Cuatros Vientos is 3,000 ft. above sea level and the Spanish army tests included landing on and taking-off from a freshly ploughed field. The only other competitor, a German, declared this feat to be impossible, and Pixton, too, was worried about the loss of power at this altitude. Then Busteed arrived on Boxkite No. 60 and made short work of the ploughed field test and subsequently both machines were demonstrated to King Alfonso and his staff; the Spanish Government then adopted Bristol aeroplanes as standard equipment for its School of Military Aviation, both aircraft were purchased and two more Prier monoplanes and a further Boxkite were ordered.

When the Spanish trials ended Pixton was summoned to Döberitz, near Berlin, to demonstrate No. 74, which had been shipped to Germany when Valentine returned from Paris. Pixton flew the machine several times before German staff officers at Döberitz and once before the Kaiser at Potsdam. Once when Pixton was challenged by a Rumpler pilot to fly in very gusty conditions he easily out-manœuvred his rival, but misjudged his height and touched down at high speed, bounced high and then landed safely. Frank Coles, Pixton's mechanic, remarked that this was a test of the undercarriage and was able to warn Pixton before he had time to apologise for an error of judgment, but later a German pilot tried to do the same and came to grief. These demonstrations marked the formation of the Deutsche Bristol-Werke and its associated flying school at Halberstadt, to which No. 74 was handed over on 30 March 1912.

Meanwhile, on 11 January, the War Office had ordered a Prier monoplane for the Army Air Battalion, and on 17 February Lt. Reynolds took delivery of No. 75 at Larkhill. It was generally similar to No. 71 but had a strengthened

Warren Merriam with pupil in No. 73 at Larkhill, 1912.

rudder post and a cane tail skid with an aluminium shoe on the end. Like all Prier monoplanes, it was fitted with a Rubery Owen quick-release catch which could be attached to a rope and picket before starting and released from the cockpit, thus dispensing with wheel chocks and the helpers who were always liable to damage the floating elevator. The last of the initial batch, No. 76, was a two-seater like the others, but was equipped for alternative use as a long-range single-seater, with a combined auxiliary fuel and oil tank to fit the front seat and a waterproof cover for the front cockpit. No. 76 was delivered to the Italian Government on 4 April, and a similar machine from the second production batch, No. 84, followed on 1 June.

The second batch (Nos. 81–91 and 94–98) comprised both single-seaters and two-seaters, and several of the latter were an improved model introduced by Capt. Dickson, having a fixed tailplane and a hinged elevator and the fuselage lengthened by 30 in. The first of this Prier-Dickson type was No. 82, which was sent to Larkhill on 27 July 1912 and proved very successful. No. 81 was a single-seater with Anzani engine similar to No. 68 and was sent to Spain in April, together with No. 83, a two-seater similar to No. 72. No. 83 crashed before acceptance by the Spanish authorities, and No. 82 was then sent to Spain as a replacement, but not before the advantages of the revised fuselage and tail had been noted by the Royal Flying Corps at Larkhill.

Single-seater No. 81, sold to Spain in March 1912.

63

Prier-Dickson No. 75 (*256*) at Farnborough in March 1913.

Consequently, when No. 75 needed repairs in June, it was modified to the new standard and redelivered as a Prier-Dickson, bearing its new military number *256*. Almost at once it crashed, but was again repaired at Filton and returned to service on 23 July 1912. Only two more 'short' Prier two-seaters were built, No. 90 which went to Italy in September and No. 94 (largely a rebuild of No. 71) which was demonstrated by Pixton at Bucharest in May and then returned to Brooklands as a trainer, being finally crashed by Lindsay Campbell on 10 August 1912. No. 85 was a Prier-Dickson for the German Government and was delivered on 4 June; Nos. 86 and 88 were similar machines with 70 h.p. Gnomes for the Turkish Government and were dispatched in July to Constantinople, where Coles erected and Pixton tested them. No. 87 was delivered to the Bulgarian Government at Sofia on 16 September; it was flown in the Balkan War and once carried Hubert Wilkins (later famous as a polar explorer) as a passenger to take films for a London newspaper. No. 89 was the third two-seater for Italy, shipped on 14 August, while No. 91 was the second machine for the Royal Flying Corps, who took delivery on 23 August 1912, allotting it serial *261*. The remainder of the second batch were Anzani-engined single-seaters generally similar to No. 81; Nos. 95 and 96 were sent to Italy in May 1912 and were returned to Filton, intact but well worn, as late as January 1914. No. 97 was built for the Larkhill school in May 1912, but was wrecked a month later, when No. 98 was built as its replacement; the latter had a fixed tailplane, as did the final Prier single-seater, No. 102, which went to Larkhill in November as an additional school machine.

After Prier left the Company in 1912, Coanda perpetuated the long-fuselage model for school duties, and three more were built before December 1912. Of these, No. 130 crashed on a test flight, being rebuilt as No. 155 and retained at Larkhill school. No. 156 was sold to the Deutsche Bristol-Werke school at Halberstadt. Coanda also introduced a side-by-side variant of the Prier-Dickson, of which three were built, No. 107 for the Halberstadt school in June, with No. 109 following as a spare airframe in December, while No. 108 was delivered to the Larkhill school in October and was crashed by Major Hewetson on 18 July 1913. The side-by-side variant was described in one of the Company's catalogues as the 'Sociable' model, the tandem two-seater being called the 'Military' and the single-seater the 'Popular', but these appellations failed to gain currency. Thirty-four Prier monoplanes were built in all between July 1911 and December 1912.

SPECIFICATION AND DATA

Type: Prier Monoplanes
Manufacturers: The British & Colonial Aeroplane Co. Ltd., Filton, Bristol
Power Plants: One 50 hp Gnome (P-1 and 2-seaters)
One 70 hp Gnome (2-seater long-body)
One 35 hp Anzani ⎫
One 40 hp Isaacson ⎬ single-seaters
One 40 hp Clément-Bayard ⎭ only

Model	P-1	single seat school	two seat short body	two seat long body	two-seat side-by-side
Span	30 ft 2 in	30 ft 2 in	32 ft 9 in	34 ft	35 ft 6 in
Length	24 ft 6 in	24 ft 6 in	24 ft 6 in	26 ft	26 ft
Height	9 ft 9 in	9 ft 9 in	9 ft 9 in	9 ft 9 in	9 ft 9 in
Wing Area	166 sq ft	166 sq ft	185 sq ft	200 sq ft	200 sq ft
Empty Weight	640 lb	620 lb	650 lb	660 lb	660 lb
All-up Weight	820 lb	780 lb	1,000 lb	1,080 lb	1,080 lb
Speed	68 mph	58 mph	65 mph	65 mph	65 mph
Accommodation	1	1	2	2	2
Production	3	7	11	10	3
Sequence Nos.	46 56 57	68 81 95– 98 102	58 71–76 83 84 90 94	82 85–89 91 130 155 156	107–109

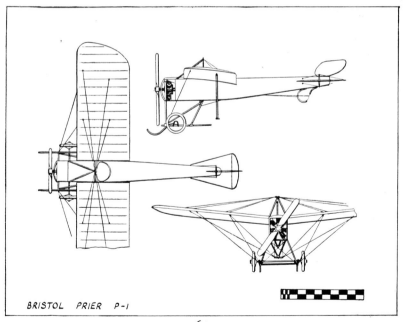

BRISTOL PRIER P-1

G.E.1 No. 64 in its original form at Larkhill, March 1912.

The Bristol Gordon England Biplanes

Eric Gordon England gained his Royal Aero Club aviator's certificate (no. 68) on 25 August 1911 at the Bristol flying school at Brooklands. Previously he had helped José Weiss in gliding experiments at Amberley in Sussex, and before joining the Bristol school he had had some experience of flying a Hanriot monoplane at Brooklands. Soon after gaining his certificate he joined the Company as a staff pilot and almost his first assignment was to fly a T-type biplane in the Circuit of Britain race. Later the same year he made several demonstration tours on a Boxkite with Graham Gilmour in Dorset and Hampshire and the Isle of Wight.

He soon showed promise as a designer, and his conversion of a T-type biplane into a tractor machine, No. 59, has already been described. His second venture, the G.E.1 biplane (No. 64), was entirely original and much more successful. The design was begun as early as August 1911 in an attempt to provide a sturdy military two-seater with wings which could be quickly detached to facilitate transport in an army column. Most of the structure was of spruce and the front of the fuselage was plywood-covered. Side-by-side seating with dual hand-wheel control was provided and a Bosch self-starting trembler coil and battery were installed. A sturdy undercarriage with a central skid gave good taxying qualities on rough ground and protected the large slow-running airscrew, which was driven at half-engine speed through a chain by a neatly installed 50 h.p. Clerget upright four-cylinder watercooled engine, with a frontal radiator and hinged bonnet like a car. The wings were of equal span and the tail surfaces were long and tapered. It was an advanced and logical design, but the engine was hardly powerful enough to do it justice. After tests during May and June it was fitted with a large balanced rudder to improve stability, and on 19 June 1912 it was sold to the Deutsche Bristol-Werke, who, however, found it unsuitable for school use and returned it on 21 September 1912 to Filton, where it was scrapped.

66

No. 64 with modified radiator and empennage at Larkhill, July 1912.

The G.E.1 was at one point taken as the basis for Lt. C. D. Burney's hydrovane seaplane, and the X.1 derived from it is described later. Although underpowered, it was considered to be worth developing and an improved design, G.E.2, was put in hand for the Military Aeroplane Competition of August 1912. Two G.E.2 biplanes were built, No. 103 having a 100 h.p. double-row Gnome engine direct-coupled to the airscrew, while No. 104 had a 70 h.p. watercooled Daimler-Mercedes engine with a two-to-one chain drive and nose radiator as in No. 64. No. 104 also had an Eisemann dual-ignition set for self-starting and was the only entry in the competition to be efficiently silenced, as required by the rules. Both aircraft were similar in construction to No. 64, but had round-tipped wings with increased gap and the fuselage was raised above the lower wing to improve airscrew clearance.

The G.E.2 biplanes (competition numbers *12* and *13*) were to be flown, respectively, by Gordon England himself and Howard Pixton. The Daimler engine failed to develop full power and the unlucky number *13* had to be withdrawn early in the trials, but soon afterwards England damaged number *12* in a heavy landing and had to retire also. Just before this accident, England had a somewhat hair-raising experience. He had flown for 90 min., without much use of the controls, for the machine was remarkably stable, but found

G.E.2 No. 104 (Daimler) at Larkhill in August 1912.

67

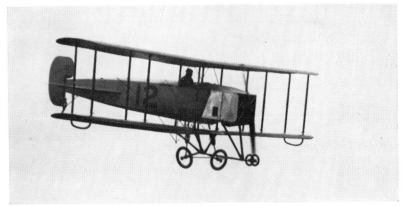

G.E.2 No. 103 (Gnome) flying at Larkhill in August 1912.

when he came in to land that the elevator movement was very restricted. He landed safely by using the engine switch, which was arranged to cut the ignition of one row of cylinders at a time, so providing some measure of engine-speed control. It transpired that England's mechanic, Temple Robins, had been making adjustments in the cockpit and had tied the elevator cables together to prevent their movement in the wind, and that England had been in a hurry to fly and had omitted the customary check for control freedom.

Gordon England's final Bristol design, the G.E.3, was a large long-range biplane to a Turkish Government specification, with two seats in tandem and an 80 h.p. Gnome engine. The fuselage was faired to a circular section and large brass fuel and oil tanks were fitted in the fairings between the cockpits, giving a duration of 3 hours. The tanks were pressurised by a wind-driven air pump under the fuselage and delivered fuel to a gravity tank in the decking between the cockpits. The wings were similar to those of G.E.2 and readily detachable for road transport.

Two G.E.3 biplanes were built, Nos. 112 and 113, but when flown the wing spars were found to bow upwards between the struts. The design was then abandoned, because by this time the Italian blockade of Turkish ports pre—

G.E.3 No. 113 at Filton in November 1912; note kingpost bracing to stiffen rear spars.

vented delivery. Gordon England left the Company shortly afterwards to join James Radley in a seaplane project and subsequently became a well-known figure in the motor-car and petroleum industries.

SPECIFICATION AND DATA

Type: Gordon England Biplanes

Manufacturers: The British & Colonial Aeroplane Co. Ltd., Filton, Bristol

Model	G.E.1	G.E.2	G.E.2	G.E.3
Power Plant	50 hp Clerget	70 hp Daimler	100 hp Gnome	80 hp Gnome
Span	33 ft 8 in	40 ft	40 ft	39 ft
Length	29 ft	31 ft	31 ft	28 ft 5 in
Wing Area	320 sq ft	400 sq ft	400 sq ft	387 sq ft
Empty Weight		1,100 lb	1,080 lb	1,096 lb
All-up Weight		2,000 lb	1,980 lb	1,996 lb
Speed	65 mph	62 mph	68 mph	65 mph
Accommodation	2	2	2	2
Production	1	1	1	2
Sequence Nos.	64	104	103	112 113

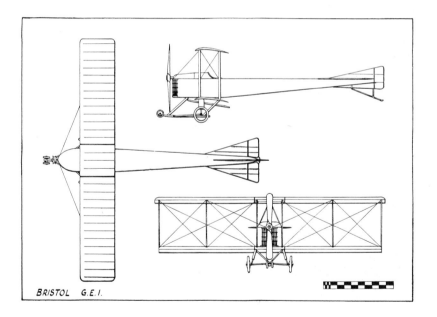

BRISTOL G.E.1.

Coanda School monoplane No. 132 at Filton in November 1912.

The Bristol-Coanda Monoplanes

Henri Coanda, son of Gen. Coanda the Rumanian War Minister, had trained as an engineer in France and was an artist of merit as well. He had studied under Eiffel, whose wind-tunnel at Auteuil was the first to be built in Europe. At the Paris Salon of 1910, Coanda exhibited a novel biplane whose engine drove, not an airscrew, but a small-diameter ducted fan. It is uncertain whether this biplane ever flew, as has been claimed, but Coanda deserves due credit for originating this form of propulsion unit. Another of Coanda's projects was a tandem-wing monoplane with a submerged engine driving an airscrew mounted half-way along a streamlined circular-section fuselage.

Coanda joined the Company's staff in January 1912, and his first product at Filton was an orthodox tandem two-seater monoplane (No. 77) derived from the Prier-Dickson. The wings were structurally similar to Prier's, having two tubular steel spars filled with wood, on to which the ribs were threaded and located by clips so that they were free to rotate round the spars for warping. In Prier's design the front spars were always longer than the rear, giving a forward rake to the tip, but this somewhat restricted the range of warping movement available. Coanda's wings had their tips raked the opposite way, with the rear spar longer than the front, which resulted in a longer flexible trailing edge. The wings were braced above and below to steel tube pylons, the control pulleys being enclosed in streamline fairings at the apex of each pylon. The 50 h.p. Gnome engine was surrounded by a circular cowling, which prevented oil from being thrown back to the cockpits. The undercarriage had steel-tube skids of the type originated by Grandseigne, and the cockpits were furnished with wicker seats and had non-inflammable celluloid windows in the fuselage sides. No. 77 was sent to Larkhill on 27 March 1912 and remained there for testing for some weeks. A second monoplane, No. 80,

70

was similar but had side-by-side seats with dual controls. It was built in May 1912 and remained in continuous use as a school machine at Brooklands and Larkhill until crashed by Merriam and Gipps on 26 January 1914. Both these models were offered as suitable for training purposes and eventually five more of the tandem version and six more of the side-by-side version were built, all with 50 h.p. Gnomes, during 1913. Of the tandem version, No. 132 went to Italy and Nos. 185, 186, 188 and 189 to Rumania; and of the side-by-side version, Nos. 110 and 165 went to Italy and Nos. 164, 166 and 176 to Rumania, while the last, No. 177, was retained at Larkhill and was finally converted into the one and only side-by-side Coanda biplane No. 218.

On 15 May 1912 the War Office announced conditions for the Military Aeroplane Competition, and it was found that the competing aircraft had to be designed and built by 15 July! It was, of course, impossible to produce a new design specially to meet the conditions in only two months, and in any case the prize money, limited to £5,000 to any one entrant, hardly justified an all-out effort of this kind. However, Coanda had already made good progress with a new design for a military monoplane and two of these were entered, together with the two G.E.2 biplanes, in the competition. The rules laid great emphasis on suitability for reconnaissance and ease of maintenance and transport. Dual controls were required, together with a good view downwards and good stability, and the pilot was expected to start his engine and operate from unprepared fields without assistance. The aircraft had to be tendered at Larkhill packed in a rail transport crate not longer than 32 ft. and had to be capable of being towed on its own wheels or trolley in an army column. The flying tests were stringent and included duration, speed, altitude and climb minima, together with landing on various surfaces and quick take-off from a harrowed field. At least one flight had to be made in a wind averaging 25 m.p.h.

Coanda's two competition monoplanes, Nos. 105 and 106, were both equipped with the new 80 h.p. Gnome engine. Great attention had been paid to drag reduction and the usual pyramids of cabane struts were replaced by a pair of vertical steel pylons on the fuselage centre-line carefully faired with wood. The passenger's cockpit was between these pylons and the pilot's just behind, so that from a distance the machine appeared to have a crew of four. The wings were of the same type as on No. 77 and their cables had quick release clips for easy dismantling. The cockpit sides had celluloid windows and the trailing edges were cut back at the wing roots to improve the pilot's view. Like all Coanda monoplanes they had a semicircular fixed tailplane and a one-piece elevator, with a balanced rudder above. Busteed experienced directional instability on No. 105 with the original rudder, and a smaller Prier-type rudder was tried in conjunction with a fixed fin, but this was no better and the trouble was finally cured by a balanced rudder of re-vised outline. Nos. 105 and 106 (competition numbers *14* and *15*) were flown by Busteed and Valentine, respectively. Valentine, attempting the duration test of 3 hours in *15* had engine failure while approaching a flock of sheep and struck a fence in attempting to avoid them. The damage was soon repaired, but Valentine withdrew from the trials and Pixton was allowed to take his place.

Both Busteed and Pixton did well in the ensuing tests and eventually shared third place with the British Deperdussin in the final assessment and were awarded £500 each. Pixton excelled in the rough weather test, with Capt. Patrick Hamilton, R.F.C., as passenger, when he took-off and remained up for over 15 min. in violent gusts whose recorded speed varied from 17 to 44 m.p.h. Pixton also headed the list in the range test with 420 miles, while Busteed was third in the high speed test with 73 m.p.h., only 2 m.p.h. less than the best. Neither succeeded in taking-off from a harrowed field and Coanda quickly appreciated that the wing-loading was somewhat too high; all subsequent monoplanes of the type had larger wings and the details were carefully redesigned to save weight. These improvements could have been made before the competition began, had more time been available.

Busteed in Coanda No. 106, competing at Larkhill in August 1912.

Both Nos. 105 and 106 were bought by the War Office and received military serials *263* and *262* respectively. Training was begun on them in preparation for the autumn manœuvres, and on 10 September Edward Hotchkiss, by then a second-Lt. in the Special Reserve, with Lt. C. A. Bettington, R.F.C., as passenger, left Larkhill to fly to Hardwick, near Cambridge, on *263*. They intended to land at the Port Meadow, Oxford, and while gliding down from 2,000 ft. above Wolvercote Hotchkiss lost control; the descent became a steep dive and the starboard wing fabric tore off, both men being killed instantly. It appeared that the quick-release clip of one of the flying wires had become detached, but, as this was not the first of several similar accidents, the War Office somewhat summarily banned the flying of all monoplanes by pilots of the Military Wing, R.F.C.; no such ban was imposed on Naval pilots by the Admiralty and indeed the War Office ban was lifted five months later, but it ended the Company's hopes of supplying Coanda monoplanes in quantity to the Royal Flying Corps. Foreign interest in the design remained, however, and enquiries were received from Italy and Rumania for the improved model with span increased from 40 ft. to 42 ft. 9 in., which became standardised for production.

A single experimental variant, which was not a success, emerged in September 1912 alongside the first of the production batch. This was No. 111, nicknamed *The Elephant*. It was intended to compete with the strongly built Etrich and D.F.W. monoplanes favoured by the German Army and had a welded steel-tube landing gear with a central skid; the shock absorbers were telescopic struts containing coil springs and the half-axles could be moved by a tiller-bar for ground steering. The engine was the 70 h.p. Daimler-Mercedes from the unlucky G.E.2 biplane, and the machine was sent to Larkhill for testing with two sets of wings, one set being of normal profile, while the other had a very pronounced camber based on the aerofoil section known as the 'Phillips Entry'. It was seriously overweight and failed to fly successfully with either set of wings, so was never sent to Deutsche Bristol-Werke as had been intended.

The first production Coanda military monoplane, No. 118, had extra fuel and oil tanks and an enlarged rudder and was taken to Bucharest in September by Prince Cantacuzene, head of the Rumanian military aviation mission which had come to Larkhill to study 'Bristol' methods and products. Pixton demonstrated this monoplane in the Rumanian army manœuvres with great success. Two others, Nos. 121 and 122, were built for the Italian government, and No. 122 was dispatched to Turin on 13 November, but No. 121 remained at Larkhill and was destined to have a remarkable career. The fourth production monoplane in the batch was No. 123, which was Prince Cantacuzene's personal mount, but he crashed it while taxying, and after being rebuilt as No. 142, it became a static test airframe. The next of the series, No. 131, was specially finished for the Paris Salon of 1912, with a streamlined chassis with filleted strut junctions. It so impressed the Italian authorities that they purchased it in preference to No. 121 and ordered 12 more for urgent delivery. Rumania also ordered ten, and both countries had sent officers to Larkhill for instruction in December. No. 131 was despatched to Turin on 6 December 1912, together with school monoplane No. 132, as initial equipment for the Italian military aviation school.

Enthusiasm for the Coanda monoplane increased as experience was gained, and the Company appeared to have overcome the set-back caused by the War Office ban. A new production batch of 12 monoplanes was laid down, numbered 143 to 154 inclusive, the first two being retained at Larkhill for test and demonstration, and No. 145, which had a modified chassis, being sent to Spain on 23 December after a marathon effort to dispatch it before the Christmas holiday. No. 146, the first of four for Rumania, was not ready until February 1913, having been held up while Coanda rechecked the stress calculations and performed static tests with sand-bags on the inverted airframe of No. 142, at the request of Prince Cantacuzene. Satisfied with the results, all was ready for acceptance flight testing to begin as soon as the weather permitted, and on 5 March 1913 Gordon England's younger brother Geoffrey undertook a 1 hour duration test on No. 146 although the wind was still too strong for the altitude test. After flying for 39 min., the machine was struck by a violent gust which caused the port wing to collapse and Geoffrey

Coanda Military monoplane No. 150 flying at Halberstadt in 1913.

England was killed. Prior to this accident the Coanda monoplane had been selected for purchase by the Italian National Subscription, which had raised nearly £800,000 to buy aeroplanes for the army and had ordered 36 more of the type to be built in Italy by Italian labour. The Company had been asked to grant a manufacturing licence to an established firm in Italy, and Caproni & Faccanoni, of Vizzola Ticino, had been recommended as the most reliable of the three or four constructors of that time. A condition for granting the licence was that the first few Italian-built machines should be test-flown by Bristol pilots, and the formal agreement setting up the Societa Italiana Bristol Aeroplani was signed on 31 December 1912 by Henry White Smith, who, with Capt. Dickson, had supervised the Caproni factory arrangements. These included the supply from Filton of a complete skeleton monoplane (No. 154) as a pattern and the loan of a picked party of Filton erectors to teach their Italian colleagues 'Bristol' methods in addition to the normal provision of drawings and data.

Delivery tests of Nos. 122, 131 and 132 were undertaken by Sidney Sippe, who had just joined the Bristol staff, and in December Pixton went to Turin on his return from Rumania and put No. 131 through its paces, breaking records for climb and speed with full load. He then went to Madrid and during the trials of No. 145 at Cuatros Vientos repeated his Turin performance. He also took up as passengers the Infante of Spain and his uncle, Prince Leopold of Battenburg. Meanwhile Sippe remained in Italy to await assembly of the first two Caproni-built monoplanes. These were generally satisfactory in workmanship, but the warp control was found to be immovable and on examination it was found that the ribs had been bolted to the spars, thus destroying the flexibility of the wing which was an essential feature of the design. In January a new flying school, based on Larkhill practice, was opened at Malpensa and Collyns Pizey went out to begin instruction. He stayed until April when new Italian military aircraft trials were to be held between Turin and

74

Milan, for which two Caproni-Bristols had been entered. The events were ruined by incessant rain, turning the flying ground into a sea of mud, and the Caproni-Bristols proved unequal to the task. As a result the Italian Government cancelled the Bristol contract and after a prolonged dispute which lasted until January 1918 the Caproni-Bristol licence was cancelled.

After the loss of No. 146, delivery of the remainder of the Rumanian monoplanes was held in abeyance, but a specially finished Coanda monoplane, No. 153, was exhibited at Olympia in February, featuring wheel brakes and armoured glass fuselage windows. Together with Nos. 150 and 151, it was sent to the Deutsche Bristol-Werke in April 1913, but Nos. 151 and 153 were returned to Filton in August. No. 152 was held as a replacement for No. 146 on the Rumanian contract, and the final example, No. 196, was one of the Caproni-Bristols shipped to Filton in August 1913 for conversion into a biplane. The Rumanian monoplanes were fitted with strengthened wings, but this detracted seriously from their performance and eventually a happy compromise was found in the conversion of the whole batch into biplanes, which proved very successful indeed.

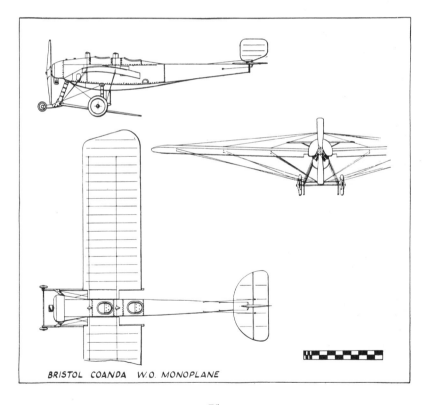

BRISTOL COANDA W.O. MONOPLANE

Type: Coanda Monoplanes

Manufacturers: The British & Colonial Aeroplane Co., Ltd., Filton, Bristol
Deutsche Bristol-Werke, Halberstadt, Germany
Caproni & Faccanoni, Vizzola Ticino, Varese, Italy

Model	School	Side by side	Competition	Daimler	Military
Power plant	50 hp Gnome	50 hp Gnome	80 hp Gnome	70 hp Daimler	80 hp Gnome
Span	40 ft	41 ft 3 in	40 ft	39 ft 4 in	42 ft 9 in
Length	27 ft	27 ft	28 ft 3 in	30 ft 9 in	29 ft 2 in
Height	7 ft	7 ft	7 ft	7 ft	7 ft
Wing Area	275 sq ft	275 sq ft	242 sq ft	260 sq ft	280 sq ft
Empty Weight	770 lb	770 lb	1,000 lb	1,200 lb	1,050 lb
All-up Weight	1,100 lb	1,100 lb	1,710 lb	1,850 lb	1,775 lb
Speed	65 mph	65 mph	73 mph	60 mph	71 mph
Accommodation	2	2	2	2	2
Production	6	7	2	1	20
Sequence Nos.	77 132	80 110 164–	105 106	111	118 121–
	185 186	166 176 177			123 131
	188 189				142–154
					(196 + one in
					Italy)

Busteed flying B.R.7 No. 157 at Larkhill, 1913.

The Bristol-Coanda Two-seat Biplanes

When the flying of monoplanes by pilots of the Military Wing, Royal
Flying Corps, was banned in September 1912, the loss of the potential War
Office market for the Coanda monoplane was partly mitigated by the award of
a contract to build the officially designed B.E.2 biplane, which, although
ineligible for the Military Aeroplane Competition, had performed rather
better than the actual prizewinners. The fact that a biplane could match the
monoplane's performance without sacrificing its advantages of strength and

76

stiffness led Coanda to draft a Bristol biplane design, and by November enquiries for a long-range two-seater had come from both Spain and Germany. Coanda preferred the well-tried 80 h.p. Gnome engine, but the enquirers insisted on engines already in use in their own fleets; consequently the Spanish specified the 70 h.p. Renault because it was standardised for their Maurice Farmans, while the Deutsche Bristol-Werke were under government pressure to use the 90 h.p. Daimler-Mercedes. In November 1912, therefore, Coanda began the design of a two-seater biplane suitable for either the Renault or the Daimler-Mercedes. Early in 1913 a Spanish purchasing mission, led by Col. Pedro Vives-y-Vych, visited Filton and Larkhill, and five Renault-engined biplanes were ordered. Designated B.R.70 (later shortened to B.R.7) these were built alongside the first four B.E.2s and the first B.R.7, No. 157, was finished in time to be shown at Olympia in February 1913, together with Coanda monoplane No. 153. No. 157 was flown at Larkhill in March, but was overloaded with wings of the normal section used on monoplanes. A more cambered profile had been specified for the Daimler-engined biplane, which was being built at Halberstadt, and a set of wings of this shape was tried out on the B.R.7 in April with better results, but still not good enough to meet the contract, so the Spanish government declined to accept delivery. Only seven B.R.7s were built and the second one, No. 158, was tried out with a four-bladed airscrew, without improvement, and a special two-blader with very pointed tips was also made to Coanda's design. On 26 May 1913, Pizey, with his mechanic Fellows as passenger, was flying No. 158 when the carburettor caught fire. He was able to land promptly and both occupants jumped out immediately after touching down, but the B.R.7 was totally destroyed in a few minutes. After this No. 157 remained at Larkhill as an advanced trainer, but the rest of the batch, Nos. 160–163, were rarely flown, although No. 163 was tested with a plain two-wheeled Vee landing gear. A final B.R.7, No. 178, was built in December 1913 with increased span, but never left Filton works.

In Germany, the Daimler-engined biplane underwent considerable modification and finally emerged with extended upper wings having large inversely tapered ailerons, also a supplementary rudder below the stern which nearly doubled the vertical surface area of the tail. This was test-flown by Henri Jullerot in July and August during his term as instructor-in-charge at the Halberstadt school.

In January 1913 Coanda designed a central-float seaplane, which resembled in some ways the G.E.3 and may have owed something to it, for the fuselage was faired to a circular section and mounted midway between the wings; the fuel tanks and system were also arranged in the same way as in Gordon England's design. On completion, this seaplane, No. 120, was sent to Cowes and was fitted with a wide central float built of mahogany designed by Oscar Gnosspelius, who had pioneered the design of hydroplanes on Lake Windermere and had produced similar floats for seaplanes. Stability afloat was ensured by two small torpedo-shaped floats under the wing-tips; there was no

77

Busteed and party with No. 120 at Cowes, April 1913, showing original float.

tail-float, but two water rudders were fitted at the rear of the main float. The two tandem cockpits had dual handwheel controls and there was a gap between the upper wing-roots above the front cockpits. The 80 h.p. Gnome was installed in a close-fitting aluminium cowling and had a starting handle in the cockpit, with an interconnected hand-starting magneto. A standard Coanda rudder and tailplane were fitted, but an extra rectangular rudder was later added under the tail to offset the keel surface of the main float. In the early buoyancy tests, the Gnosspelius float was satisfactory, but after being moored out for some days it soaked up an excessive weight of water and at his first attempt Busteed was unable to take-off. He therefore arranged with S.E. Saunders and Co. of Cowes to build a specially light float, using their patent wire-sewn plywood; this float was attached to the seaplane during the first week in April, and on the 15th Busteed succeeded in taking-off. His troubles had only just begun, however, for the Gnome engine was too closely cowled and quickly overheated. Losing power rapidly, Busteed had to alight abruptly and the impact was too much for the light-weight float, which burst open, throwing the pilot into the Solent. He was a strong swimmer, but was near exhaustion before being seen and rescued half an hour later by a dredger.

No. 120, although begun as a private venture, had been purchased, subject to acceptance trials, by the Admiralty and was to have carried the R.N.A.S. number *15*. The Admiralty had also ordered a landplane derived from the Coanda monoplane; this was a fairly straightforward conversion of No. 121, which had returned to Filton in February 1913 for overhaul after service at the Larkhill school since the previous October. It thus became the prototype of the Gnome-engined biplane known as the T.B.8, and in July and August at Larkhill soon showed that it had a much better performance than the B.R.7. It was next converted into a twin-float seaplane, for which purpose No. 120's original Gnosspelius float was divided down the centre line and made into a

Busteed taxying No. 121 at Dale in September 1913.

pair of narrower floats. In this form, with a steerable tail float and extra fin area added, No. 121 was sent to Dale on Milford Haven on 20 September 1913. It was flown through all its tests satisfactorily by Busteed and his assistant G. B. Dacre, until rough weather made further flying impossible. It was then returned to Filton in December, stripped, overhauled and rebuilt with a new fuselage as No. 205 and delivered to Calshot as the agreed substitute for No. 120, receiving the latter's intended serial *15*. It had a tendency to fly nose down and in April 1914 it was again rebuilt at Filton with new floats, staggered wings with ailerons and a revised fin; in this form it was flown at the Spithead naval review in July 1914. Before agreeing to accept No. 205, it seems that the Admiralty had asked for a larger seaplane, and drawings have survived of a project called B.C.2, showing a tandem two-seater with a fuel system similar to No. 120's, and a circular monocoque fuselage, with a 200 h.p. eight-cylinder watercooled Clerget engine, for which Coanda designed an ingenious two-speed reduction gear, with internal clutches for changing speed, in place of the chain gear formerly employed. The design is dated between April and June 1913, after which it seems to have been discontinued. The Admiralty's order for a landplane was fulfilled by converting monoplane No. 144 to a T.B.8. This was first flown as a biplane on 12 August 1913 and was delivered to Eastchurch as number *43* on 7 October 1913. After a crash it was rebuilt with a two-wheeled Vee landing gear as No. 225, and redelivered to the R.N.A.S. in this form in April 1914, still with its original number *43*.

The remarkable success of the T.B.8 quickly eclipsed the remaining Coanda monoplanes, and ten of the latter delivered earlier in the year to Italy, Germany and Rumania were brought back at the end of 1913 for conversion to biplanes. One of them was the special Olympia show model, No. 153, which underwent a record number of metamorphoses. It had gone to Halberstadt, together with Nos. 150 and 151, in April and in August Nos. 151 and 153

79

were returned to Filton and converted to biplanes. No. 151, equipped with a simple form of bomb rack, was sent to Rumania in October, but No. 153 was taken to Spain by Sippe, where it beat all comers in trials at Cuatros Vientos, and in particular took-off from the ploughed field, always a favourite test with the Spaniards, in 60 yd. from axle-deep mud. Even these severe conditions had no effect on No. 153, which returned to Filton intact in February 1914 and was overhauled for another lease of life as No. 227. Its later career included tests with an 80 h.p. Clerget rotary engine at the Royal Aircraft Factory; modification to take a 100 h.p. Monosoupape Gnome engine, in which form it was sent to compete at Vienna in June 1914; finally it was purchased by the Admiralty (*917*) in October 1914 and ended its days at Eastchurch as a trainer.

Pixton and Jullerot in No. 121 at Larkhill, July 1913; note bomb held by mechanic.

The first two T.B.8s built from scratch as biplanes were Nos. 197 and 198, completed in November 1913. No. 198 was specially finished for the Paris Salon de l'Aéronautique and was the sole British exhibit there. It had a number of improvements over the earlier monoplane conversions, notably a simpler landing gear with shorter skids and a separate tail skid, also a new aerofoil section characterised by a flattening of the upper surface between the spars. This had been developed by Coanda, who had also designed a new type of airscrew with tapered wide-chord blades, a complete change from the square-tipped Lang type. At one stage it was proposed to fit double rudders to both the B.R.7 and the T.B.8, as on the German Daimler-engined biplane, but this modification was never carried out in practice. No. 198 had single controls in the aft cockpit only, the forward cockpit being equipped with a prismatic bomb-sight and a bomb release trigger which operated a revolving carrier for 12 small bombs mounted below the cockpit floor. Each bomb weighed 10 lb. and contained 2 lb. of T.N.T.; the trigger released the lowest bomb and then revolved the carrier to bring the next into the release position; it also fused the bombs, which had to fall about 100 ft. before a wind-mill arming vane rendered them live.

The French military authorities were attracted by the workmanlike appearance of No. 198 and would have bought it outright, but their terms of reference limited them to the purchase of French-built aircraft. They urged the Company to arrange for Bristol aeroplanes to be built in France, and a few weeks later a licence was granted to the Société Anonyme des Atéliers d'Aviation Louis Breguet, with factories at Vélizy near Paris and at Douai.

After returning from the Paris Salon on 9 January 1914, No. 198 was equipped with a two-wheeled undercarriage and purchased by the Admiralty as number *153*, being delivered to Eastchurch on 19 March 1914. Meanwhile No. 197, which had been tested with an 80 h.p. Gnome engine at Larkhill in January and February, was fitted with an 80 h.p. Le Rhône engine and sent to the Breguet works at Vélizy on 4 March for demonstration to the French army. Flown by Sidney Sippe, it climbed to 3,000 ft. in $7\frac{1}{2}$ min. with a useful load of 715 lb. and attained 74 m.p.h. It was damaged at the end of the demonstration, but repaired at Filton in July 1914 and eventually delivered to the Admiralty as number *916* on 17 September 1914. Satisfied with the T.B.8's performance, the French government approved it for manufacture by Breguet, and the Company supplied their licensee with the same range of data and manufacturing aids as in the case of Caproni & Faccanoni, including a complete sample skeleton airframe, No. 228, delivered to Douai in May 1914. In this month also was delivered the only T.B.8 ever sold to a private owner; this was No. 143, originally built in January 1913 as a Coanda monoplane, converted to a biplane in October 1913, modified to increase the wing stagger in January 1914, overhauled and equipped with an 80 h.p. Clerget rotary engine in May 1914 and finally purchased by Mr. R. P. Creagh, a graduate of the Brooklands school, on 3 July 1914 for £700. Mr. Creagh hoped to convert it to a seaplane like No. 205, but was frustrated by the outbreak of war in August.

The Admiralty also invited tenders for two larger Bristol seaplanes, but specified the use of the 200 h.p. Canton-Unné radial engine, and R.N.A.S. numbers *147* and *148* were reserved for them. Several layouts were investigated, but neither a price nor a satisfactory design could be agreed and in June 1914 the Company asked to be allowed to decline the order. A feature of this design, carried over from the earlier B.C.2 project, was a clutch-controlled two-speed airscrew reduction gear to permit maximum engine revolutions for take-off and direct drive for cruising.

As already stated, the six Coanda monoplanes originally built for Rumania early in 1913 were all delivered later that year as T.B.8 conversions. They comprised Nos. 118, 147, 148, 149, 151 and 152, and Prince Cantacuzene was sufficiently satisfied with their performance to place an order for a much improved derivative, for which he provided a new 75 h.p. Monosoupape Gnome engine. This biplane, No. 223, designated G.B.75, was a complete redesign with only a superficial resemblance to the T.B.8, incorporating many features due to Frank Barnwell. The fuselage was faired above and below and the streamline shape was continued forward by a large hemispherical spinner and cowl enclosing the engine, to which cooling air was admitted by louvres

81

in the spinner. Warping wings were fitted and the tail unit had a fixed vertical fin. Equipment included an electric intercommunication system for the crew. The G.B.75 was first flown at Larkhill on 7 April 1914, but the spinner gave trouble and was removed, and the wings were rigged with increased stagger to compensate for nose-heaviness. It was flown again on 28 April and offered for delivery to Bucharest on 15 June, but never dispatched, the order being cancelled a fortnight later. The reason for this is obscure, but may be related to a single general arrangement drawing which has survived of a biplane with a single cockpit containing two staggered seats, and is dated 27 May 1914. There are also records of requests by Prince Cantacuzene to deliver a new biplane, which could not be done during the war, and it is probable that this is a reference to Type RB, which may have been substituted for the G.B.75. At all events, Type RB was never built, and the G.B.75 was delivered with a standard 80 h.p. Gnome to the R.F.C. at Farnborough on 2 August 1914, receiving number *610*.

After the outbreak of war, 12 improved T.B.8s, Nos. 331–342, were built, with ailerons instead of warp control; initially they were intended for the R.F.C., but were all diverted in October 1914 to the R.N.A.S. at Gosport and Eastchurch, receiving numbers *1216–1227*. Three T.B.8s went to France with

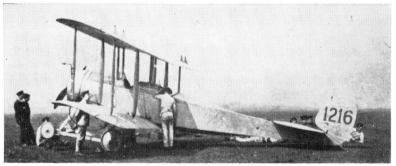

T.B.8 of R.N.A.S. at Eastchurch in March 1915.

the Eastchurch Squadron and one bombed German batteries at Middelkerke on 25 November 1914. When No. 1 Squadron R.N.A.S. went to France from Gosport on 26 February 1915, one T.B.8 was still on its strength; but in general, apart from a period of coastal patrol duty by four T.B.8s of No. 1 Squadron detached from Gosport and based on Newcastle-on-Tyne in the winter of 1914–15, the type's war service was confined to training duties. It proved sufficiently valuable in this role for 24 more to be ordered by the Admiralty in August 1915. These were built at Brislington and delivered between 24 September 1915 and 24 February 1916. The first eight, Nos. 870–877 (*8442–8449*), were fitted with 50 h.p. Gnomes and went to Chingford and Redcar. The next 13, Nos. 878–890 (*8450–8453* and *8562–8570*), had 60 h.p. Le Rhônes, and were issued to Barrow-in-Furness, Killingholme and

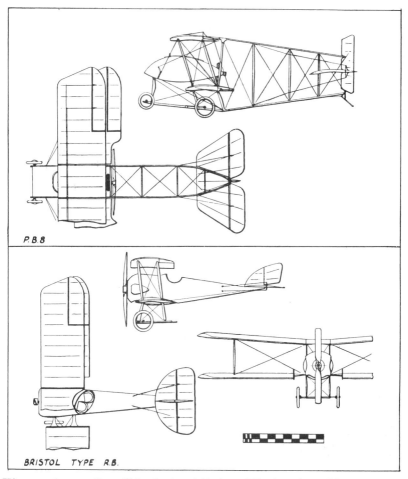

P.B.8

BRISTOL   TYPE   R.B.

Kingsnorth as well as Chingford and Redcar. The last three, Nos. 891–893 (*8571–3*), were delivered as airframes to the White City stores depot.

One further Bristol-Coanda two-seater biplane was built and was Coanda's only pusher biplane design. This was No. 199, the P.B.8, which was intended to serve as a Boxkite replacement at the Brooklands school. Although the design was begun in November 1913, construction proceeded on very low priority, and the complete machine was not delivered to Brooklands till July 1914. Hardly had it arrived when its 80 h.p. Gnome engine was requisitioned by the War Office and so it never flew. The P.B.8 was relatively small, with wings of equal span having upper and lower ailerons. The overall length was equal to the span and the tail booms were parallel in plan view at a fairly close pitch, the lower booms being continuous with the chassis skids. Initially the nacelle nose shape was a horizontal knife-edge, but as finally built this was changed to

83

a vertical knife-edge. The crew occupied a common cockpit, and access to the aft seat was not easy because of the low clearance under the upper wing. A much more satisfactory trainer was No. 218, the only side-by-side version of the T.B.8, which was rebuilt in April 1914 from monoplane No. 177. It had ailerons and a separate tail skid, as on the G.B.75, and was used at Larkhill.

SPECIFICATIONS AND DATA

Type: Coanda Two-Seat Biplanes

Manufacturers: The British & Colonial Aeroplane Co. Ltd., Filton and Brislington, Bristol
Deutsche Bristol-Werke, Halberstadt, Germany
Société Anonyme des Ateliers d'Aviation Louis Breguet, Vélizy and Douai, France

Model	Hydro 120	B.R.7	Daimler	T.B.8	T.B.8H	G.B.75	P.B.8
Power Plant	80 hp Gnome	70 hp Renault	90 hp Daimler	80 hp Gnome 80 hp Le Rhône 100 hp Mono-Gnome 50 hp Gnome 60 hp Le Rhône	80 hp Gnome	75 hp Mono-Gnome	80 hp Gnome
Span	38 ft 8 in	38 ft	57 ft	37 ft 8 in	37 ft 8 in	37 ft 8 in	27 ft 6 in
Length	27 ft 10 in	27 ft 5 in	27 ft 5 in	29 ft 3 in	30 ft 6 in		27 ft 6 in
Wing Area	436 sq ft	440 sq ft	570 sq ft	450 sq ft	450 sq ft	420 sq ft	
Empty Weight		946 lb	1200 lb	970 lb		970 lb	
All-up Weight		1826 lb	2100 lb	1665 lb		1650 lb	
Speed		63 mph	65 mph	65–75 mph		80 mph	
Duration		5 hours	5 hours	5 hours	4 hours	5 hours	
Accommodation	2	2	2	2	2	2	2
Production	1	7	1	53	1	1	1
Sequence Nos.	120	157, 158 160–163 178	(1 in Germany)	118, 121, 143 144, 147–149 151–153 196– 198 218, 225 227, 228 331–342 870–893	205	223	199

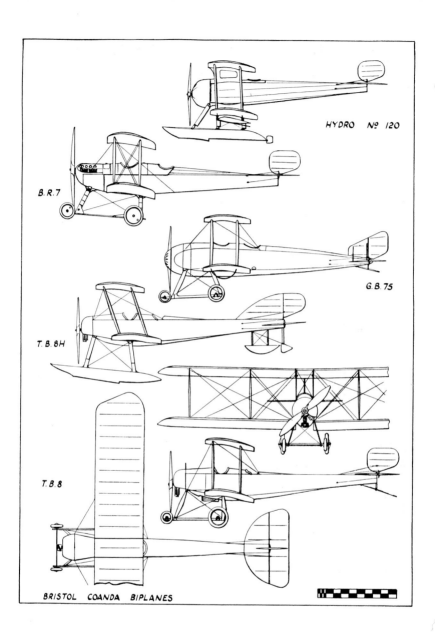

HYDRO Nº 120

B.R.7

G.B.75

T.B.8H

T.B.8

BRISTOL COANDA BIPLANES

85

Lt. C. D. Burney, R.N., with model of proposed X.1 hydroped biplane.

The Bristol-Burney Flying Boats

Coanda's biplane, No. 120, was not the first Bristol seaplane, for over a year earlier there had begun a very interesting series of experiments, which continued in a great secrecy almost up to the outbreak of war in 1914. In October 1911 Howard Pixton undertook a series of overwater flights from Hayling Island in a Boxkite (No. 29) fitted with flotation bags under the wings, with Lt. Charles Dennistoun Burney, R.N., son of Admiral Sir Cecil Burney, as his passenger. Lt. Burney was very enthusiastic about the possibility of operating naval aircraft with the Fleet independently of shore bases and had studied the pioneer work of Forlanini and Guidoni on the use of hydrofoils for lifting motor boats above rough water to reduce drag at high speeds. On his father's advice, he approached Sir George White privately with several ideas which he wished to patent jointly with the Company, so as to ensure their adequate exploitation.

Burney's specification for a naval aeroplane comprised the following novel features: a buoyant hull; hydrofoils for take-off from rough water; wings which could be folded for stowage of the aircraft on an ordinary boat deck and unfolded while taxying; separate air and water propellers, the latter to be driven for taxying by either one of two independent engines, both of which would be used together for flight. Further proposals envisaged inflatable wings and fuselage and 'means of varying the area of pneumatic planes by furling'. As all these very original ideas would require a great deal of research into materials and methods, he suggested, to start with, that the G.E.1 biplane, No. 64, then being built, should be equipped with a water undercarriage consisting of three 'hydropeds' or legs carrying a cascade of hydrofoil vanes. Five torpedo-shaped pneumatic floats under the fuselage and wing would support the aircraft while at rest, but were not intended to act as running surfaces.

The Directors were interested in this project and, having been assured of Admiralty support, set up a secret design office, called 'X Department' to develop it. 'X Department' was entirely detached from the main drawing office at Filton House and began work just after Christmas 1911, consisting only of Frank Barnwell and one assistant, Clifford Tinson, who joined him in the first week of January 1912. Frank Barnwell, who had been apprenticed to the Fairfield Shipbuilding Company on Clydeside, had helped his elder brother Harold to build and fly the first successful Scottish aeroplane, which in 1911 had won the Law prize of £50. After this success, the brothers came south to Brooklands, where Harold joined Vickers as a test pilot, while Frank was on the point of going in with A. V. Roe when he received a much more exciting offer from Sir George White to take charge of the new secret design office at Filton.

Burney proposed to equip his first biplane, designated X.1, with a 60-80 h.p. E.N.V. engine driving both air and water propellers through clutches, with bevel gears and shafts running inside the hydroped legs. The counter-shaft carrying both clutches was to be mounted between the cylinder banks above the engine, which drove it through a chain. Barnwell examined Burney's scheme carefully and concluded that success would only be attained with a larger and cleaner design; he proposed a monoplane with a boat hull and buoyant wing-tips. Experiments were done on the stiffness of a long cylindrical pneumatic tube, and a wing was designed using eight such tubes side by side spanwise within lightweight ribs which maintained the aerofoil profile. But the rubber-proofed fabric, which was the only material then available, was too heavy when made up to the required strength and so the idea of a pneumatic wing was rejected.

Barnwell's layout for a monoplane flying boat with hydropeds was approved for construction and was designated X.2, having sequence No. 92. The hull was planked with thin mahogany veneer covered with sailcloth and varnished. The wings, of three-spar design, had warp control and were rigged at a pronounced dihedral angle; they were finished with a waterproof varnish to provide lateral buoyancy. Dual controls were installed in the cockpit amidships, and the engine, an 80 h.p. Canton-Unné watercooled radial, was mounted in the nose, driving both air and water propellers through two Hele-Shaw clutches. The airscrew was a conventional two-bladed tractor, while the two water propellers were mounted at the lower ends of the two forward hydropeds.

On 9 May 1912, X.2 was put on board the lighter *Sarah* at Avonmouth and taken with great secrecy to Dale, on Milford Haven. Flotation tests were not at first satisfactory, but eventually the leaks were stopped and taxying trials began. Propelled by its water screws, the boat got away quickly, but after about 50 yd. the streamline fairings of the hydroped tubes were torn off by water friction. Static tests with the airscrew clutched-in showed some vibration in the front bearing carrying the primary chain drive from the crankshaft, and this had to be remedied. Towing tests behind a Naval torpedo boat were fairly satisfactory, but the craft was unstable at moderate speeds.

X.2 taxying under power from water-screws at Dale, September 1912.

Underwater stability was eventually obtained by reducing the area of some of the hydrofoils and adding water rudders and a controllable water elevator on the aft hydroped. Although these were adequate for towed stability, it was found impossible to prevent the craft heeling over when the water screws were clutched in, due to unequal torque reactions. It was necessary also to fit wing-tip floats because of the yaw caused by the drag of whichever wing was in the water.

In September stronger streamline casings were fitted to the hydropeds, and it was decided to rely on towing for the preliminary air test. Tests under power had been delayed because the engine stalled when both water and air propellers were engaged, so the engine was removed and 500 lb. of ballast substituted for it. On 21 September 1912, X.2 was towed by the torpedo boat into a 12-knot wind, and at 30 knots airspeed rose clear of the water in a climbing attitude. Burney's colleague George Bentley Dacre was in the cockpit reading instruments, but the controls were preset for level flight and locked, so he had no means of correcting the nose-high attitude, but the aircraft would certainly have regained a level path if the towing party had not been too prompt in slipping the tow, with the result that the craft stalled, sideslipped and crashed, fortunately without injury to Dacre.

The Admiralty agreed to continue helping with man-power and dockyard facilities, but it was decided that X.2 was not worth a major repair, so in March 1913 a second flying boat, X.3, was put in hand at Filton, incorporating many improvements. This craft, No. 159, was larger than X.2 in both beam and wing area. The hull framework was made at Filton and sent to Cowes for Saunders to cover it with their Consuta sewn plywood, and the completed aircraft was shipped to Dale in the *Sarah* in August. One major change in X.3 was that the water screws were contra-rotating and mounted back-to-back, being driven by a single shaft running in a separate vertical tube located midway between the front hydropeds, so that the thrust-line was central and torque reaction was cancelled out. The wings were rigidly braced and lateral control was by inverse-tapered warping ailerons; only a single set of controls was installed in the side-by-side cockpit. At first it was proposed to power X.3 by two 70 h.p. Renault engines, but the Admiralty offered to lend a 200 h.p. Canton-Unné radial, and this was accepted. Preliminary taxying tests were done with an 80 h.p. Gnome, dummy outriggers being substituted for the wings to carry the wing-tip floats. The latter carried small hydrofoils, and the main hydropeds were fitted with controllable water rudders and a water elevator. Stability under tow was very good and taxying performance satisfactory, although the nose dipped when the airscrew was clutched in. To counteract this tendency, Barnwell devised a supplementary front elevator just aft of the airscrew, its control being co-ordinated with the clutch operation so as to lift the nose while the airscrew drive was being taken up. The wings and the 200 h.p. engine were then installed, and the aircraft was ready for flight testing by Busteed in June 1914, when it was unfortunately grounded on a hidden sandbank, necessitating major repairs. The Company then asked

X.3 aground in Milford Haven after taxying into sand-bank in June 1914.

the Admiralty for more substantial backing in order to continue the trials, but this was refused and, after a visit to Dale by Sir George White on 8 July 1914, the programme was discontinued and X.3 was brought back to Filton, where it remained in store until 1920, when it was scrapped.

Barnwell was well aware of the deficiences of bevel gears and long shafts, and in a letter to Stanley White in December 1913 he sketched out a much simpler hydrovane flying boat having chain-driven outboard airscrews powered by a central engine; the airscrews were arranged to swing up for taxying and take-off, and to a lower position giving an optimum thrust-line for flight; no water screws were necessary and all gearing and torque shafts were eliminated. Although not developed in 1914, this layout was briefly revived by Barnwell in 1921 in his Type 66 project, which featured retractable hydrovanes and a Napier Lion engine, but this was never built. So ended a series of experiments which, though unsuccessful so far as their primary objects were concerned, led to Burney's invention and development of the Paravane mine-sweeping device in 1915.

SPECIFICATION AND DATA

Type: Burney Flying Boats

Manufacturers: The British & Colonial Aeroplane Co. Ltd., Filton, Bristol

Model	X1	X2	X3
Power Plant	60 hp E.N.V.	80 hp Canton-Unné	200 hp Canton-Unné
Span	34 ft	55 ft 9 in	57 ft 10 in
Length	30 ft	30 ft 8 in	36 ft 8 in
Wing Area	325 sq ft	480 sq ft	500 sq ft
Accommodation	2	2	2
Production	nil	1	1
Sequence Nos.	—	92	159

Original Scout, No. 206, at Larkhill, February 1914; Busteed in cockpit, Barnwell holding up tail.

The Bristol Scouts A-D, S.S.A., G.B.1 and S.2A

Apart from improved replicas of the Anzani-engined Prier monoplanes, Coanda designed only one single-seat monoplane; this was the S.B.5, No. 183, a smaller version of the military monoplane, for the Italian government. When the Caproni-Bristol contract fell through in November 1913, the unfinished fuselage was still in the works awaiting disposal. There was a growing interest in single-seater biplanes for high-speed reconnaissance and Barnwell was given permission to convert the S.B.5 into a scout biplane, as 'X Department' was not fully occupied. The drawings were sketched in a manifold book under the reference 'SN.183', although the result, when completed, received the new No. 206.

The 'Baby Biplane', or Scout, was very simple in outline and economical in manufacture. The single-bay wings of 22 ft. span were similar to those designed by Coanda for the P.B.8 and had the same ailerons and stagger. A two-wheeled Vee chassis was fitted and the tailplane, elevators and balanced rudder were made from light steel tubing. A reconditioned 80 h.p. Gnome engine* was installed in a close cowling open at the bottom and the machine when finished weighed only 950 lb. complete with pilot and 3 hours' fuel.

No. 206 was sent to Larkhill on 23 February 1914, and Busteed, who had had a considerable hand in the design, was delighted with it; after a very few flights to familiarise himself with so lively a mount he attained 95 m.p.h. The little biplane was then sent to the Olympia Aero Show, together with the G.B.75 two-seater. When the Show opened on 16 March, No. 206 was the smallest biplane there, but without doubt the most sensational.

After the Show was over, the Scout went back to Larkhill, and at the end of April returned to Filton to be fitted with a new set of wings of slightly greater

* Actually No. 1916, salvaged from hydro-biplane No. 120.

area, which increased the span to 24 ft. 7 in. These reduced the landing speed and improved handling without affecting the maximum speed. At the same time the engine cowling was modified to an annular shape, allowing more airflow through the central opening. On 14 May 1914 Busteed put the modified Scout through an A.I.D. performance test at Farnborough and recorded a speed range of 97·5 m.p.h. to 40 m.p.h.; he then flew to Brooklands, where he gave a spectacular demonstration and in a handicap race was beaten only by seconds by Harold Barnwell in the 100 h.p. Gnome-engined Sopwith Tabloid.

The Scout was entered for the Aerial Derby round London on 23 May, but the race was postponed until 6 June, and on that day visibility was so bad that Sippe was not allowed to fly the Scout. However, another competitor, Lord Carbery, who owned a Morane monoplane, was so impressed by the Scout that he asked to buy it, and was allowed to because two more of the type, Nos. 229 and 230, were being built. Carbery paid £400 for the airframe without engine and installed the 80 h.p. Le Rhône from his Morane. He took delivery at Hendon on 17 June, having already entered it for two cross-country races, the first being London-Manchester and back on 20 June.

Scout A modified; Carbery starting from Hendon in London-Manchester Race, July 1914.

During practice flying, Carbery reached a true speed of over 100 m.p.h., but on the day the weather was very rough and having averaged 89 m.p.h. to the compulsory landing point at Castle Bromwich, Carbery landed across wind and tipped up on his nose, breaking the port lower wing and the chassis. Repairs at Filton were completed by 7 July, just in time for the second race, from London to Paris and back. In this event Carbery was scratch man and on the day of the race his engine was not giving full power. Nevertheless, he would not give up, and although he had to circle Hendon three times to gain height with 5 hours' fuel on board, and the weather was foggy into the bargain, he reached Buc safely. Unfortunately the mechanics who refuelled the Scout at Buc, during the compulsory 2 hours' stop, only filled one tank and Carbery did not check both tanks before taking-off on the return flight. Consequently he had only just crossed the French coast near Hardelot when his engine began to fail; he operated the fuel changeover cock, only to find the second tank empty also. He just had time to glide down on to the Channel beside a convenient tramp steamer; the water was calm and he was rescued without even getting his feet wet, but in salving the aircraft the fuselage was broken and all but the engine and mountings fell back into the sea.

Concurrently with No. 206, Coanda had been engaged on a different single-seater biplane project at the request of the French government. This was No. 219, the S.S.A. (Single Seat Armoured) biplane, whose principal feature was the bullet-proof construction of the whole of the front fuselage and cockpit as a single monocoque unit of sheet steel, colloquially known as 'The Bath', enclosing the engine and fuel and oil tanks as well as the pilot's seat, the latter being formed by the shaped contour of the rear bulkhead. The 80 h.p. Clerget rotary engine was enclosed in a sheet cowling with a large steel spinner in front; the spinner was perforated to allow cooling air to enter, but contained a central cone which prevented direct entry of bullets from ahead. The wings were staggered and set very far forward to counteract nose-heaviness, the lower wings being attached to a framework which left a gap between the wing roots and the fuselage. The chassis was of the two-wheeled type, with two skids extended aft so that no tail skid was necessary. The wheels were arranged to castor for cross-wind landing, this being a Blériot feature esteemed by French pilots. The rear fuselage was very slender and carried a large balanced rudder and Scout-type tailplane and elevators.

When finished, No. 219 was flown at Larkhill by Sippe on 8 May 1914, with a temporary aluminium cowling because of vibration in the steel spinner. A week later the S.S.A. was fitted with a larger rudder before going to Farnborough, but was damaged in a heavy landing. After repairs Busteed flew it again at Filton on 25 June, but an undercarriage bracing wire failed on landing, and he was catapulted out of the cockpit injuring his knees and shoulder. The S.S.A. was badly damaged, but the French authorities agreed to take delivery of it for rebuilding in the Breguet works at Douai, whither it was consigned on 3 July 1914. The S.S.A. was unarmed and was not further developed at Filton, but may be considered a forerunner of the armoured trench fighter exemplified by the Sopwith Salamander of 1918. The very similar RB two-seater, described earlier, may also have been intended as an armoured machine, and was exactly contemporary with the S.S.A.

Nos. 229 and 230 differed from No. 206 only in detail, notably the wing bracing and engine cowling, and were designated Scout B to distinguish them from the prototype, which became Scout A in retrospect. Barnwell sketched out a version of the Scout with a Statax engine, a small diameter swash-plate design which showed initial promise but was never properly developed. He also designed a racing single-seater, the G.B.1, for the 1914 Gordon Bennett race. This was discussed by the Directors on 26 June, but they decided not to built it. It was to have had a 100 h.p. Mono-Gnome engine mounted between horizontal bearers, as in the Sopwith Tabloid, and a tapered fixed fin.

The two Scout Bs had not been flown when war broke out on 4 August 1914, but they were at once requisitioned by the War Office and delivered to Farnborough on 21 and 23 August, respectively. They were then sent to France, where their high speed and rate of climb won the approval of discerning pilots, who nicknamed them 'Bristol Bullets'. They were allotted R.F.C. numbers *633* and *648* and were flown by Lt. Cholmondeley and Major J. F. A. Higgins, of Nos. 3 and 5 Squadrons, respectively. The former armed his Scout with two rifles, on either side of the cockpit and offset from the line of flight so as to miss the airscrew.

Although committed to ordering Royal Aircraft Factory designs, for which large contracts had been placed when war was imminent, the War Office was sufficiently impressed by its new Bristol, Martinsyde and Sopwith Scouts to place small production contracts for them, and the Company received an order for 12 of a further improved version, Scout C, on 5 November 1914. The Admiralty wanted them too and ordered 24 Scouts on 7 December, but this led to a dispute between the two Services, who both demanded priority in delivery. A compromise was reached whereby the first Scout C, No. 450 (*1243*) was completed urgently and delivered to the Admiralty on 16 Febru-

First production Scout C at Grain in March 1915.

ary 1915. It was followed by Nos. 451–462 (*1602–1613*), delivered to the War Office between 23 April and 13 June 1915, followed by 17 more for the Admiralty, Nos. 463–479 (*1244–1260*) between 3 June and 18 July 1915. Meanwhile the War Office had placed a second contract for 75 Scout Cs on 16 March and the first six of these, Nos. 480–485 (*4662–4667*) were delivered between 10 and 29 July, followed by the remaining six, Nos. 486–491 (*1261–1266*), for the Admiralty between 29 July and 24 August 1915. All these Scouts were fitted with 80 h.p. Gnome engines. Manufacture of the Scout C was undertaken at Brislington because the Filton factory was fully committed to B.E.2c production. The next 32 for the War Office, Nos. 492–523 (*4668–4699*), were completed between 9 August and 12 November 1915, all after

94

the first four being fitted with 80 h.p. Le Rhône engines after delivery because of a growing shortage of Gnomes. The Admiralty, however, insisted on having Gnomes because of their greater reliability, particularly for over-water flying, and had ordered 50 more on 6 June 1915; the first of the batch, No. 524 (*3013*), was delivered on 5 September, but the shortage of Gnome engines caused progressive delay until early in the New Year, and the 37th machine, No. 560 (*3049*), was delayed until 9 February 1916. However, it was followed quickly by the remaining 13, Nos. 771–783 (*3050–3062*), between 11 February and 25 March.

Meanwhile, the remaining 37 Scouts for the War Office, Nos. 784–820 (*5291–5327*), with Le Rhônes, had gone ahead smoothly and were dispatched between 13 November 1915 and 18 February 1916. This completed the production of the Scout C, of which 161 in all were produced, 74 for the Admiralty and 87 for the War Office; 65 of the latter had 80 h.p. Le Rhône engines and all the others had 80 h.p. Gnomes. At least one R.N.A.S. Scout (*3035*) was tested with an 110 h.p. Clerget.

Bristol Scouts were dispersed among many R.F.C. squadrons, but never formed the sole equipment of any squadron. They were not armed when issued and much ingenuity was displayed by individual units and pilots in adapting them to an offensive role. How effective they could be was demonstrated on 25 July 1915 by Capt. Lanoe G. Hawker of No. 6 Squadron, who on an evening patrol forced down three enemy two-seaters all armed with machine-guns, although he himself had only a single-shot Martini carbine mounted at an angle on the starboard side; for which feat he was awarded the Victoria Cross. Other weapons, similarly mounted to miss the airscrew, included the larger 0·45 in. Martini carbine firing incendiary bullets, the Lewis gun and even a breech-loading duck-gun firing chain-shot. The fowling-piece was useless, but good use was made of Lewis guns.

Most Naval Scouts were unarmed, but carried canisters of Ranken darts, designed to set fire to Zeppelin airships. Each Scout had two containers on the cockpit floor, each holding 24 darts, which could be released three at a time. Some Naval Scouts had a Lewis gun mounted above the centre-section, and a few had one mounted parallel to the top longeron and firing through the airscrew disc, sometimes but not always synchronised by a Scarff-Dibovski interrupter gear. The long duration and rapid rate of ascent of the Zeppelins made them particularly difficult to attack, except with small fast Scouts which had insufficient range to intercept them. In an attempt to overcome the range problem several Isle of Man steamers had been converted into seaplane carriers, and one, H.M.S. *Vindex*, was equipped with a flying-off deck forward. On 3 November 1915 the first take-off from this deck was made by Flight-Lt. H. F. Towler in a Scout C (*1255*), and thereafter two Scouts were carried by *Vindex* on anti-Zeppelin patrols. Another of the *Vindex* Scouts (*3028*) was loaned to Squadron Commander John Porte at Felixstowe for an experiment in which it was successfully launched from a large three-engined Porte Baby flying boat, flown by Porte himself. The Scout was carried on the upper wing of the flying boat, and its pilot, Flight-Lt. M. J. Day of *Vindex*, switched on his engine and climbed away when the composite aircraft had reached a height of 1,000 ft. above Harwich Harbour, landing safely soon afterwards at Martlesham Heath. This experiment took place on 17 May 1916, but was not repeated because Flight-Lt. Day was killed in France soon afterwards and newer aircraft able to tackle Zeppelins more effectively were coming into service by that date.

During the period of Scout C production at Brislington few modifications had been made to Barnwell's design, and meanwhile Barnwell had joined the R.F.C. and Tinson had gone to the Admiralty Air Department. The principal change necessary was a rearrangement of the tanks so as to bring the oil tank forward from its original position behind the cockpit; here it had insufficient head to maintain oil supply while taxying, particularly with the Le Rhône engine, whose oil pump was less effective than the Gnome's. In August 1915, however, Barnwell was released from active service to resume duty at Filton as Chief Designer, and he quickly took action to remedy some of the shortcomings of the existing Scout C, as reported by both Services. Some requests, such as the Admiralty's for a fixed fin and a rudder area of 5 sq. ft. he rejected. (There is a note in his handwriting in reply to the Admiralty overseer, Lt. W. P. Kemp, saying, 'We have already given them a rudder of 5·13 sq. ft.— do they want a negative fin area?') But he took steps to improve detail design and performance, substituting streamline Rafwires for stranded cable and ensuring better interchangeability and reliability of quick-wearing parts. Provision was made for a synchronised Vickers gun, and tank design was improved to overcome fuel leaks caused by vibration. Loss of fuel from this cause forced Flight-Lt. Freeman of *Vindex* to break off an engagement with Zeppelin *L.17* after hitting it with his Ranken darts; he had to ditch his Scout, but was rescued by a Belgian ship and interned in Holland for a few days before being repatriated as a 'shipwrecked mariner'.

The revised design, Scout D, completed in November 1915, matched a new War Office contract awarded on 3 August for 50 Scouts, Nos. 1044–1093

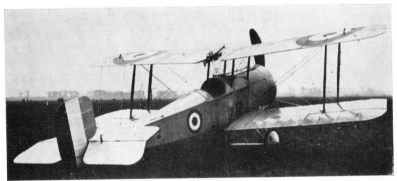

Scout D of R.N.A.S. (100 hp Mono-Gnome) with large ailerons, large rudder and cut-out for Lewis gun; Cranwell 1916.

96

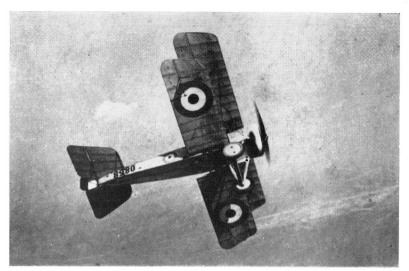

Scout D of R.N.A.S. with 100 hp Mono-Gnome and small ailerons. (*Crown copyright.*)

(*5554–5603*). These were delivered without engines between 14 February and 3 June 1916 and retained the same wing rigging and aileron area as the Scout C, but an alternative wing design was already approved for a smaller aileron combined with increased dihedral; in this type the wing-tip skids were moved outboard from below the interplane struts. The production drawings confirm that both types of wing were manufactured for the Scout D and that aileron size is not a criterion in recognising a Scout C from a Scout D. Two sizes of rudder were designed for Scout D, the larger being fitted in conjunction with long ailerons, the so-called 'medium' in conjunction with short ailerons; both the Scout D rudders were larger than the Scout C type in height and chord, but differed from each other only by $2\frac{1}{2}$ inches in height. A repeat contract for 30 Scout Ds, Nos. 1094–1123 (*7028–7057*), was placed by the War Office on 18 October 1915, and these were equipped with standardised gun mountings and the modified wings; they were delivered without engines between 7 June and 15 July 1916, and followed by a further 50, Nos. 1381–1430 (*A1742–A1791*), delivered between 22 July and 27 September 1916. Meanwhile the Admiralty ordered 50 with the 100 h.p. Monosoupape-Gnome, Nos. 1124–1173 (*8951–9000*), on 9 November 1915; their delivery was spread over the period 18 April to 5 August 1916 and they had a modified cut-away centre section with a mounting for a movable Lewis gun. The cowling for the Monosoupape engine was larger in diameter than for the 80 h.p. engines and had a bulge on the starboard side to improve exhaust scavenging. A final production batch of 30 Scout Ds, Nos. 1837–1866 (*N5390–N5419*), covered by an Admiralty contract on 1 November 1916, was delivered between 2 November and 16 December 1916, but by this time the Company had begun production of the F.2A two-seater fighter at Brislington and declined an Admiralty invitation in

97

Scout D of R.F.C. with 110 hp Clerget, spinner and large ailerons.

March 1917 to tender for a further 40 Scouts. The first ten of the final batch had 100 h.p. Monosoupape-Gnomes, but the remainder reverted to 80 h.p. Gnomes and went to R.N.A.S. flying schools. The R.F.C. also expressed interest in a more potent version of the Scout D, and three, *5554, 5555* and *5556*, were modified to take the 110 h.p. Clerget, which like the Monosoupape, required a larger diameter cowling. In March 1916 Barnwell designed hemispherical spinners to suit each engine, and *5555* was fitted with the largest and provided data for the Clerget installation proposed for the M.1A monoplane. The other spinners were also tested, as well as a Morane spinner, which was flown extensively on a Scout D with a 110 h.p. Le Rhône by Lt. Frank Courtney at Farnborough. A conical spinner tested on *5556* suffered badly from distortion and vibration and no spinners were approved for production aircraft. The number of Scout Ds produced was 210, 130 for the R.F.C. and 80 for the R.N.A.S., so that the total of all Scouts A to D was 374, a not inconsiderable progeny from a project which started as a carbon-copy stop-gap.

Scouts C and D found their way to most theatres of war in small numbers and saw service with the R.F.C. on the Western Front, in Palestine with Nos. 14, 111 and 67 (Australian) Squadrons, in Mesopotamia with Nos. 30 and 63 Squadrons and in Macedonia with No. 47 Squadron. With the R.N.A.S. they were flown by No. 2 Wing from Mudros, Thasos and Imbros in the Dardanelles campaign, from H.M.S. *Vindex* in the North Sea, and from coastal stations at home. Both services employed them extensively for training and communications, and *8976* went to the Australian Central Flying School at Point Cook; another, rebuilt by No. 1 (Southern) Aeroplane Repair Depot, R.F.C., as *B763* was sent to McCook Field, Dayton, Ohio, where it was tested by the U.S. Army Engineering Division as Project no. *P32*.

Only one Scout D, No. 1060 (*5570*), delivered new on 18 March 1916, survived the war to enter private ownership as *G-EAGR* in the British Civil

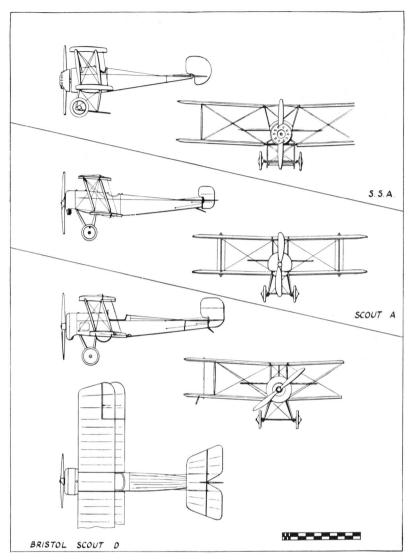

S.S.A.

SCOUT A

BRISTOL SCOUT D

Register. It was first owned by Major J. A. McKelvie, who sold it in 1926 to Squadron Leader Champion de Crespigny, who sold it a year later to Flight-Lt. A. M. Wray; it was stored for a time at Hedon, Hull, awaiting renewal of its certificate of airworthiness, which was refused because no approved fireproof bulkhead was fitted, and it was finally scrapped in 1930. In 1919 a Spanish private pilot, Juan Pombo, wished to order a new Scout D, but the Company declined to build a single new specimen and could not recommend any of those still in store at that date as being fit for reconditioning.

One other Bristol biplane, the S.2A, deserves notice here, although it was a two-seater. It was derived from the Scout D and was designed to meet an Admiralty specification for a two-seater fighter. Powered by a 110 h.p. Clerget rotary engine installed between horizontal bearers as proposed for the G.B.1, it had the same tail surfaces as Scout D but less rake at the wing tips. Two seats were installed side by side in the single cockpit. The design was rejected by the Admiralty, who preferred the Sopwith 1½ Strutter, but the War Office were interested in it as a potential advanced trainer and ordered two prototypes on 10 March 1916. These, Nos. 1377 and 1378 (*7836* and *7837*), were built and flown in May and June 1916, being delivered to the Central Flying School at Upavon on 11 June and 30 July, respectively. One of them was later flown at Gosport, where it had been fitted with a 100 h.p. Monosoupape-Gnome in a modified cowling. Its performance was quite good in spite of its girth, which earned it the nickname 'Tubby' at Filton as well as other appropriate epithets at the C.F.S.

SPECIFICATIONS AND DATA

Type: Scouts A-D, S.S.A., S.2A

Manufacturers: The British & Colonial Aeroplane Co. Ltd., Filton and Brislington, Bristol

Type	Scout A	Scout B	Scout C	Scout D	S.S.A.	S.2A
Power Plant	80 hp Gnome or Le Rhône	80 hp Gnome	80 hp Gnome, Le Rhône Clerget	80 hp Gnome, Le Rhône or Clerget, 100 hp Mono-Gnome, 110 hp Clerget or Le Rhône	80 hp Clerget or Gnome	110 hp Clerget, 100 hp Mono-Gnome
Span	22 ft / 24 ft 7 in	24 ft 7 in	24 ft 7 in	24 ft 7 in	27 ft 4 in	28 ft 2 in
Length	19 ft 9 in	20 ft 8 in	20 ft 8 in	20 ft 8 in	19 ft 9 in	21 ft 3 in
Height	8 ft 6 in	8 ft 6 in	8 ft 6 in	8 ft 6 in		10 ft
Wing Area	161 sq ft / 198 sq ft	198 sq ft	198 sq ft	198 sq ft	200 sq ft	
Empty Weight	617 lb / 750 lb	750 lb	760 lb	760 lb / 925 lb	913 lb	
All-up Weight	957 lb / 1,100 lb	1,100 lb	1,200 lb	1,250 lb / 1,440 lb	1,200 lb	1,400 lb
Max. Speed	95 mph / 100 mph	100 mph	93 mph	100 mph / 110 mph	106 mph	95 mph
Initial Rate of Climb	800 ft/min	1,000 ft/min	1,000 ft/min	1,100 ft/min		
Duration	3 hours / 5 hours	2½ hours	2½ hours	2½ hours / 2 hours	3 hours	3 hours
Accommodation	1	1	1	1	1	2
Production	1	2	161	210	1	2
Sequence Nos.	206	229, 230	See Appendix B		219	1377, 1378

First S.2A *7836* at Filton in June 1916.

Second T.T.A. *7751* at Filton in May 1916.

The Bristol T.T.A. and F.3A

When Frank Barnwell returned to Filton in August 1915 he sought a technical assistant to work with him on new projects. He interviewed Leslie G. Frise, who had just graduated from Bristol University, and persuaded him to resign his R.N.A.S. commission to join the Company; together in September 1915 they laid out the preliminary design of a twin-engined local defence two-seater to a War Office requirement. Four R.A.F.4a engines of 150 h.p. were promised for two aircraft, and the aim was to design a compact biplane with a fuselage of the minimum size that would accommodate a pilot and gunner, giving the latter a maximum field of fire. Although both the crew could not be given equally good fields of vision, the pilot's location aft of the trailing edge gave a good view forward and downward. The gunner in the nose had an unobstructed field of fire in the forward hemisphere for two free-mounted Lewis guns and had five spare drums of ammunition, also a vertical camera. The pilot had a single Lewis gun firing aft, with three spare drums.

Dual controls were fitted for emergency use only, with pedals in the front cockpit because the nose was too narrow for a normal rudder bar. The wings were of equal span and designed to fold back. Two sets of ailerons were designed, those actually constructed being of high aspect ratio. The tail unit comprised a single balanced rudder and flat tailplane of Scout D shape. The engine nacelles were midway between the wings and their rear fairings enclosed the oil and gravity fuel tanks. Below each nacelle was a small two-wheeled chassis of low drag, while the fuselage was protected by a fixed skid under the nose and a sprung tail-skid. The biplane, designated T.T. (Twin Tractor), promised to fulfil all the requirements, and was smaller than the F.E.4 designed at Farnborough to do the same job, which had a span of 75 ft.

After tendering, the Company was informed that all R.A.F.4a engines were earmarked for the B.E.12 and R.E.8 programmes, and that 160 h.p. or 120 h.p. Beardmores would be issued instead. At length the smaller engines materialised, and in January 1916 the amended design was finished as T.T.A., two prototypes being ordered on 15 February 1916 at a price, less engines, of £2,000 each. These identical aircraft, Nos. 1375 and 1376 (*7750* and *7751*), were test flown and accepted on 26 April and 27 May, respectively, by Capt. Hooper, Commanding Officer of the R.F.C. Acceptance Park at Filton. The first T.T.A. was flown to Upavon on 11 May for trials by A.I.D. pilots and achieved a top speed of 87 m.p.h., and an initial rate of climb of nearly 400 ft. per minute, which was better than the F.E.4's performance in spite of the reduced power available, but the design was adversely criticised on other grounds and not recommended for squadron service.

Concurrently with the building of the T.T.A.s the Admiralty released to the War Office a few 250 h.p. Rolls-Royce engines for experimental use, and the Company was invited to tender for an escort and anti-Zeppelin fighter using this power unit. Many firms submitted designs and Armstrong Whitworth, Bristol, Sopwith and Vickers all received orders for two prototypes each. The Bristol design, F.3A, was ordered on 16 May 1916 and sequence Nos. 1485 and 1486 were reserved, the corresponding R.F.C. serials being *A612* and *A613*. The F.3A utilised many of the T.T.A.'s components, including wings, tail unit and rear fuselage with pilot's cockpit, but the contract was cancelled soon after being awarded, so it was never built. The landing gear was unorthodox and consisted of one T.T.A. chassis unit, suitably strengthened, under the fuselage with a small-wheeled outrigger under each wing-tip. Two gunners' nacelles were provided above the top wing, with a forward and a rearward gun in each, mounted on telescopic pillars swinging through 90 degrees to fire on the beam. Probably it was intended to install the Davis gun if this had developed satisfactorily. Duration of seven hours for night-fighting against Zeppelins was specified, but the project was abandoned as soon as reliable gun-synchronising gear became available.

SPECIFICATIONS AND DATA

Types:　　　　　T.T.A. and F.3A.

Manufacturers:　The British & Colonial Aeroplane Co. Ltd., Filton, Bristol

Type	T.T.A.	F.3A
Power Plant	Two 120 hp Beardmore	One 250 hp Rolls-Royce
Span	53 ft 6 in	53 ft 6 in
Length	39 ft 2 in	36 ft 5 in
Height	12 ft 6 in	12 ft 11 in
Wing Area	817 sq ft	817 sq ft
Empty Weight	3,820 lb	3,400 lb
All-up Weight	5,100 lb	5,300 lb
Maximum Speed	87 mph	—
Accommodation	2	3
Production	2	nil (2 cancelled)
Sequence Nos.	1375, 1376	(1485 1486)

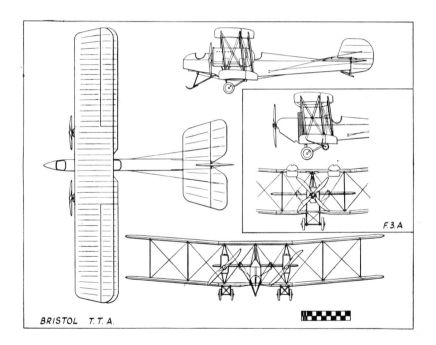

F.3.A

BRISTOL T.T.A.

First prototype F.2A *A3303* with original side radiators at Filton in September 1916.

The Bristol Fighter F.2A and F.2B

By March 1916 the Company had contracts for over 600 B.E. two-seaters of various types, and had delivered over 400; a further 550 B.E.2d and B.E.2e were to be produced before production of official designs ended in 1917. The shortcomings of the B.E. series and the requirements of the War Office for new designs were well known to Capt. Barnwell, and he held no high opinion of the R.E.8, the Royal Aircraft Factory's designated successor to the B.E.2e, so he set about producing a similar biplane having none of its defects. The result was the R.2A, which was laid out in March 1916 as a light two-seater powered by a 120 h.p. Beardmore engine, with the pilot in the front cockpit, with a synchronised Lewis gun on the starboard upper longeron, and an observer close to him in the rear cockpit, which contained dual controls, wireless, camera and message-launching tube. The observer could fold his seat and stand up to fire a single Lewis gun carried on a rotating ring mounting. To improve the observer's field of fire, the fuselage tapered to a very small cross-section aft, and more than a third of the fin and rudder area was below tail-plane level. For the same reason, the fuselage was mounted high between the staggered wings, so that the observer could fire over the pilot's head at quite low elevations. The upper wing was thus placed so as to minimise the pilot's blind spot. The design was promising though underpowered, and it was hoped that a 150 h.p. Hispano-Suiza engine might be released later, so in May 1916 a modified design, R.2B, was sketched round this engine. This had wings of unequal span with a partial Warren girder lift bracing intended to simplify rigging in the field. Then in July Barnwell was offered one of the new 190 h.p. Rolls-Royce engines as well as the Hispano-Suiza, and he immediately redesigned the R.2A to suit both engines. He was not content to adapt what he had already drawn, but started afresh from the Rolls-Royce installation diagram, designing a new cowling and fuselage to accommodate all the R.2A's equipment in perfect harmony with the new fuel and oil tanks required; at the same time he incorporated the latest improvements in armament.

104

He sent Frise on a fortnight's course on the Vickers gun at Hythe, with instructions to find out all about it. Frise returned with the information and a complete Vickers gun as well. Various positions for it were tried, but in the end Barnwell decided that only a mounting on the centre line would be satisfactory, with the cocking handle immediately in front of the pilot, so that jams could be readily cleared. This involved making a tunnel through the upper fuel tank, but this complication had the advantage of keeping the gun in the

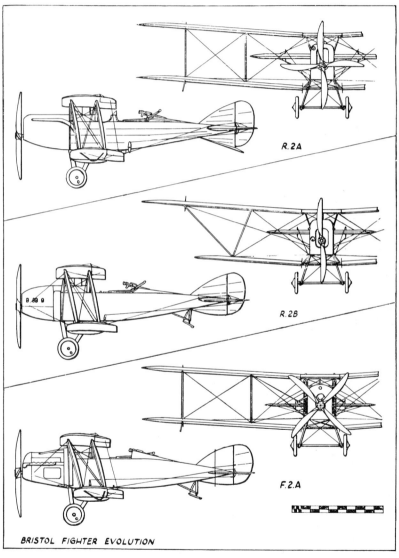

R. 2A

R. 2B

F. 2. A

BRISTOL FIGHTER EVOLUTION

warm air behind the engine, free from stoppages from frozen oil. The tail unit was redesigned and the top of the fuselage cambered to a horizontal knife-edge stern, thus reducing still more the observer's blind area. The rear cockpit arrangement was also revised, and the observer's tip-up seat was mounted to slide fore-and-aft so that he could sit facing either way. This gave him a better look-out while using his wireless and placed him within arm's reach of the pilot to give him instant warning of attack by a thump on the shoulder. An important innovation was the adjustable tailplane, whose incidence could be varied to give stable 'hands-off' flying over a wide range of speeds. The dual control was removed, but a small emergency lever could be plugged into a socket for elevator control, and there were hand-grips on the rudder cables, which enabled the observer to minimise the effect of a crash landing with a dead or unconscious pilot. The new design was renamed F.2A to mark its ability as a fighter, and 'Bristol Fighter' was the name universally bestowed on it from the start. The Company was instructed to proceed at once with two prototypes, one with the Rolls-Royce engine and the other with the Hispano-Suiza. On 28 August 1916 a contract was awarded for the two prototypes and 50 production aircraft.

Work commenced on the two prototypes during July, and the first, No. 1379 (*A3303*), was ready for flight on 9 September 1916; the second, No. 1380 (*A3304*), followed on 25 October. The first flight was eagerly awaited by everyone in the factory, and there was dismay when Capt. Hooper reported that he was unable to climb higher than 6,000 ft. Rigging was checked but small alterations of incidence and stagger had no effect, and finally Capt. Barnwell sent for his brother Harold, Vickers' chief test pilot, who in turn reported a maximum altitude of 6,000 ft., although he felt certain he had climbed very much higher. Then the penny dropped, the altimeter was changed and the fault was found. In fact, the F.2A had climbed to 10,000 ft. in 15 min. *A3303* was flown to Upavon on 21 September, and in its official trials exceeded its estimated performance by a handsome margin. Originally, the Rolls-Royce installation had two separate radiators mounted vertically on either side of the fuselage just ahead of the wings. This arrangement obscured

A3303 at Upavon with nose radiator fitted and lower wing-root end-plates removed.

106

Second F.2A *A3304* at Filton in December 1916, with longerons and lower centre section modified to F.2B standard.

the pilot's view for landing, and a new circular radiator was designed to fit into the nose, equipped with shutters in front; a similar radiator, but with shutters behind, was installed on the second prototype. As further Hispano-Suiza engines were not immediately available, Rolls-Royce engines were standardised for production aircraft, and in November the contract was amended to call for 200 more of an improved model, the F.2B. In accordance with A.I.D. recommendations the gap in the lower wing was filled by a lower centre section, and the upper longerons forward of the pilot's cockpit were sloped down so as to improve the view. All production Bristol Fighters had raked wing tips instead of the B.E. shape chosen for the two prototypes. Production aircraft numbered 1431–1480 (*A3305–A3354*) for the 50 F.2As and 2069–2268 (*A7101–A7300*) for the 200 F.2Bs were assembled at Brislington, because Filton works were full of B.E.s and deliveries began on 20 December 1916; six left the factory before the year ended, and the fiftieth was dispatched on 23 March 1917.

The second prototype, *A3304*, was modified to incorporate the F.2B's lower centreplane and sloping longerons, and these were approved for production; deliveries of the 200 F.2Bs began on 13 April, but before this the first squadron of F.2As had gone into action over Arras. Deliveries of Bristol Fighters had begun early in the year to experimental stations, where they were intensively flown in mock battle by pilots with front line experience. Their reports were enthusiastic, and two squadrons were formed and trained for the spring offensive of 1917. The first squadron, No. 48, received F.2As in February and arrived in France on 8 March, but was held back from action in order to achieve the maximum surprise effect. Early in April the squadron was based at Bellevue, near Arras, under the command of Major A. Vere Bettington. As a result of numerous applications from experienced pilots and observers, weary of the odds against them and eager to fly the Bristol Fighter, No. 48 Squadron contained the cream of the R.F.C. and numbered more than one V.C. amongst its crews. All were convinced that the Bristol Fighter would prove fast and manœuvrable enough to outfly the notorious

Albatros D.IIIs used in formations or 'circuses' by Baron von Richthofen to establish local air superiority.

On 5 April 1917 the first offensive reconnaissance over Arras was made by six F.2As led by Capt. Leefe Robinson, V.C. They were met near Douai by Richthofen with five Albatros and attempted to fight back in the orthodox two-seater manner, with the pilots manœuvring to give their gunners a good field of fire, but four Fighters were shot down, two by Richthofen personally, and Leefe Robinson was taken prisoner. Six days later, four Fighters were attacked by four Albatros and shot down two of the latter without loss, but later in the patrol one had to return to Bellevue with a jammed gun and the other three were shot down by four more Albatros. On 16 April six more of No. 48 Squadron's machines patrolled over Douai for over half an hour without meeting any enemy, which beguiled the formation leader into straying too far downwind, so that five ran out of fuel while still over the enemy lines. All but one were burned by their crews to avoid capture, and this sequence of losses was a disastrous debut for the new Fighter, from which so much had been expected. Some of the pilots then began to fly the Fighters as if they were single-seaters, using the front gun for the main attack and the observer's only as secondary rear cover. Immediate and striking success resulted from this change of tactics, and on 30 April a patrol of six F.2As fought their way home from Douai without loss. The tip was passed on to the second Bristol Fighter Squadron, No. 11, which had just re-equipped after flying Vickers Gunbus pushers.

No. 11 Squadron went into the line in May and for some weeks performed photographic reconnaissance without interference from the enemy. On 20 June 1917, the first attack by an Albatros was made on one of No. 11's Fighters, flown by Lt. A. E. McKeever with Sergt. Powell as observer. Mc-Keever held his fire until his attacker crossed his sights at close range, when a short burst from the front gun proved decisive. He repeated the performance the next day and within a week had scored four victories. In September he met eight enemy fighters, shot down one and disabled five others, for which he was awarded the Military Cross. By the end of October he had destroyed 20 enemy aircraft and had won a bar to his M.C. On 30 November, returning from a long patrol into enemy territory, he was attacked by seven Albatros and two two-seaters. He shot down one of the latter and in the *mêlée* that followed three of the single-seaters were destroyed, two by Powell with the rear gun. This final demonstration of prowess not only gained McKeever a D.S.O., but proved the magnificent fighting ability of the Bristol Fighter, when handled by a determined crew, and similar feats by many other pilots soon avenged the early casualties suffered by No. 48 Squadron.

Both Nos. 48 and 11 Squadrons had received F.2Bs as soon as they became available, and the production contract was twice revised until by July the quantity on order was 602. Capt. Hammond tested the first F.2B, *A7101*, on 10 April 1917, three days before its despatch to the Acceptance Park. Of this batch, the first 150 were fitted with the 190 h.p. Rolls-Royce engine, now named Falcon I, and 50 with the 220 h.p. Falcon II. Later the first 275 h.p. Falcon III was installed in *A7177*, and this engine was standardised for future production, as long as supplies lasted. With the extra performance the Falcon III provided, the Bristol Fighter was one of the really great aeroplanes of 1917 and 1918. In a letter to Capt. Louis Strange after his posting to the Central Flying School, Major Vere Bettington, C.O. of No. 48 Squadron, wrote from France on 13 May 1917:

"Regarding the Bristol, she is a topping fighting two-seater, the best here; not excepting the D.H. as she is much handier than that and communication between pilot and passenger in the Bristol is splendid whereas D.H.4 is not. . . . She is faster than the Hun two-seater but cannot touch the latest Albatros Scout for speed. Where she does score tremendously is in her power to dive, in this she is alone among English or Allied machines. Many Huns who have dived on the tail of one, missed and gone on diving, have been dived after, overtaken and destroyed. They are dived plumb vertically for thousands of feet until the noise is like that of a million sabres cleaving the air. The indicated speed on a Clift or Ogilvie Indicator is then generally 60 to 90 m.p.h. the second time round the dial. The indicator reads normally to 130 m.p.h. then a space so probably the speed is considerably over 230 m.p.h. . . . She loops well . . . she will do a fine spinning nose dive (if held in but will come out soon if left alone). . . . She stands an enormous amount of punishment in the way of being shot about and several have been very hard hit and come home, to be written off charge as beyond repair. . . . The Norman sight for the Lewis seems to be awfully good; observers have done well with it and many a Boche diving on the tail of a Bristol possibly mistaking it for a wretched Quirk (B.E.) has been badly stung; up to now observers have got about as many Huns as the pilots have done with their front guns."

Production of the F.2B at Filton began with Nos. 2269–2518 (*B1101–B1350*), which were delivered between 18 July 1917 and 18 February 1918, while Brislington continued with Nos. 2851–2950 (*C4801–C4900*) delivered concurrently between 17 October 1917 and 2 March 1918. The B.E.2e line at Filton ended at last, and in July 1917 the War Office adopted the Bristol Fighter for the re-equipment of all fighter-reconnaissance squadrons; a second production line began at Filton with a contract for 500 placed on 4 September covering Nos. 2951–3450 (*C4601–C4800*) and (*C751–C1050*) delivered between 30 November 1917 and 28 May 1918. This was increased in October by a further 300 shared by both factories, Nos. 3451–3750 (*D7801–D8100*), which were delivered between 29 March and 11 July 1918. But the Bristol factories were already working to their limit and still more drastic steps were needed to accelerate production, large contracts being let from November onwards to firms outside the aircraft industry; these firms included Angus Sanderson and Armstrong Whitworth, both of Newcastle-on-Tyne; Austin Motors and Harris & Sheldon of Birmingham; the Gloucestershire Aircraft Co. of Cheltenham; Marshall and Sons of Gainsborough; National Aircraft

Factory No. 3 (managed by Cunard) at Aintree; and the Standard Motor Co. of Coventry. Each of these undertakings received orders for between 100 and 500 airframes, the total number being nearly 2,000.

Soon it was obvious that Rolls-Royce Falcons could not be produced fast enough for all the Bristol Fighters ordered, and the first alternative sought was the Hispano-Suiza, of which the 200 h.p. geared version was being produced by the French motor industry and in England also by Wolseley Motors. As the power was less than that of the Falcon III, Fighters with the latter engine were reserved for fighter-reconnaissance squadrons and those with alternative engines were to be issued to corps-reconnaissance units. As there would still not be enough Hispano-Suizas to meet the whole programme, because of the concurrent adoption of the S.E.5a Scout which used only this engine, a second alternative engine, the 200 h.p. Sunbeam Arab, was chosen; at Filton, Arabs were specified for 300 Fighters, *C751–C1050*. Unfortunately all these engines had been rushed into production before being fully developed and suffered severely from 'teething troubles'. Wolseley-built Hispanos averaged only 4 hours' life before crankshaft failure; Brasier-built Hispanos were no better, and although those built by Mayen were more reliable, all these were taken for the S.E.5a programme. Only 80 out of a promised 1,800 Sunbeam Arabs had been accepted by the end of 1917, because of severe vibration, and even these gave endless trouble when installed. It was then hoped to use a larger Hispano-Suiza of 300 h.p. which, having direct drive, was immune from reduction gear trouble, and the Sunbeam Arab installation was modified to accommodate it, but this too was delayed in production.

The effect of these cumulative troubles and delays was to postpone the changeover from R.E.8s to Bristol Fighters from April 1918 till September, and large numbers of F.2B airframes delivered early in the year remained in storage and did not reach France in time to take any active part in the fighting, apart from Bristol-built Rolls-Royce machines. At the Armistice, the Royal Air Force had on charge about 900 of the latter and 720 with other engines, out of a total of 1,349 from Filton, 853 from Brislington and 1,600 from other contractors.

When supplies of both types of Hispano-Suiza failed, it was decided to substitute the Siddeley Puma of 240 h.p., but as this was a six-cylinder vertical engine it was difficult to install, and in particular the front gun had to be moved from its successful central position. Even the Puma was delayed in delivery, due to foundry difficulties. In the summer of 1918 the direct-drive 300 h.p. Hispano-Suiza at last became available, and this proved to be entirely reliable, but deliveries had hardly commenced before the war ended. It was the original Falcon-engined version which never failed in production and proved invincible in action. It equipped six squadrons in France, one in Italy, two in Palestine and five for home defence. The Arab-engined version also rendered valuable service with five long-range corps-reconnaissance flights in France.

In the great German offensive of March 1918, the Bristol Fighter squadrons

F.2B of No. 22 Sqn at Vert Galand on 1 April 1918, the birthday of the R.A.F. (*Crown copyright.*)

in France took a major part in strafing the advancing enemy infantry, flying almost at ground level with guns blazing and blasting enemy batteries with 20 lb. Cooper and 112 lb. Hale bombs in support of the hard-pressed Third and Fifth Armies. Nothing came amiss to the Bristol Fighter. In the arid wastes of the Palestine desert, No. 67 (Australian) Squadron gained superiority over the enemy air forces in October 1917 with the arrival of five F.2Bs, for the first time since the campaign began. The Australian pilot Capt. Ross Smith and his observer Lt. E. A. Mustar flew the same Bristol Fighter, *B1229*, throughout the campaign, during which time they destroyed 17 enemy aircraft between them and twice rescued the crews of other stranded machines.

On the home front daylight raids by Gotha bombers caused heavy civilian casualties and at first met little opposition, but on 7 July 1917 an attempt was

Veteran F.2B *F4891* on show at Filton in September 1919.

F.2B night-fighter *B1252* of No. 39 Sqn, showing wing-tip lights and pilot's ring-sight.

made by Home Defence units to intercept the raiders. The only aircraft to get within range was a Bristol Fighter, and later the type was chosen to re-equip three H.D. squadrons; they were equipped with a sight set to face forward at an elevation of 45 degrees from the pilot's eye. The rear gunner fired over the pilot's head at the same elevation while the pilot aimed the aircraft, and at 100 m.p.h. the trajectory remained straight for 800 yards. Rolls-Royce-engined fighters equipped the Home Defence squadrons and were painted matt dull green, with all white stripes and rings in the insignia obscured.

Although the Falcon installation varied only in minor detail during the entire period of production, there were several changes in external appearance when alternative engines were used. The 200 h.p. Hispano-Suiza employed a nearly circular radiator slightly taller than wide, and its oil tank was mounted externally beneath the cowling. The Sunbeam Arab at first had a similar radiator of larger area and more nearly rectangular, but the simple tubular engine mounting was found to be too flexible for this very rough-running engine and a deep braced girder had to be substituted making the bottom line of the cowling square and horizontal; this mounting was combined with

F.2B *C906* with Arab and S.E.5a radiator at Filton in April 1918.

an S.E.5a radiator for a time, but had to be increased in area for the 300 h.p. Hispano-Suiza, raising the top cowling to pent-roof shape. Finally an improved mounting and radiator was designed to accommodate either the Sunbeam Arab or the 300 h.p. Hispano-Suiza, and this pattern was standardised for 1918 production. The Puma installation, designed at Farnborough, resembled that of the D.H.9, with a similar underslung radiator. Some late Falcon installations had enlarged radiators with a squarer shape, and a few Fighters had the aircooled R.A.F.4d engine; most of these were flown for test purposes at Farnborough.

When the United States entered the war in 1917 the Bristol Fighter was among the British types proposed for large-scale production in America; 2000 were ordered first from the Curtiss Aeroplane and Motor Corporation

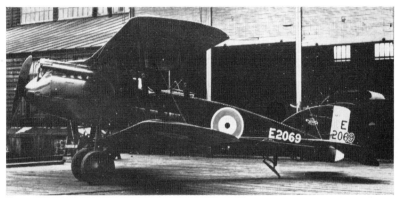

F.2B built by Armstrong Whitworth and fitted with Puma at Elswick Works, Newcastle-on-Tyne, in 1918.

of Buffalo, N.Y., and later from a group of other firms to be supervised by the Engineering Division of the Bureau of Aircraft Production at McCook Field, Dayton, Ohio; all were originally to be fitted with the 300 h.p. Hispano-Suiza, licence-built by the Wright-Martin Corporation. These plans met with approval from the Company, and several of the Filton staff went to America to supervise the arrangements, taking with them two sample airframes. To their dismay, they found that the engine actually chosen was the 400 h.p. Liberty 12, which was too heavy and badly installed. Capt. Barnwell predicted trouble but was overruled; when the first Curtiss-built F.2B flew and crashed he was proved correct, but the U.S. Army blamed the aircraft rather than the power plant, and only 27 of the contract were built, the rest being cancelled. Technical opinion at McCook Field was less biased and the two Filton-built aircraft were flown, one (*P 30*) with a 300 h.p. Hispano-Suiza and the other (*P 37*) with a 290 h.p. Liberty 8. *P 37* crashed before any performance tests could be made, but on 18 November 1918 *P 30* was flown by Major Schroeder to a height of 29,000 ft. above Dayton, an unofficial

Filton-built F.2B *P30* with the first American 300 hp Hispano-Suiza, at McCook Field, Dayton, Ohio, in 1918. (*Photo via Peter M. Bowers.*)

world's altitude record for which homologation was never sought. A Hispano-Suiza-engined F.2B variant with semi-monocoque veneer fuselage was built at McCook Field with the designation XB-1A (*P 90*) in July 1919, and 40 more were produced for the U.S. Army by Dayton-Wright in 1920.

XB-1A of U.S. Army Air Corps built by Dayton-Wright in 1921.

Although production of Bristol Fighters by outside contractors ceased on 26 November 1918, the Company was allowed to continue deliveries of all machines contracted for and started at that date, and production at Filton continued until September 1919, by which time a total number of 4,747 Bristol Fighters had been completed, 2,081 at Filton, 1,045 at Brislington and 1,621 by other contractors. Contracts placed with the Company from March to September 1918 covered Nos. 3754–4253 (*E2151–E2650*) and Nos. 4257–5424 (*F4271–F4970* and *H1240–H1707*). Of the last batch, 153 aircraft (*H1240–H1389, H1399–1400* and *H1407*) were completed with Arabs and the final 18 (*H1690–H1707*) with Pumas; all the rest had Falcons.* The last three

* Apparently only four F.2Bs were included in Imperial Gifts to Dominion Air Forces in 1919: *D7869* (later *G-CYDP*) and *F4336* (later *G-CYBC*) to Canada, and *H1557* and *H1558* to New Zealand. *H1248* (*G-AUEB*) was purchased ex-Disposals with a 300 h.p. Hispano-Suiza in 1920.

Rolls-Royce machines, *H1687–9*, were specially fitted with long-range tanks and dual controls, without armament. In addition 56 were taken over for completion from the Standard Motor Co., Nos. 5659–5714 (*E5253–E5308*), and delivered with Pumas.

When the Royal Air Force became re-established on a peacetime footing, the Bristol Fighter was adopted as the standard Army Co-operation type, and in December 1919 a new machine, No. 5893 (*J6586*), was tested with a wide range of desert equipment and a tropical cooling system for use in India and

F.2B Mk II *J6790* with desert wheels and oleo undercarriage for service trials; Filton 1920.

Iraq. This was followed by 214 similar new machines, Nos. 5894–6107 (*J6587–J6800*), and these together with successive batches of Fighters reconditioned in accordance with specification No. 21/21, totalling 435 machines during the next five years, were issued to the overseas squadrons of the R.A.F., which maintained law and order in Iraq, Baluchistan and the North-West Frontier of India. At home they equipped the four Army Co-operation Squadrons, well known for their message-hook technique as demonstrated annually at Hendon, also No. 24 (Communications) Squadron and the Royal Aircraft Establishment; amongst the R.A.E. stud was one with square-tipped metal wings of biconvex section, incorporating leading edge condensers for evaporative cooling experiments. All the reconditioned aircraft received new sequence numbers, but normally retained their original serials, although

F.2B Mk II *J6721* of the R.A.E., with steel biconvex (R.A.F. 34) wings and evaporative cooling; Farnborough, January 1930. (*Crown copyright.*)

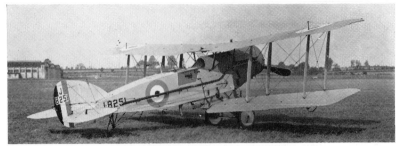

F.2B Mk III *J8251* at Filton in October 1926.

in 1925 a batch of 84 built from spares, Nos. 6721–6804, became *J7617–J7699*. After this batch a further 144 were reconditioned in 1926, and during that year one machine, *H1420*, was specially modified to a revised lay-out and exhaustively tested at the School of Army Co-operation, Old Sarum. This variant, which was structurally redesigned throughout for higher loads, was designated Bristol Type 96 and officially named Bristol Fighter Mark III, and 50 new aircraft, Nos. 7040–7089 (*J8242–J8291*), were delivered between 16 October and 23 December 1926. The final production batch consisted of 30 similar machines, but with dual controls instead of armament; these, Nos. 6988-7017 (*J8429–J8458*), were completed between January and June 1927 and included *J8430* specially furnished as a personal transport for H.R.H. the Prince of Wales, for whom it was flown and maintained by No. 24 Squadron. The 3576th and last new Bristol Fighter to be built at Bristol for the Air Ministry was No. 7122, one of two Mark IIIs delivered to the R.N.Z.A.F., in July 1927, together with a dual-control trainer, No. 7120. All the Mark IIIs of the R.A.F. were converted in 1928 into Mark IVs with a still higher gross

F.2B Mk IV *F4587* converted from Mk II in May 1928; this aeroplane was flown in the 1937 R.A.F. Display at Hendon and registered *G-AFHJ* in 1938, but was destroyed during the war. (*Crown copyright.*)

weight, strengthened longerons and landing gear, Handley Page auto-slots and enlarged fin and horn-balanced rudder. The prototype of the Mark IV was *H1417*, which initially had slot-and-aileron controls on a square-tipped upper wing.

Bristol Fighters Mark IV were issued to the Oxford and Cambridge University Air Squadrons in July 1928 until finally superseded in 1931, when a few were released for sale and came on to the Civil Register. Apart from Royal Air Force service, Bristol Fighters were supplied in small quantities to many foreign air forces, including Belgium, Greece, Mexico, Norway, Peru and Spain, as well as to Australia, Canada, New Zealand and the Irish Free State. A large proportion of these were sold in 1920–23 from war disposal stocks and were fitted with 300 h.p. Hispano-Suizas; in Belgium, S.A.B.C.A. acquired a manufacturing licence after 16, Nos. 6223–6238, with Frise ailerons and oleo landing gear, had been purchased new. Twelve similar new Fighters, Nos. 6510–6521, were supplied to Spain between July and October 1924, and ten more with further revised control surfaces and oleo landing gear, Nos. 7222–7231, went to Mexico in 1927. The grand total of all Bristol Fighters built, excluding the Jupiter-engined variant described later, was 5,308. The last Bristol Fighters in service, those of the R.N.Z.A.F., were scrapped in 1938, No. 7121 having crashed during air-firing practice at a range near Christchurch in February 1936. Only two Bristol Fighters now survive and are being preserved for posterity. One is *E2581*, still in its 1918 camouflage, in the Imperial War Museum, London; the other is *D8096*, maintained in airworthy condition and flown on suitable occasions by the Shuttleworth Trust, at Old Warden, Beds.

The Shuttleworth Trust's veteran F.2B flying at Filton in July, 1961.

SPECIFICATIONS AND DATA

Types: R.2A, R.2B, F.2A and F.2B

Manufacturers: The British & Colonial Aeroplane Co. Ltd., Filton and Brislington, Bristol

The Bristol Aeroplane Co. Ltd., Filton, Bristol;

Angus Sanderson & Co. Ltd., Newcastle-on-Tyne;

Sir W. G. Armstrong, Whitworth & Co. Ltd., Gosforth and Elswick, Newcastle-on-Tyne;

Austin Motors Ltd., Longbridge, Birmingham;

Cunard Steamship Co. Ltd., National Aircraft Factory No. 3, Aintree, Lancs.

Gloucestershire Aircraft Co. Ltd., Sunningend, Cheltenham;

Harris & Sheldon, Ltd., Stafford Street, Birmingham;

Marshall & Sons, Ltd., Gainsborough, Lincs.

Standard Motor Car Co. Ltd., Coventry;

Curtiss Aeroplane & Motor Corporation, Buffalo, N.Y., U.S.A.;

Dayton-Wright Airplane Co., Dayton, Ohio, U.S.A.

Engineering Division, Bureau of Aircraft Production, McCook Field, Dayton, Ohio, U.S.A.

Power Plants:

(R.2A)	One 120 hp Beardmore;
(R.2B)	One 150 hp Hispano-Suiza;
(F.2A)	One 190 hp Rolls-Royce Falcon I / One 150 hp Hispano-Suiza
(F.2B)	One 190 hp Rolls-Royce Falcon I One 220 hp Rolls-Royce Falcon II One 275 hp Rolls-Royce Falcon III One 200 h.p. Hispano-Suiza One 200 hp Sunbeam Arab One 200 hp R.A.F.4d One 180 hp Wolseley Viper One 230 hp Siddeley Puma One 300 hp Hispano-Suiza
(USA O-1)	One 400 hp Liberty 12 / One 290 hp Liberty 8

Span:
(R.2A) 40 ft 8 in
(R.2B) 39 ft
(F.2A & F.2B) 39 ft 3 in

Length:
(R.2A) 26 ft 3 in
(R.2B) 25 ft 5 in

(F.2A & F 2B) { Falcon 25 ft 10 in / Arab & Hispano 24 ft 10 in / Puma 26 ft

(USA O-1) { Liberty 12 26 ft 2 in / Liberty 8 25 ft 5 in

Height: 9 ft 6 in

Wing Area: (R.2A) 430 sq ft
                 (R.2B) 320 sq ft
                 (F.2A) 389 sq ft
                 (F.2B) 405 sq ft

Weights:

Type	Engine	Empty Weight	All-up Weight
F.2A	Falcon I	1,700 lb	2,700 lb
	Hispano	1,500 lb	2,500 lb
F.2B	Falcon III	1,930 lb	2,800 lb
	Arab	1,890 lb	2,800 lb
	Hispano 200	1,740 lb	2,700 lb
	R.A.F.4d	2,000 lb	2,800 lb
	Puma	1,920 lb	2,810 lb
	Hispano 300	2,070 lb	3,000 lb
Mark II	Falcon III	2,095 lb	3,160 lb
Mark III	Falcon III	2,150 lb	3,250 lb
Mark IV	Falcon III	2,200 lb	3,350 lb
USA O-1	Liberty 12	—	2,940 lb

Maximum Speed:

(F.2A: Falcon I)	110 mph	(F.2B: Puma)	116 mph
(F.2A: Hispano)	102 mph	(F.2B: Hispano 300)	120 mph
(F.2B: Falcon III)	125 mph	(Mark II & III)	112 mph
(F.2B: Arab)	115 mph	(Mark IV)	110 mph
(F.2B: Hispano 200)	115 mph	(USA O-1)	138 mph

Service Ceiling: 20,000 ft
Endurance: 3 hours
Accommodation: 2

Production Sequence Nos. } : see Appendices B and D

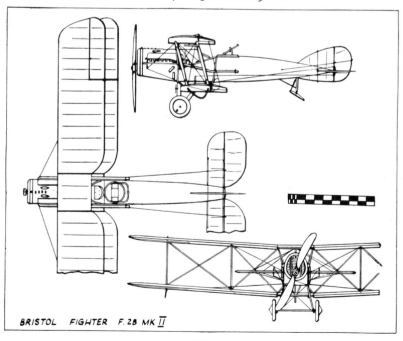

BRISTOL FIGHTER F. 2B MK II

M.1A as first flown by F. P. Raynham at Filton in June 1916.

The Bristol M.1A, M.1B and M.1C Monoplane Scouts

In the spring of 1916 the Royal Flying Corps was woefully short of properly-armed fighting Scouts, and the pusher-type two-seaters which bore the brunt of the fighting were no match for the Fokker monoplanes with their two or three synchronised machine guns firing through the airscrew. British gun interrupter gears had not been reliable until the hydraulic Constantinesco-Colley gear was invented, and, as soon as this device had been put into production, aircraft firms were urged to submit designs using Vickers guns firing through the airscrew disc. The officially-designed B.E.12 was a makeshift attempt to turn the outworn B.E.2c into a single-seat fighter, and its success was so limited that in June 1916 Sir Douglas Haig had condemned its continued use on the Western Front. The demand for better fighting machines became acute as casualties among pilots and observers mounted, and soon after the Battle of the Somme began, on 1 July 1916, the first prototype of a new single-seater designed by Capt. Barnwell had been built. This was the M.1A, No. 1374, a monoplane incorporating all the experience gained with the Scout D and refined aerodynamically to the limit of practicability.

In March a few Scout Ds had been equipped with hemispherical spinners, and a marked reduction of drag had been gained thereby. Comparative tests between Scout *5555* with this spinner and Scout *5556* with an equivalent pointed spinner had revealed structural instability in the latter which made it unusable because of vibration, whereas the domed spinner gave no trouble. Both Scouts were equipped with the 110 h.p. Clerget, and this engine, with a similar spinner and cowling, was taken as the basis of Barnwell's new monoplane. The fuselage was conventional in structure, but the wire-braced four-longeron girder was faired throughout its length to a circular section. The monoplane wings, raked at the tips, were attached to the top longerons, wire-braced below to the bottom longerons and above to a cabane formed from two hoops of streamline section tubing. The undercarriage was a simple Vee type carrying two wheels on a rubber-sprung cross-axle. The pilot's cockpit was located under the cabane which thus gave protection in the event of overturning in a forced landing. The empennage was conventional, with a fixed fin of generous area.

The M.1A, a private venture, was first flown at Filton on 14 July 1916 by Fred P. Raynham, the foremost free-lance test pilot of his day. In his hands the little monoplane, as yet unarmed, achieved the astounding speed of 132 m.p.h. and he even flew it under Clifton Suspension Bridge! In October the M.1A was purchased by the War Office for evaluation by the A.I.D. and four more of similar type were ordered. These had a Vickers gun on the port wing root, a cut-out panel in the starboard wing root and a revised cabane consisting of four straight struts arranged in a pyramid, and were called M.1B. The M.1A, revised to the new standard, was delivered to the Central Flying School as *A5138* on 29 November 1916 and was followed by No. 1481 (*A5139*) on 15 December and No. 1482 (*A5140*) on 19 January 1917. All three had 110 h.p. Clerget rotaries, but the third M.1B, No. 1483 (*A5141*), was

Second M.1B *A5140* at Filton in December 1916.

Fourth M.1B *A5142* modified to M.1C standard with central gun; Orfordness, April 1917. (*Crown copyright.*)

fitted with a 130 h.p. Clerget when dispatched on 8 February. A further engine change was made in the last M.1B, No. 1484 (*A5142*), which left Filton with a Bentley A.R.1 rotary of 150 h.p. on 22 March 1917. It was hoped that a large production order would follow the official trials, in view of the great advance in performance, but to the Company's (and many R.F.C. pilots') intense disappointment, the landing speed of 49 m.p.h. was considered too high for operation from small airfields on the Western Front. The pilot's view was also criticised, but Capt. Barnwell himself flew one of the monoplanes at Upavon and found no difficulty in landing, although he was well known to be a somewhat erratic pilot.

Eventually a production order was given, on 3 August 1917, for only 125 aircraft, Nos. 2719–2843 (*C4901–C5025*), delivered between 19 September 1917 and 25 February 1918, and these were relegated to Middle East squadrons as replacements for the Scout D. The production version, M.1C, was fitted with the 110 h.p. Le Rhône engine and had its single Vickers gun centrally mounted so that the windscreen was divided by the sight, which had a padded surrounding frame, with the cocking handle ready to hand, making stoppages very easy to clear; cut-outs were made in both wing-roots to improve the downward view. This location for the gun had been tried out experimentally on the fourth M.1B, and the Sopwith-Kauper interrupter gear was sometimes employed, when C.C. gears were in short supply.

M.1Cs of No. 72 Sqn in Mesopotamia in 1917. (*Crown copyright.*)

Only five squadrons were partly equipped with M.1C for active service, although a fair number of the monoplanes were issued without guns to flying schools at home, where they were highly esteemed as senior officers' personal mounts. Nos. 17 and 47 Squadrons, based on Salonika, operated against the Turks and Bulgars in January 1918 with one flight of each equipped with M.1Cs, and these two flights were merged in April to form No. 150 Squadron. No. 111 Squadron in Palestine flew a few monoplanes for a time, and in March 1918 No. 72 Squadron went to Basra with one flight of monoplanes, which later operated from Mirjana in support of the Third Army Corps. In 1917 six M.1Cs were sent to the Chilean government in part payment for two warships built for Chile, but commandeered by the Admiralty before completion. One was flown by Lt. Godoy from Santiago to Mendoza, Argentina, and back on 12 December 1918; this was the first flight across the Andes and entailed climbing to over 13,000 ft. to clear the

Uspullata Pass. On 4 April 1919 this exploit was repeated by Lt. Cortinez, but without official permission; on being reprimanded after arriving at Mendoza, he flew back again and found himself a popular hero.

G-EASR at Filton in 1924.

These two flights after the Armistice drew attention to the M.1C's capabilities, and the Company bought back from the Aircraft Disposal Board four of them for reconditioning and resale. One of them was an M.1B, and this machine, *G-EAVP*, was modified as a flying test-bed for the three-cylinder Bristol Lucifer radial engine, under the new designation M.1D, which is separately described later in this book. Of the other three, one was sold in America, one, formerly *G-EAVO*, in Spain to Senor Juan Pombo in 1921 and one, *G-EASR*, remained at Filton. Two other M.1Cs were bought from the

Larry Carter with *M-AFAA* (formerly *G-EAVO*) at Croydon in November 1921.

Harry Butler and H. A. Kauper with M.1C *C5001* bought from the Aircraft Disposals Board at Waddon in July 1919.

Disposal Board by private owners in 1919; one was *C4964*, registered *G-EAER*, and flown in the 1919 Aerial Derby by Major C. H. Chichester Smith; the other was *C5001*, purchased at Waddon in July 1919 by an Australian pilot, Capt. Harry Butler, A.F.C., who in partnership with H. A. Kauper (formerly Harry Hawker's assistant), flew it in the neighbourhood of Adelaide from a field at Minlaton, S.A., as *G-AUCH*, winning the first Australian Aerial Derby on 8 September 1920. Harry Butler died in July 1923 from injuries received in a crash in another aeroplane and his M.1C was then stored until it was bought in 1930 by H. Miller, who replaced the Le Rhône engine by a Gipsy II engine in 1931; with this combination, now *VH-UQI*, he won the Adelaide Aerial Derby in 1931 and 1932 and also competed in the Victorian Aerial Derby in 1932, but had to retire with engine trouble. After some years' further flying with the Commercial Aviation Co., the machine was flown from Adelaide to Perth in 1938, and was then stored in the roof of a hangar at Guildford Airport. It was rediscovered there in 1956 by C. B. Tilbrook, who raised a fund to build an exhibition hall to house it permanently at Minlaton as the Harry Butler Memorial. Painted red and

Harry Butler's M.1C re-engined in 1931 with Gipsy II, restored in 1957 and now preserved at Minlaton, S.A.

bearing the name *Puck*, *VH-UQI* is now the only surviving M.1C, although until 1960 the mouldering remains of Lt. Godoy's monoplane still existed at Santiago de Chile. A replica M.1C was produced by Don Cashmore using original drawings and flown in 1987 with a Warner Scarab engine. It has been donated to the RAF Museum and is being put on display at Hendon with a 110 h.p. Le Rhône engine installed.

SPECIFICATION AND DATA

Type:	M.1A, M.1B and M.1C
Manufacturers:	The Bristol & Colonial Aeroplane Co. Ltd., Filton, Bristol
Power Plants:	One 110 hp Clerget (M.1A & M.1B); 110 hp Le Rhône (M.1C); 130 hp Clerget (M.1B); 150 hp A.R.1. (M.1B)

Span:	30 ft 9 in	*Length:*	20 ft 4 in
Height:	7 ft 10 in	*Wing Area:*	145 sq ft
Empty Weight:	900 lb	*All-up Weight:*	1,350 lb
Max. Speed:	(M.1A) 132 mph	*Accommodation:*	Pilot only
	(M.1B) 125 mph		
	(M.1C) 130 mph	*Production:*	1 M.1A, 4 M.1B,
Service ⎫	(M.1A) 17,000 ft		125 M.1C
Ceiling ⎭ :	(M.1B) 15,000 ft		
	(M.1C) 20,000 ft	*Sequence Nos.:*	1374, 1481–1484,
Endurance:	(M.1A) $2\frac{3}{4}$ hours		2719–2843 (rebuilt: 5885–5887)
	(M.1C) $1\frac{3}{4}$ hours		

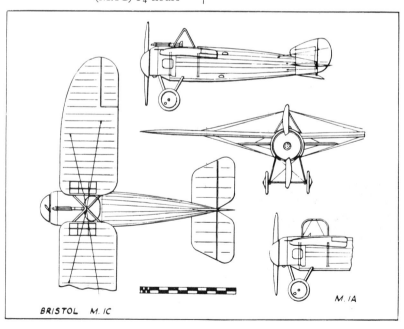

BRISTOL M. 1C

M. 1A

First M.R.1 (originally *A5177*) after having metal wings fitted; Filton, 1918.

The Bristol M.R.1 Metal Biplane

Some of the earliest pioneers of flying, including the Wright Brothers and Louis Blériot, had been makers and riders of bicycles before their first attempts at aviation, and the materials and methods of bicycle construction were well known to aircraft builders from the beginning. Thin-walled carbon-steel seamless tubing, brazed or soldered into machined sockets, bolted together and braced with piano-wire, must have seemed the logical aircraft structure to military engineers desiring to attain serviceability in such aircraft as they considered to be practicable. Many attempts were made to design aeroplanes along these lines, such as the official R.E.5 and R.E.7, but always the weight was excessive, and if very thin-walled tubes were chosen, they would not stand up to manhandling on the ground because they buckled too easily. When the first useful aluminium alloys were produced, having a strength–weight ratio better than mild steel, they were found to be very easily corroded and impossible to braze or solder. Vickers Ltd. were among the first in the field with their all-metal monoplanes based on the patents of Robert Esnault-Pelterie, and in 1911 Sir George White had commissioned in France a monoplane of steel-tube construction designed by Gabriel Voisin, but it was far too heavy to fly.

The Company's interest in metal construction continued, and in July 1914 they undertook the detail design and construction of four all-metal derivatives of the B.E.2c, called the B.E.10. The aerodynamic design of this two-seater biplane was by a syndicate of Farnborough designers led by H. P. Folland and included such refinements as full-span trailing edge flaps to reduce landing speed. After the outbreak of war, the urgent need for quantity production of the B.E.2c at Filton caused the B.E.10 to be abandoned early in 1915, when the few components and details already manufactured were delivered to the Royal Aircraft Factory for mechanical testing.

During the ensuing 12 months, aircraft production all over the country expanded enormously and the authorities foresaw the risk, if war continued, of a severe shortage of timber suitable for aircraft manufacture; already stocks of Grade A silver spruce were declining and Grade B was being substituted wherever safety allowed. In July 1916 Capt. Barnwell drafted the revised layout of the R.2A reconnaissance biplane to match the 190 h.p. Rolls-Royce engine, thereby creating the Bristol Fighter. The need for a reconnaissance two-seater still remained for use where enemy air support was not paramount, and, as such fronts were mainly in a tropical climate, there seemed to be a strong case for adopting metal construction.

With the shortcomings of the B.E.10 design in mind, he approached the problem logically and drew on his early training on the Fairfield shipyard. He believed that duralumin sheet could be used in a monocoque structure if properly protected by a good quality marine varnish and adopted this method for the fuselage of the M.R.1, as the metal biplane was designated. The fuselage was built up in four sections bolted together; the front section was a semi-monocoque open channel with channel-section struts at each frame bracing the top longitudinals to the centre of the bottom frame member. This carried the engine bulkhead and bearers at its forward end and the tanks and centre section struts above and below. The next section aft was similar and contained the pilot's cockpit, with a Vickers gun and ammunition box above. The third section was a self-contained parallel-sided monocoque unit carrying the observer's seat with a Scarff gun mounting above, and the tapered monocoque rear fuselage boom was bolted to the back of this section; the design was so arranged that the observer's cockpit section could be left out altogether and the aircraft then became a single-seater to which wings of smaller area could be attached. This versatility would have been a valuable investment in a machine for which a long storage life was envisaged, but in fact the contract awarded on 2 November 1916 was for only two prototypes for evaluation and mechanical test.

As Barnwell and Frise were under extreme pressure to get the Bristol Fighter into quantity production, the detail design of the M.R.1 was handed over to W. T. Reid, who faithfully translated Barnwell's ideas into metal, using relatively small amounts of mild steel. The duralumin monocoque fuselage was one of the first examples of double-skin construction, the smooth outer skin being riveted to a longitudinally corrugated inner skin. The original wing structure was a direct adaptation from wood to duralumin, using duplicated plates on edge to form the spars, but this was found to be much too flexible on test and in the end wing design and construction were sub-contracted to The Steel Wing Company of Gloucester, who had developed a method of using rolled high-tensile steel strip and had already produced successful sample steel wings for the B.E.2d and Avro 504. Two other methods, using both steel and duralumin, the subject of patents by the Krieger Electric Car Syndicate and a Mr. Mayrow, respectively, were also tested.

By mid-1917 the first M.R.1, No. 2067 (*A5177*), was complete except for the wings, which were making slow progress at Gloucester, and it was decided to build a set of conventional wooden wings (with upper ailerons only) so as not to delay flight tests. The latter were entirely successful and *A5177* was handed over to the Air Board on 23 October 1917, its contract

Bristol M.R.1 with temporary wooden wings (ailerons on top wing only) before first flight;
Filton, October 1917.

price of £2,000 having been reduced to £1,600 on account of the wooden wings. The second M.R.1, No. 2068 (*A5178*), was delayed until late in 1918 before receiving its metal wings, but was then successfully flown, a Wolseley Viper engine of 180 h.p. being fitted instead of the 140 h.p. French Hispano-Suiza of the first machine. After the Armistice *A5178* was piloted frequently

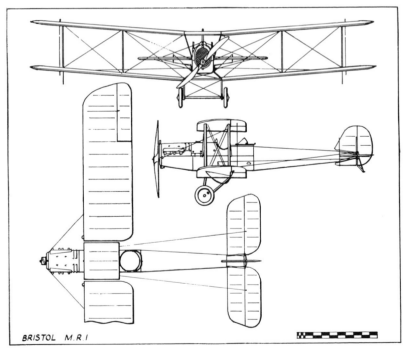

BRISTOL M.R.I

by Capt. Barnwell, and eventually it was accepted for delivery to the Royal Aircraft Establishment; it was flown to Farnborough by Capt. Barnwell personally on 19 April 1919, but on arrival he collided with a pine tree near the North Gate of the R.A.E. and crashed on the aerodrome, bringing down the top of the tree with the aeroplane. He was shaken, but otherwise unhurt; the M.R.1, however, was considerably damaged and no attempt was made to repair it. Meanwhile, *A5177* (renumbered *A58623*) was being structurally tested and much valuable information on metal construction was gleaned from it. For its day, the M.R.1 was a considerable technical achievement, its disposable load amounting to more than 40% of its all-up weight. Moreover, it had been constructed almost entirely without using specialised tools and equipment, and the necessity of developing these for quantity production was perhaps the most valuable of the lessons learned.

SPECIFICATION AND DATA

Type:	M.R.1
Manufacturers:	The British & Colonial Aeroplane Co. Ltd., Brislington, Bristol
Power Plants:	One 140 hp Hispano-Suiza One 180 hp Wolseley Viper
Span:	42 ft 2 in
Length:	27 ft
Height:	10 ft 3 in
Wing Area:	458 sq ft
Empty Weight:	1,700 lb
All-up Weight:	2,810 lb
Max. Speed:	110 mph
Endurance:	5 hours
Accommodation:	2
Production:	2
Sequence Nos.:	2067, 2068

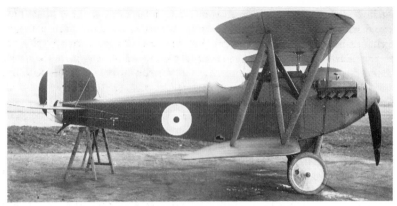

First Scout F *B3989* with Arab at Filton in January 1918.

The Bristol Scouts E and F

In the autumn of 1916, before the Bristol Fighter had been issued to the Royal Flying Corps squadrons in France, desperate efforts were being made to produce single-seater fighting Scouts capable of outflying their German opponents, in the struggle to gain local air superiority over the artillery lines. A limit had almost been reached in the power available from rotary engines and attention turned to various alternative designs, both in-line and radial. Typical of the former was the Hispano-Suiza, but its reliability was poor and supplies of serviceable engines so limited that they were reserved for the officially-designed S.E.5a Scout, the first prototype of which flew in December 1916.

Designers looked hopefully around for other engines, and Capt. Barnwell was informed of a proposal by Harry R. Ricardo and Frank B. Halford for a ten-cylinder two-row watercooled radial of 200 h.p., the 'Cruciform'. This engine gained no official support and was not built even as a prototype, but nevertheless Barnwell designed round it two alternative single-seater schemes, one a tractor biplane and the other a pusher. The latter, drawn by W. T. Reid on 25 January 1917, remained a preliminary layout only, and showed a conventional equal-span two-bay biplane with the pilot's cockpit in a nacelle mounted high up, as in the contemporary Vickers F.B.26; armament comprised two Lewis guns. The tractor design, drawn by Barnwell himself, was dated two days earlier and showed a neat single-bay biplane combining the aerodynamic refinement of the M.1C with the compact layout of the Scout D. The wings had rounded raked tips as in the monoplane and four small strut-linked ailerons of equal area. The fuselage was a wire-braced structure aft, but a Warren girder forward of the cockpit. The undercarriage was a simple Vee type with rubber-sprung cross-axle, and the engine was installed with a annular radiator forward, to which air was admitted through a large diameter annular spinner surrounding a cone at the centre; this arrangement foreshadowed the low-drag cowling developed 30 years later by Napiers for the Hawker Tempest. Armament consisted of a single synchronised Vickers gun recessed into the top of the fuselage ahead of the pilot and a Lewis gun on the top centre section which could be elevated through 45 degrees from its lowest position, which was arranged just to clear the airscrew.

A fair amount of design work was done on the tractor project, Scout E, during February and March 1917, and sequence number 2844 was reserved for a prototype; but then it became apparent that the Cruciform engine would not be built, and early in May the Company was promised a few 200 h.p. Hispano-Suiza engines and a contract for six prototypes of a modified design. Barnwell at once revised Scout E to suit the Hispano-Suiza and changed the wing arrangement to one of unequal span with ailerons only on the top wing; at the same time the Lewis gun was deleted and two synchronised Vickers guns were arranged side-by-side in place of the single one. The revised project was named Scout F and retained the rear fuselage and tail unit of Scout E almost unchanged, but the deeper front end necessitated a new, shorter undercarriage. When the contract was issued on 4 June it specified the Sunbeam Arab engine, because of the shortage of Hispano-Suizas, and this was accommodated without much difficulty, but the cooling system gave some trouble and the header tank had to be raised to a position where it made a slight bulge in the top of the cowling. The radiator layout of Scout F matched that of Scout E in neatness and imagination, for it comprised a rectangular block mounted in an under-belly tunnel fairing, with two independent shutters, which could be set to various angles to maintain optimum water temperature. This permitted a low-drag nose design with a conical spinner over the airscrew boss. A good many revisions were made in cockpit details, flying controls and gun installation while construction of the prototype proceeded, and the design was not completed until November 1917, by which time the first few Sunbeam Arabs had begun to demonstrate the incurability of their vibration trouble. It was therefore decided to complete only the first two Scouts F, Nos. 2845 and 2846 (*B3989* and *B3990*), with Arabs and to seek a better alternative engine for the others.

The first Scout F was flown in March 1918 and had a remarkably fine performance, reaching 138 m.ph. at sea level and 128 m.p.h. at 10,000 ft. The second Scout F was flown at the Central Flying School by all the most experienced fighter pilots of the day, amongst them Major Oliver Stewart, who rated it as a better aerobatic machine than the S.E.5a; but it was condemned by its engine and no attempt seems to have been made to revert to the Hispano-Suiza version. By this time, however, a new and promising small-diameter radial engine had arrived; this was the Cosmos Mercury of 315 h.p. designed originally for an Admiralty application by A. H. R. Fedden and L. F. G. Butler of Brazil Straker and Co. Ltd. of Fishponds, Bristol, who had been awarded a contract for 200 production engines of the type.

Third Scout F *B3991* with Cosmos Mercury at Filton in October 1918.

Seeking a suitable aeroplane in which to install the Mercury engine for flight testing, Fedden approached Barnwell, who was looking for a substitute for the Sunbeam Arab and was predisposed in favour of a radial since his study for Scout E. The upshot of this meeting was the modification of the third Scout F, No. 2847 (*B3991*), to take the Mercury, which was installed in a low-drag cowling with only the cylinder heads and exhaust stubs exposed.

Known as the Scout F.1, *B3991* made its first flight at Filton on 4 September 1918 and was the first Bristol prototype to be flown by Cyril Uwins. The flight lasted 20 minutes and the aircraft reached 6,000 ft. and was both spun and rolled. The second flight, on 6 September, was also made by Uwins.

Although the Armistice put an end to any hope of production of the Scout F.1, it was very successful in its trials and in December 1918 was delivered to Farnborough. There, in April 1919, it put up unofficial records by climbing to 10,000 ft. in 5·4 min. and to 20,000 ft. in 16·25 min; its maximum speed at sea level was 145 m.p.h. After these trials no further development took place because the Cosmos Mercury contract had been cancelled; the fourth Scout F, No. 2848 (*B3992*), was completed as a spare airframe, but the last two aircraft of the order were still unfinished in April 1919; the question did arise of completing one of them with a Hispano-Suiza for offer to Senor Juan Pombo instead of the Scout D he had asked for, but he accepted the alternative offer of an M.1C, as recorded earlier. The mainplanes of *B3992* were the subject of static strength tests at the R.A.E. in 1919, and as late as March 1921 Capt. Barnwell suggested adapting this airframe as a flying test-bed for a new Curtiss engine, but this proposal was not approved.

SPECIFICATION AND DATA

Type:	Scout F
Manufacturers:	The British & Colonial Aeroplane Co. Ltd., Filton, Bristol
Power Plants:	One 200 hp Sunbeam Arab
	One 315 hp Cosmos Mercury
Span:	29 ft 7 in
Length:	(Arab) 20 ft 10 in
	(Mercury) 20 ft
Height:	8 ft 4 in
Wing Area:	260 sq ft
Empty Weight:	1,440 lb
All-up Weight:	(Arab) 2,200 lb
	(Mercury) 2,260 lb
Max. Speed:	(Arab) 138 mph
	(Mercury) 145 mph
Climb to 10,000 ft:	(Arab) $9\frac{1}{2}$ min
	(Mercury) $5\frac{1}{2}$ min
Accommodation:	Pilot only
Production:	4
Sequence Nos.:	2845–2848

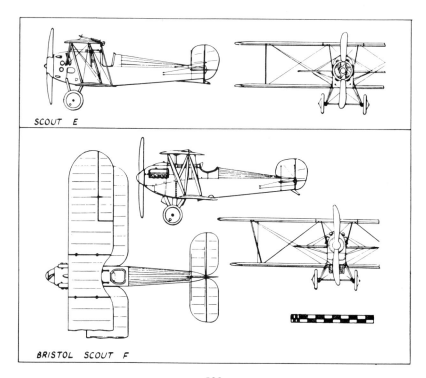

SCOUT E

BRISTOL SCOUT F

Badger I *F3495* as rebuilt with improved Dragonfly installation and larger rudder; Filton, February 1919.

The Bristol F.2C and Badger

The designation F.2C was first applied in February 1917 to a proposed variant of the Falcon-engined Bristol F.2B Fighter having improved landing gear, tail unit and engine installation. As these affected interchangeability and jigs had already been designed for large production, this variant was abandoned in March 1917 and the designation was revived in October for a new two-seater fighter-reconnaissance biplane designed for rapid production. It was severe in outline with unstaggered two-bay wings of equal span and small gap, and the pilot and observer were placed close together and high up so as to have the best possible view for fighting. The pilot's seat was below the centre section, which had a circular hole in it for the pilot's head. Armament comprised a pair of synchronised Vickers guns forward of the pilot firing through the airscrew and two separate pillar-mounted Lewis guns for the observer, one forward and one aft.

The engine proposed was a nine-cylinder Salmson water-cooled radial of 260 h.p. with tall rectangular radiators on each side of the flat-flanked fuselage in line with the pilot's position. At the end of November it was evident that the Salmson engine would not be available and the design was revised, with wings of reduced area, to suit the Bentley B.R.2 rotary of 230 h.p. Neither of these layouts met with official approval because the engines selected were not powerful enough to permit overloads to be carried without performance penalties.

Barnwell realised that at least 300 h.p. was required to meet the specification, and in April 1918 he submitted a new design based on the 320 h.p. A.B.C. Dragonfly air-cooled radial. This was a single-bay staggered biplane of unequal span and clean appearance, having many features derived from the Scout F. A fuselage mock-up was built and the layout of guns, camera, wireless and other equipment was agreed with specialist R.A.F. officers. Detail design went ahead, but no prototypes were ordered until September. By this time the Dragonfly engine had shown itself to be no more reliable than the Sunbeam Arab and was achieving an average life of only 17 hours before crankshaft failure occurred.

Meanwhile Fedden and Butler of Brazil Straker had designed a new nine-cylinder radial engine of 400 h.p. called the Cosmos Jupiter. The contract for three prototypes of the F.2C, officially named Badger, allowed the second machine to be fitted with a Jupiter for comparison with the other two which were to have Dragonflies. Six weeks later the war ended and all production contracts were terminated, but experimental contracts were kept in being and the first two Badgers, Nos. 4254 and 4255 (*F3495* and *F3496*), were completed. The first, with a Dragonfly, suffered engine failure from an airlock in the fuel system on its first take-off on 4 February and Uwins made a crash landing in which the landing gear and engine mounting were destroyed. It was repaired with a more pointed cowling and a larger rudder, and delivered to the Air Board on 15 February 1919. The Jupiter engine was late completing its bench tests, and the second Badger did not fly until 24 May 1919. Barnwell shared Fedden's faith in the Jupiter as a promising civil aero-engine and gave him every assistance in installing it in the Badger, which was flown without armament, with the rear cockpit partly enclosed. No engine trouble occurred in the early flight tests, but the lateral control of the Badger was not satisfactory and so the third prototype, No. 4256 (*F3497*) was cancelled before delivery. The second Badger was formally purchased by the Air Board on 5 September, after having had a Dragonfly engine substituted for the Jupiter, with full armament and equipment installed; a fixed fin, added to improve handling with the heavier Jupiter engine and airscrew, was retained. When the Badger had been designed and before construction was completed, Barnwell had sent a 1/10th scale model for test in the N.P.L. wind-tunnel, to confirm the aerodynamic design; he was therefore concerned that the tunnel tests had given no warning of the lateral control deficiencies which appeared in full-scale flying. He had already emphasised the importance of the Company's having its own wind-tunnel and in March he and Frise designed a simple rectangular fuselage of spruce and plywood in which was installed a 240 h.p. Siddeley Puma engine bought very cheaply from the Disposal Board. To this were attached a spare set of Badger wings, tail surfaces and landing gear, and the result was a single-seat laboratory biplane whose flying qualities could be directly compared with wind-tunnel tests on a model. Known at first as the Badger Experimental, soon shortened to Badger X, this machine, No. 5658, cost only £250 to build and was the first Bristol aeroplane to be entered on the British Civil Register, with the mark *K110*, which was revised to *G-EABU* on 30 May 1919. By that date it had already been written off, for, although Uwins made a successful first flight on 13 May, Barnwell himself nosed it over

Badger X at Filton in May 1919.

on 22 May and had to be released by onlookers from the safety harness in which he hung, helpless and cursing, upside down. He was uninjured and the aeroplane was not beyond economic repair, but the Directors decided not to go to the expense of doing so in a machine which could not easily be developed into a commercial two-seater. Barnwell himself had hoped to use the Badger X as a runabout and it was nicknamed 'Barnwell's Week-ender', though whether this referred to its proposed use or the extreme shortness of its design time is not certain.

The Air Board were sufficiently impressed with the Jupiter's performance to order a fourth Badger equipped to full military standard. This was No. 5657(*J6492*) and was named Badger II. As at first built it had the same rudder as *F3496*, but this was replaced by a horn-balanced unit in conjunction with redesigned wings featuring large-area ailerons with 'park-bench' balances designed by Frise. Unknown to him, an exactly similar device had just been

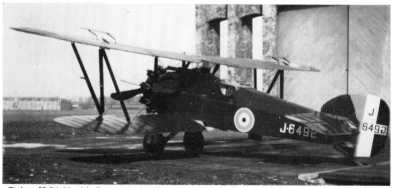

Badger II *J6492* with Cosmos Jupiter I and park-bench aileron balances, at Filton in March 1920.

patented by A. V. Roe and Co. Ltd., who wrote to the Company pointing out the infringement; the matter was settled amicably and Frise then sought an alternative method of aerodynamic balancing, which later became world-famous as the Frise aileron, for which royalties were paid for fifteen years by many other manufacturers, including A. V. Roe and Co. The Badger II was formally purchased by the Air Council on 11 March 1920 and loaned to the Company thereafter for development testing of the Jupiter engine, of which the Company acquired the whole design and manufacturing organisation in July 1920. Several different engine cowlings were tested on the Badger II, the last being a polygonal type designed for the Handley Page O/10 installation in July 1921.

Badger II with Jupiter II and polygonal cowl in 1921.

SPECIFICATIONS AND DATA

Type: F.2C and Badger

Manufacturers: The British & Colonial Aeroplane Co. Ltd., Filton, Bristol

Type	F.2C	F.2C	Badger I	Badger II	Badger X
Power Plant	260 hp Salmson	230 hp B.R.2	320 hp A.B.C. Dragonfly Ia	400 hp Cosmos Jupiter I	230 hp Siddeley Puma
Span	36 ft 5 in	31 ft 5 in	36 ft 9 in	36 ft 9 in	34 ft 2 in
Length	23 ft 8 in	23 ft 7 in	23 ft 8 in	23 ft 8 in	24 ft
Height	6 ft	8 ft 9 in	9 ft 1 in	9 ft 1 in	9 ft
Wing Area	408 sq ft	348 sq ft	357 sq ft	357 sq ft	340 sq ft
Empty Weight	—	—	1,950 lb	1,950 lb	—
All-up Weight	—	—	3,150 lb	3,150 lb	—
Max. Speed	—	—	135 mph	142 mph	—
Service Ceiling	—	—	19,000 ft	20,600 ft	—
Accommodation	2	2	2	2	Pilot only
Production	nil	nil	3	1	1
Sequence Nos.	nil	nil	4254–4256	5657	5658

Braemar II in flight over Bristol in February 1919.

The Bristol Braemar, Pullman and Tramp

In the summer of 1917 dismay at the success of the Gotha raids on London led to an urgent demand for retaliatory bombing on German industrial targets and in October the 41st Wing R.F.C., or Independent Air Force, was formed for this purpose. Very large aircraft were needed for the long-range heavy bombing of Berlin itself, if necessary, and both the Handley Page and Bristol firms submitted suitable designs. Capt. Barnwell drafted his first layout, called B.1, in October 1917. It was a triplane with internal stowage of six 250 lb. bombs and a central engine-room for four engines in a fuselage of good streamline shape. The engines were geared in pairs to shafting so as to drive one large four-bladed tractor airscrew on each side of the fuselage. The B.1 had a four-wheeled landing gear with wheel brakes, a castoring tail wheel and folding wings and was to carry a crew of six, comprising two pilots, a wireless operator, an engineer and two gunners (one also acting as bomb-aimer) over a range of 1,000 miles.

This layout was passed to W. T. Reid for detailing and emerged as a less ambitious design having four engines disposed in tandem pairs on the centre wing. The fuselage had flat sides to facilitate construction, with spruce compression members locally reinforced with plywood and braced by swaged tie-rods. The design was accepted by the Air Board, a contract for three prototypes, Nos. 3751–3753 (*C4296–C4298*), being awarded on 26 February 1918. The Company had earlier investigated the possible production of large flying-boats for the Air Board, and had this project gone forward new hangars of adequate size would have been built. As things were, the only way of erecting the prototype bombers under cover was to occupy one bay of the Acceptance Park hangars; this was wide enough for the length of the bomber but not its full span. Consequently the bombers had to be assembled one at a time and slewed out sideways on trolleys running on rails out of the hangar door.

The first prototype, named Braemar Mark I, was completed in August 1918 with four 230 h.p. Siddeley Puma engines, substituted because the intended 360 h.p. Rolls-Royce Eagles were not available. F. P. Raynham made a successful first flight on 13 August and flew it to Martlesham Heath for acceptance trials on 13 September, having achieved the very creditable top speed of 106 m.p.h. at a gross weight of 16,200 lb. At Martlesham it was flown during October by Major R. H. Carr and Capt. G. Gathergood, who found the performance and handling generally satisfactory, but criticised the pilot's controls and view and complained of fuselage vibration during taxying. The method of bracing the top and bottom wings to the centre wing was thought to be responsible for tie-rod breakages, which occurred frequently in the outer bays. From Martlesham the Braemar I was sent to Farnborough, where it ended its days in 1920.

Most of the features criticised at Martlesham were improved in the second prototype, Braemar Mark II, for which 400 h.p. Liberty engines were available; it was first flown by Cyril Uwins on 18 February 1919 and its speed and climb with full load were better than predicted. On 17 April it was flown to Martlesham Heath, where it remained at least until February 1920. As late as November 1921 there was a proposal to fit a torpedo rack under the Braemar II's fuselage, but about this date it was wrecked when it swung during take-off run and collided with a hangar at Martlesham Heath. In April 1919 the Air Board had agreed that the Company should finish the third prototype as a civil transport for 14 passengers, but Barnwell would not permit it to be flown with its enlarged fuselage until a model had been tested in a wind-tunnel.

The third Braemar, renamed Pullman, flew early in May 1920 and created a sensation at the International Aero Show at Olympia in July. It was the largest aeroplane ever seen inside Olympia and its interior decorations were greatly admired. After the show it went to Martlesham Heath, where it was purchased on 7 September, but no attempt was made to operate it as a passenger transport and it was finally dismantled. Although the enclosed crew cabin gave the pilots an unsurpassed view, it was not liked by service

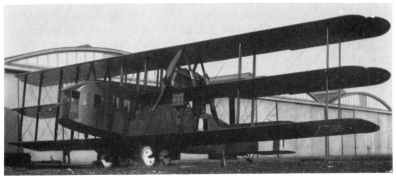

The Pullman at Martlesham Heath in August 1920.

pilots, who made a point of carrying fireman's axes so as to be able to escape quickly in an emergency. The Pullman carried its original serial *C4298* throughout its life, although it had been entered temporarily on the Civil Register as *G-EASP* from 14 April to 13 May 1920. The Pullman was not entered for the Air Ministry Civil Aircraft Competition in August 1920 because its landing speed was too high.

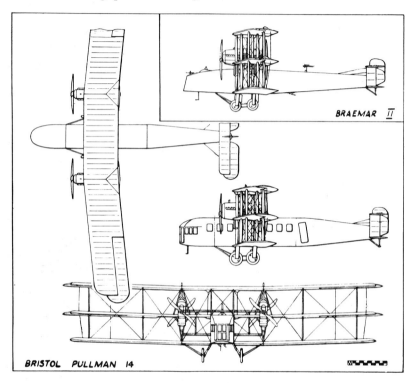

While the Braemars were under test by the R.A.F. several ambitious projects for civil transports derived from them were proposed, and in February 1919 Capt. Barnwell had discussed the use of flying boats as ancillaries to ocean liners with the Royal Mail Steam Packet Co., who had pressed strongly for a steam turbine power unit if feasible. It was hoped that the Air Ministry might support such a project and the Company intended to start with a civil transport derived from the Braemar, but with a central engine-room. This would be powered at first with four petrol engines designed as a unit which could be replaced later by a steam turbine power plant of equivalent power. As a first step, W. T. Reid laid out a Pullman for 50 passengers, powered by four 500 h.p. Siddeley Tiger engines. Enquiries were made into the feasibility of a steam plant comprising a pair of 1,500 h.p. turbines, and it was proposed at one stage to use the Braemar I as a steam turbine test-bed. Fraser and Chalmers of Erith undertook to design a turbine of the Ljungstrøm type, and the Bonecourt Waste Heat Company offered to design a high pressure flash boiler, but their quotation was considered too high. In May, Reid reduced the number of passenger seats to 40 and recommended that a similar flying boat should be designed by Major Vernon, who had joined the drawing office staff from Felixstowe, where he had been assistant to Major Rennie, John Porte's chief designer. In July the 40-passenger project was dropped because the Air Ministry would not support it, but discussions continued on a

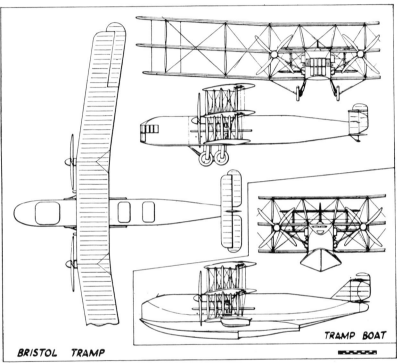

BRISTOL TRAMP

TRAMP BOAT

smaller test-bed triplane. Eventually a contract was awarded for the design and construction of two prototypes, equivocally described as 'spares carriers', powered by four Siddeley Pumas in a central engine room, with gear-boxes and transmission shafts supplied by Siddeley-Deasy. The contract price for each of these triplanes, named Tramp, was £23,000, of which £7,500 was Siddeley's price for a set of four engines and transmission gears. A flying boat of similar size with a Porte type hull, the Tramp Boat, was laid out by Major Vernon. It was found difficult to scale down the steam turbines to a maximum output of 750 h.p. each, which was all the Tramp could safely accommodate, and the condenser and boiler posed still more severe problems; in the end the difficulties of making a reliable lightweight high-pressure closed-circuit system proved insuperable.

First of the two Tramps at Filton in January 1922, ready for ground running.

The two Tramps, Nos. 5871 and 5872 (*J6912* and *J6913*), were not completed until the end of 1921, and even then neither of them ever flew, because the transmission system, particularly the clutches, gave continual trouble. Work on them at Filton was stopped in February 1922 when both of them were transported to Farnborough for development and experiment by the R.A.E. as ground rigs. Quite a large 'greenhouse' grew up round *J6913*, which remained in use for a year, during which a working party from Filton carried out further modifications to the flight deck and engine controls.

Had it been feasible to produce a safe, reliable and economic steam plant within the permissible weight limits, flying boat passengers in the 1920's might have enjoyed the speed, silence and comfort so vividly pictured by Squadron Commander Hallam, a former Felixstowe pilot, in the last chapter of *The Spider Web*, which he wrote under the pseudonym 'PIX'. That ideal was not to be realised for 25 years, when the Saro Princess took the air powered by Bristol Proteus gas-turbines, and by then the flying boat was already extinct as a commercial proposition.

SPECIFICATIONS AND DATA

Types: Braemar, Pullman and Tramp
Manufacturers: The British & Colonial Aeroplane Co. Ltd., Filton, Bristol
The Bristol Aeroplane Co. Ltd., Filton, Bristol

Type	Braemar I	Braemar II	Pullman	Pullman 40	Tramp
Power Plant	Four 230 hp Siddeley Puma	Four 400 hp Liberty 12	Four 400 hp Liberty 12	Four 500 hp Siddeley Tiger	Four 230 hp Siddeley Puma
Span	81 ft 8 in	81 ft 8 in	81 ft 8 in	122 ft	96 ft
Length	51 ft 6 in	51 ft 6 in	52 ft	76 ft 6 in	60 ft
Height	20 ft	20 ft	20 ft	32 ft 6 in	20 ft
Wing Area	1,905 sq ft	1,905 sq ft	1,905 sq ft	—	2,284 sq ft
Empty Weight	10,650 lb	10,650 lb	11,000 lb	—	12,809 lb
All-up Weight	16,500 lb	18,000 lb	17,750 lb	—	18,795 lb
Max. Speed	106 mph	125 mph	135 mph	—	—
Absolute Ceiling	14,000 ft	17,000 ft	15,000 ft	—	—
Accommodation	4	4	2 crew 14 passengers	3 crew 40 passengers	3
Production	1	1	1	nil	2
Sequence Nos.	3751	3752	3753	nil	5871 5872

Second of the three F.2B's built with long-range tanks and dual controls in July 1919.

The Bristol Tourer

In January 1919 a request was made by Sir Frederick Sykes, Controller of Civil Aviation, for three of the Bristol Fighters still in production to be delivered as unarmed communications two-seaters, with extra tankage for 5 hours' duration and dual controls. Another of the same batch was fitted with a hinged coupé cover over the passenger's seat, specially furnished to provide maximum comfort; the cockpit enclosure gave a useful reduction in drag, resulting in a top speed of 128 m.p.h. In this aeroplane, *H1460*, Uwins flew Herbert Thomas from Filton to Hounslow on 1 May 1919 to meet General Seely in London; on that day civil aviation became lawful in the United Kingdom for the first time since August 1914. The Bristol Coupé, as *H1460* was called, was purchased by the Air Board on 19 May 1919.

Three days later, Barnwell crashed the Badger X, which had been intended both as a laboratory machine and as his personal runabout; it was not repaired and Barnwell installed the Puma engine from it in a Fighter airframe converted to civil standards, in the same way as the three Falcon-engined

G-EAIZ, the first Puma-engined Tourer, at Filton in September 1919.

143

dual-control Fighters, *H1687* to *H1689*, which were delivered in July 1919. The Puma-engined version, No. 5867, was registered as *G-EAIZ* on 7 August and received a certificate of airworthiness on 16 September 1919. It was used at first as a Puma test-bed and soon became so popular as a general Company hack that it was named the Tourer, and a second Tourer, No. 5868, was built and registered as *G-EANR* on 23 September. This was exhibited at the Paris Salon in December 1919 with a four-bladed airscrew. Barnwell had never liked the underslung cooling system designed by the R.A.E. for the Puma-engined Bristol Fighter, and preferred a nose radiator high up, where pump and thermal siphon effects were complementary, with vertical shutters for temperature control. The pilot's view for landing was unaffected and the system could be kept working even if the pump failed; moreover, the damage in a forced landing was less extensive and easier to repair. Both these considerations were of prime importance for world-wide operation over undeveloped terrain.

For its peacetime design programme, the Company aimed at producing a two- or three-seat biplane suitable for such applications, and Barnwell had begun to design one with a three-cylinder Cosmos Lucifer engine of 100 h.p., at first known as the Rancher and later renamed the Colonial. This design had made little progress by July 1919, when an enquiry came in for a version of the Tourer to carry two passengers. Barnwell designed a simple modification of the Tourer with a wide rear cockpit seating two passengers side-by-side; a coupé top was an alternative to the open cockpit. This was so simple to produce that the Colonial was abandoned and both two-seat and three-seat Tourers went into production for demonstration and sale in the U.S.A., where the Company's New York agent had reported a promising market, including enquiries for seaplanes. He had already sold No. 5868 (*G-EANR*) which was shipped to New York in May.

Two open three-seaters, Nos. 5873 and 5874, were put in hand as twin-float seaplanes with interchangeable wheeled chassis, together with five open three-seaters (Nos. 5876–5880) and one two-seater (No. 5881). The New York agent then asked for a three-seater Coupé, so the first of these, No. 5891, not yet completed, was substituted for No. 5876 and the rest of the batch (Nos. 5877–5881) were shipped to New York at the end of May. For the

No. 5891, the first Coupé Three-seater at Filton in August 1920 before dispatch to New York.

American market, Tourers were finished in dark battleship grey with pale blue undersurfaces, with the word 'Bristol' in longhand style painted on the fuselage sides. One of them, probably 5868, was sold to Joseph F. Thorne, who used it to fly bullion to the coast from his silver mines in Nicaragua, but the fate of the others is unknown. The three-seater Coupé, No. 5891, was exhibited at Olympia in July 1920, before being shipped to New York in August. Meanwhile No. 5876, the first of the batch, was purchased by the Instone Air Line on 3 June 1920, with the registration *G-EART*. *G-EAIZ* and a new two-seater, No. 5892 (*G-EAVU*), had been successfully demonstrated in Belgium and Norway, so 15 more Tourers, comprising six open and six coupé three-seaters and three open two-seaters, Nos. 6108–6122, were laid down in anticipation of an expanding market. But only initial deposits had been paid on the Tourers ordered in America, and when difficulties arose over import duties the New York agency was closed down, so no more machines were shipped. The two seaplanes were amongst those cancelled, but later an order was received from Siberia and work on them continued. The first

No. 5873 on tow off Avonmouth in October 1920; note the metal airscrew.

seaplane was flown from Avonmouth on 15 October 1920, when Uwins took-off from calm water in 400 yds. with two passengers and 40 lb. of ballast. The floats, designed by Major Vernon, were built of mahogany with a single step and six watertight compartments in each; they weighed 200 lb. each, and, since they were 19 ft. 6 in. long, no tail float was required. The Siberian order for the two seaplanes was cancelled before delivery, and they were then offered to Canada but apparently not sold there. However, a final two-seater Tourer, No. 6123, was shipped to Canada in May 1921 for the Newfoundland Air Survey Company; it took part in the gold rush to Stag Bay, Labrador, later that year and was flown on skis.

The beginning of 1921 found the Company with 14 unsold Tourers on hand, only one of the two-seaters, No. 6122, having been bought, in December 1920, by a private owner, Alan S. Butler, and registered *G-EAWB*. In this he left Croydon on 2 April 1921 to tour southern Europe and returned in June having had no mishaps of any kind. He entered it in the Aerial Derby on 16 July and completed the course in the fourth fastest time at an average speed of 106 m.p.h., thereby winning the third prize of £50 in the Handicap Race. These exploits so convinced Alan Butler of the value of private flying that he joined forces with Geoffrey de Havilland and was for many years Chairman of the de Havilland Aircraft Company.

No. 6112, the first open Three-seater for Spain, ferried by Maj. H. de Havilland in April 1921.

Meanwhile, in April 1921, a Spanish customer, Senor Bayo, ordered two three-seaters, one closed and one open, through the Company's agents at Bilbao. These, Nos. 6114 (*G-EAWQ*) and 6112 (*G-EAWR*), re-registered *M-AAEA* and *M-AEAA*, were flown out to Spain by Andrew Forson and Major Hereward de Havilland, respectively, at the end of April. The only authorised route of entry into Spain was via San Sebastian, whose airfield, Lasarte, was surrounded by mountains. Forson arrived safely in the Coupé, cleared Customs and then took-off into a cloud-bank; minutes later he crashed into a mountainside near Anzuola and was killed. Major de Havilland delivered the open Tourer to Madrid without incident, but found he had to give flying lessons to Senor Bayo, so the Company's dual-control demonstrator *G-EAVU*, which had taken the place of *G-EAIZ* in November 1920, went to Madrid until September 1921, when it was replaced by No. 6121 (*M-AFFA*) together with two more open three-seaters (6109, *M-AAAF* and 6110, *M-AFFF*). The remaining two-seater, No. 6120 (*G-EAXA*), was retained as a demonstrator to replace *G-EAVU*, which was scrapped after its return from Madrid. The remaining eight three-seaters were all sold in Australia; the first (6117, *G-AUCA*) was supplied in June 1921 to Colonel Brinsmead, Controller of Civil Aviation, who toured over 9,000 miles in it while surveying new air routes; six more were bought in September 1921 by Major Norman Brearley, who had secured the Federal Government's air mail contract for a weekly service between Geraldton and Perth. The six Tourers, all with coupé tops (Nos. 6108, 6111, 6115, 6116, 6118 and 6119), registered *G-AUDF* to *G-AUDK*, respectively, were shipped to Fremantle in time to start the service on 4 December 1921, but *G-AUDI* crashed the next day, killing its pilot and mechanic; after an enquiry, the service restarted and thereafter achieved 97% regularity. Five Tourers were not enough to maintain the service, and the last remaining Tourer airframe, No. 6113, supplied as a spare, is believed to have been combined with the wreck of *G-AUCA* (crashed in March 1923) to produce *G-AUDX*, which continued flying until September 1930. Another of the Western Australian Airways fleet, *G-AUDH*, which crashed in July 1924, was rebuilt as *G-AUDZ* and survived until February 1931. A famous 'Tourer', *G-AUEB*, was converted from a 300 h.p. Hispano-Suiza Fighter (*H1248*) and flown in 1922 and 1923 by Hudson Fysh and other pilots of Queensland and Northern Territories Aerial Services; later it became one of the first Flying Doctor ambulances in Northern Territories, and its career ended in the goldfields at Wau, New Guinea, in April 1928. The Tourers of Western Australian Airways had flown over 200,000 miles by September 1923 and nearly 485,000 miles by June 1926, when they were replaced in regular service by D.H.50's; during this period they had logged 6,400 flying hours and had carried more than 3,000 passengers and 400,000 letters and parcels, including valuable consignments of pearls from the north-west coast fisheries. Two of the retired Tourers were bought by a syndicate of W.A.A. pilots and No. 6119 (*G-AUDK*) was flown 2,300 miles from Perth to Sydney, carrying the first trans-Australian woman passenger, Mrs. J. W. Marshall; then it was flown round the entire continent, a distance of 7,500 miles, in 10 days and 5 hours, by Charles Kingsford Smith and Charles Ulm, in June 1927. An attempt a year later to fly the same Tourer to England was less successful, for three days after leaving Camooweal on 9 September 1928, Keith Anderson and his passenger, Hitchcock, crashed at Pine Creek, N.T., the aircraft being totally wrecked. None of the Australian Tourers escaped crash demolition in the end; but, for so worthy a scion of the Fighter breed, this was a more fitting fate in a pioneering country than to decay in a hangar, unwanted, unfuelled, and unswung.

SPECIFICATIONS AND DATA

Type: Tourer (including Advanced Trainer, see p 180)
Manufacturers: The British & Colonial Aeroplane Co. Ltd., and The Bristol Aeroplane Co. Ltd., Filton, Bristol

Type	Coupé	2-Seater	3-Seater Coupé	3-Seater Open	Seaplane
Power Plant	275 hp Rolls-Royce Falcon III	230 hp Siddeley Puma			
Span	39 ft 3 in	39 ft 5 in	39 ft 5 in	39 ft 5 in	39 ft 5 in
Length	25 ft 10 in	26 ft 1 in	26 ft 1 in	26 ft 1 in	29 ft 6 in
Height	9 ft 6 in	10 ft	10 ft	10 ft	11 ft 5 in
Wing Area	405 sq ft	407 sq ft	407 sq ft	407 sq ft	407 sq ft
Empty Weight	1,900 lb	1,700 lb	1,900 lb	1,900 lb	2,100 lb
All-up Weight	2,800 lb	2,800 lb	3,000 lb	3,000 lb	3,000 lb
Max. Speed	128 mph	120 mph	120 mph	117 mph	110 mph
Absolute Ceiling	24,000 ft	22,000 ft	20,000 ft	20,000 ft	17,000 ft
Accommodation	2	2	3	3	3
Production	1	12	10	8	2
Sequence Nos.	5178	5867 5868 5881 5892 6120–6123 6239–6242	5891 6108 6111 6113 –6119	5876–5880 6109 6110 6112	5873 5874

Babe Mk I with the 35 hp Viale engine of 1911 vintage used for early flying in November 1919.

The Bristol Babe

In February 1919, before Badger X was designed, Capt. Barnwell proposed a small single-seater for sale to private owners, including ex-service pilots who wanted to continue flying cheaply after demobilisation. Barnwell was always enthusiastic about the possibility of a genuine 'owner-driver's' aeroplane; the theme recurred throughout his career and regrettably cost him his life in 1938. He was impressed by the performance of the very small biplanes, called 'Kittens', built during the war at the Isle of Grain, which had flown well with two-cylinder A.B.C. Gnat engines of only 30 h.p.

Barnwell's Bobby, or Babe as it was renamed, was a biplane with a plywood-skinned fuselage and one-piece wings having a span of only 19 ft. 8 in. The intended engine was a five-cylinder air-cooled radial A.B.C. Gadfly of 60 h.p. designed by Granville Bradshaw. At first the Directors would not sanction any work on the Babe, but on 21 April 1919 they authorized the design and construction of two prototypes, and two Gadfly engines were ordered. Soon afterwards A.B.C. Motors Ltd. discontinued aero-engine manufacture in order to concentrate on motor-cycles. No other engine of equivalent power was available, although in June a 40 h.p. flat-twin engine, the Ounce, was promised later in the year by Siddeley, and a third Babe was put in hand as a test-bed for it.

Meanwhile the first two Babes (Nos. 5865 and 5866) were nearing completion, and Barnwell recalled that in 1911, when he had first come to Brooklands from Scotland, he had helped A. V. Roe to install a small 45 h.p. Viale radial engine in an Avro biplane, before he decided to join the British and Colonial Company. He had helped to design a mounting for it, and paid half the purchase price to the Viale agent, Maurice Ducrocq; for Roe, like so many of the early pioneers, was then living from hand to mouth. The same engine was transferred in 1912 to an enclosed Avro monoplane, but this crashed after only a few weeks' flying at Brooklands, the damaged Viale engine being taken to Manchester for storage, where it had remained during the war. Barnwell brought it to Filton, the cracked bearer was welded and a new Zenith carburettor fitted; given a fairly heavy airscrew to keep it turning at small throttle openings, the Viale ran well for periods of up to half an hour, after which it overheated and lost power.

This was good enough for the first flight of No. 5866 on 28 November 1919, when Uwins, who intended only to do preliminary taxying, was forced to take-off in order to avoid over-running a flock of sheep on Filton airfield. Uwins reported the Babe to be easy enough for an experienced pilot to fly, though rather unstable for a beginner. Development continued and the third Babe (No. 5875), with an incomplete Siddeley Ounce installed, was exhibited at the Paris Salon in December 1919, with a selling price of £400 ex works.

The Viale engine was not reliable enough for sale in the Babe, even if production replicas could have been built, and the first two Babes had to wait for more suitable engines before they could be put on the market. During the Paris Salon the Gnome et Le Rhône firm had offered an ultra-light 60 h.p. rotary engine and six of these were ordered. Fred Mayer, the Company's chief engine fitter, went to Gennevilliers to witness the acceptance tests and saw the engines running well at moderate speeds, but vibrating badly when run up above 45 h.p. He refused to take delivery, but after some argument he agreed to bring back two specially modified and tuned engines for the prototype Babes. With the Le Rhône engine the Babes were designated Mark III and both were flown and registered, No. 5866 as *G-EAQD* on 18 December 1919 and No. 5865 as *G-EASQ* on 14 April 1920. The Babe Mark II with Ounce engine was not registered and never flew.

In May 1920 Barnwell designed new wings having the ailerons on the bottom wing instead of the top; these were not manufactured but in August he designed a thick-section cantilever monoplane wing, which was assembled to *G-EASQ*. The Babe monoplane was not flown because of uncertainty about downwash effects on the elevators behind a thick wing, about which

All three Babes together; left, George Clephane with Mk II; right, Tom Bond and Ernie Knight (in cockpit) with the Babe monoplane; second Mk III biplane behind; at Patchway in 1924.

little was then known; its registration was cancelled in February 1921, *G-EAQD*'s having already lapsed in December 1920. The Viale engine, which remained Barnwell's personal property, was stored until 1959, when it was rediscovered at a garage at Alveston, Glos., restored to exhibition finish by Bristol Siddeley Engines Limited and presented to the Royal Aeronautical Society. In 1963 it was placed in the Science Museum, London.

SPECIFICATIONS AND DATA

Type:	Babe
Manufacturers:	The British & Colonial Aeroplane Co. Ltd., and the Bristol Aeroplane Co. Ltd., Filton, Bristol
Power Plants:	One 45 hp Viale
	One 40 hp Siddeley Ounce
	One 60 hp Le Rhône
Span:	19 ft 8 in
Length:	14 ft 11 in
Height:	5 ft 9 in
Wing Area:	108 sq ft
Empty Weight:	460 lb
All-up Weight:	(Viale) 683 lb (Le Rhône) 840 lb
Speed:	(Viale) 85 mph (Le Rhône) 107 mph
Ceiling:	(Viale) 10,000 ft (Le Rhône) 15,000 ft
Accommodation:	Pilot only
Production:	3
Sequence Nos.:	5865, 5866, 5875.

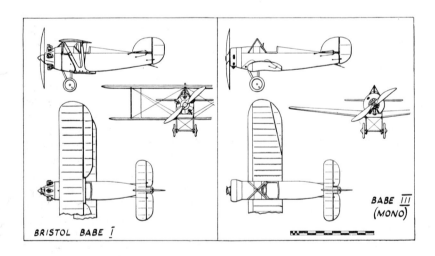

BRISTOL BABE I

BABE III (MONO)

The Bullet in its early form, with original fairing and large wings, at Filton in July 1920.

The Bristol Bullet

The Bullet was designed by Capt. Barnwell, at the instigation of Roy Fedden, with the twofold purpose of providing a test-bed for the Cosmos Jupiter engine on which the effects of high-speed manœuvres could be studied, and of bringing the Company's name into the public eye in international races. It was one of the fastest aeroplanes of its day, its top speed being little short of 160 m.p.h. It was a single-seater biplane of great strength and exquisite finish; the wing and tailplane spars were all duplicated to permit the use of thin low-drag aerofoils without sacrificing stiffness. The fuselage was a conventional four-longeron tie-rod-braced girder faired to a circular cross-section to blend with the radial engine, which was cowled similarly to that of the fourth Badger (*J6492*); the latter had just begun flight tests when the Bullet design was finalised in August 1919. In order to keep the landing speed below 50 m.p.h., Barnwell chose a wing area of 295 sq. ft.; the wings were of nearly equal span, but the upper was greater in chord than the lower; ailerons were fitted only to the upper wing, and the wing roots were joined to each other and to the cabane struts on the aircraft centre line. Only one Bullet, No. 5869, was built. It was exhibited at the Paris Salon in December 1919, but the Cosmos Jupiter engine was a partial mock-up, with no pistons or crankshaft and only a dummy wooden crankcase with a plain airscrew shaft through it; no complete engine could be spared for exhibition at that date.

No flight engine was in fact available for it until June 1920, when it was registered *G-EATS*; by this time an improved cowling had been developed for the Badger, having raised shoulders between the cylinder heads; a similar cowling was installed on the Bullet, which first appeared in the Aerial Derby on 24 July 1920, flown by Uwins. Although he achieved the third fastest time round the course, his average speed of 129 m.p.h. was disappointing and Barnwell decided that fuselage drag could be reduced if the engine were almost submerged. This required a larger diameter forward, but wind-tunnel tests confirmed the improvement, and a large hemispherical spinner was designed to match the revised cowling. When flown again the improvement was less than expected and the wing area was then reduced to 180 sq. ft., since other racing biplanes were being handled safely at a wing loading of 12 lb. per sq. ft. The ailerons were relocated on the lower wing, where control circuit friction was less, and the lower wing was given a pronounced dihedral angle. The new wings, being reduced in both span and chord, needed a correspondingly smaller gap, and this brought the upper wing roots near enough to the fuselage to permit the cabane to be reduced to a pair of short single struts on the centre-line. The tailplane area was reduced to match the new wings and the revised design was completed in February 1921.

By this time it was urgently necessary to step up the hours of flight testing of the Jupiter engine, now a Bristol product, in order to obtain Air Ministry approval as soon as possible. The Bullet shared this task with the fourth Badger and rarely left the neighbourhood of Filton, except for the 1921 Aerial Derby, in which Uwins flew it round the course in the second fastest time; he finished fourth at an average speed of 141 m.p.h., being outpaced only by the Napier Lion-engined Gloster Mars I. Minor refinements were made during the next 12 months, but the biggest improvement came from simply leaving

The Bullet in its final form at Croydon in September 1922. (*'Flight' photo.*)

off the spinner when it was flown in the 1922 Aerial Derby by Rollo de Haga Haig, who gained second place at an average speed of 145 m.p.h. In January 1923 the cowling was further improved and a long-stroke oleo undercarriage was fitted to cater for landing with maximum fuel in the King's Cup Race. The Bullet was expected to exceed 175 m.p.h. with an up-rated Jupiter IV and was entered in both the 1923 Aerial Derby and King's Cup Races, but its intended pilot, Leslie Foot, was killed six weeks earlier in the Grosvenor Cup Race and the Company then withdrew from racing for two years. After Foot's death the Bullet was stored for a time, being finally scrapped in 1924, although its registration was not cancelled until April 1925.

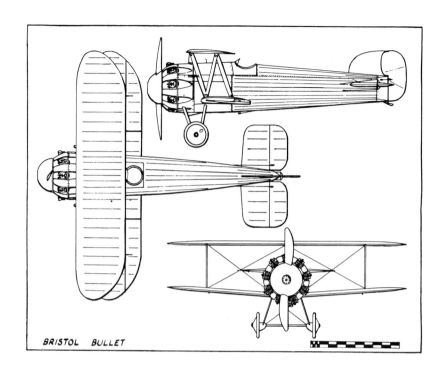

BRISTOL BULLET

SPECIFICATION AND DATA

Type:	Bullet
Manufacturers:	The Bristol Aeroplane Co. Ltd., Filton, Bristol
Power Plant:	One 450 hp Bristol Jupiter II
Span:	(early) 31 ft 2 in; (late) 22 ft 4 in
Length:	24 ft 1 in
Height:	(early) 9 ft 8 in; (late) 8 ft 10 in
Wing Area:	(early) 295 sq ft; (late) 180 sq ft
Empty Weight:	1,800 lb
All-up Weight:	2,300 lb
Max. Speed:	(early) 155 mph; (late) 170 mph
Accommodation:	Pilot only
Production:	One only
Sequence No.:	5869

The Seely at Filton in July 1920, before going to Martlesham Heath.

The Bristol Seely

In July 1919 conditions were announced for a competition for civil aeroplanes to be held by the Air Ministry in 1920, to encourage designs for safety and comfort. There were separate classes for large and small aeroplanes, with points awarded for payload and economy, and for ability to land slowly and take-off with a minimum run. It was found impossible to modify the Bristol Pullman, by increasing its span, to attain the required low speed performance, but, with the Colonial abandoned it was possible to design a Tourer derivative to meet the rules. The new project, later named the Seely, was a two-seater, with the passenger accommodated behind the pilot in a single comfortable cabin as in the F.2B Coupé, but the fuselage was deeper with the bottom longerons dropped to the level of the lower wing. The fuselage bays in front of the pilot were of steel tube instead of spruce, to give better protection in a crash, and the undercarriage had multi-disc wheel brakes and a central skid to prevent nosing over on landing. Wing area was increased, using a three-bay arrangement; a horn-balanced rudder and large fin were fitted and the sprung tail skid was steerable with the rudder. The engine was a Siddeley Puma, tuned for economy, with a large area radiator for efficient cooling at low climbing speeds. This radiator was also standardised on all Tourers from No. 6108 onwards, after Major Hereward de Havilland had reported overheating on *G-EAVU* at Cuatros Vientos, and was specially valuable in Australia. The Seely, No. 5870, was registered *G-EAUE* on 3 July 1920, a month before the Air Ministry competition began at Martlesham Heath.

Uwins piloted the Seely through all its tests without mishap, and the competition resolved itself into a slow-flying race between himself, Arthur Keep on the Westland Limousine and Harry Hawker on the Sopwith Antelope. The Limousine was about the same size as the Seely but had twice the power, while the Antelope had the same power but was smaller. Consequently the Limousine scored on take-off and the Antelope in landing run; but Hawker, in his enthusiasm to land in the shortest possible distance, stalled and smashed his undercarriage, leaving Keep the winner, with Uwins a few points behind.

After the competition ended, the Seely remained at Filton on routine duties but in 1923 was converted into a laboratory aircraft for Jupiter development. A Jupiter III engine with an exhaust-driven supercharger and a Leitner-Watts steel-bladed airscrew was installed, and on 22 December 1923 the Seely was purchased by the Air Ministry for the Royal Aircraft Establishment, as *J7004*. In the course of a comprehensive test programme during 1924, the Seely frequently climbed to 23,000 ft., a duty for which its low wing-loading and enclosed observer's cabin rendered it more popular than most aircraft of that date.

SPECIFICATION AND DATA

Type:	Seely
Manufacturers:	The Bristol Aeroplane Co. Ltd., Filton, Bristol
Power Plant:	One 240 hp Siddeley Puma
	One 435 hp Bristol Jupiter III with R.A.E. supercharger
Span:	47 ft 3 in
Length:	(Puma) 29 ft 6 in
	(Jupiter) 28 ft
Height:	12 ft
Wing Area:	566 sq ft
Empty Weight:	2,000 lb
All-up Weight:	(Puma) 3,000 lb; (Jupiter) 3,600 lb
Max. Speed:	(Puma) 110 mph at sea level
	(Jupiter) 121 mph at sea level, 137 mph at 10,000 ft
Service Ceiling:	(Puma) 18,000 ft; (Jupiter) 24,000 ft
Accommodation:	2
Production:	One only
Sequence No.:	5870

The Seely with supercharged Jupiter III at Filton in December 1923.

The first Ten-seater, in Handley Page Transport livery, at Croydon in March 1922.

The Bristol Ten-seaters and Brandon

One of the first post-war new projects considered by the Company in February 1919 was a general-purpose single-engined biplane to carry four passengers or equivalent cargo. Capt. Barnwell enquired from potential operators what layout they would prefer and found opinions as numerous as facts were few; some preferred two engines for reliability, but others considered that this doubled the risk of failure. In July Barnwell designed a biplane named Grampus I of 75 ft. span and wing area of 1,150 sq. ft. to to carry six passengers or 2,000 lb. of cargo over a range of 1,000 miles; it was powered by a single Siddeley Tiger engine of 500 h.p. It was larger than the four-passenger type preferred by the Directors, and only a few Tigers were available since their production contract had been cancelled. In any case watercooled engines were considered unsuitable for tropical work, so Barnwell had second thoughts and in October put forward a smaller Grampus II project, carrying only three passengers with a 150 h.p. R.A.F.4a air-cooled engine, the new Siddeley Lynx radial engine being the alternative for a production version if the prototype were successful. This was not approved either, nor were eight-passenger versions with either four Lucifers (Grampus IV) or two Hall-Scott engines (Grampus V, for the American market). An interesting feature of Grampus I was a small water ballast tank near the stern-post, so that the centre of gravity position could be adjusted to make the best use of the available cargo space. After February 1920, the Grampus project was abandoned, as it did not fit either of the classes specified for the Air Ministry civil aeroplane competition.

Nevertheless, the Directors believed in the usefulness of a single-engined load-carrier; and when, in January 1921, the Treasury agreed to subsidise approved air transport companies, they authorised Barnwell to proceed with a fresh layout. This was a biplane of robust design, laid out by W. T. Reid, powered by a single Jupiter engine. But the Jupiter, though making good progress, was not yet approved and an alternative had to be found. The 400 h.p. Liberty seemed the best choice, as it was available from the Aircraft

Disposal Co. at home and acceptable to the American market. Six passengers were to be carried in a roomy cabin, with the pilot and wireless operator in a cockpit forward of the upper wing; the design featured a four-wheel tandem undercarriage like the Braemar's, with brakes on the rear wheels. A little later, a Napier Lion engine of 450 h.p. was offered and the design was enlarged to take advantage of it, finally accommodating a pilot and nine passengers, which was a payload more likely to earn a profit, and was named Ten-seater.

One aircraft, No. 6124, was constructed and three further sets of details were made at the same time, but not assembled. It was ready for flight on 21 June 1921 and registered *G-EAWY*. Its early flight trials went without a hitch, the principal modification being the removal of the front pair of wheels, which experience proved to be unnecessary and not worth their weight. It arrived at Croydon on 8 July 1921 and was put into experimental service, being flown to Martlesham Heath in August and purchased by the Air Council in December. On 6 February 1922 it was demonstrated at Croydon to about 400 delegates to the Second Annual Air Conference. It was handed over to Instone's in June 1922, and thereafter flew many hundreds of hours on the London to Paris route, carrying both passengers and cargo. Later it was lent for a time to Handley Page Transport Ltd., who used it on the London–Cologne cargo service. With the same engine, it could carry twice as much payload as the official winner of the Air Ministry competition.

Meanwhile, the Jupiter passed its Type Test in September 1921 and Reid and Fedden had collaborated in designing a self-contained power-plant installation for the second Ten-Seater, No. 6145. The front end of the fuselage was blanked off by a fireproof bulkhead and the engine was mounted, complete with cowling and exhaust manifold, on a sheet-steel structure attached to the four longerons. On the port side the attachments were vertical hinges, and on the starboard side they were bolts locked in sockets by lever-operated cams. Thus the whole power-egg could be swung open like a gate for easy access to the engine rear cover, with its magnetos and carburettors. The oil tank and fuel filter were mounted on the fireproof bulkhead and connected to the engine by flexible pipes.

The Jupiter-engined Ten-Seater was first flown in July 1922 and registered *G-EBEV* on 22 August 1922. Furnished for eight passengers and a crew of two, it was demonstrated at Croydon on 5 February 1923 to delegates to the Third Annual Air Conference under the revived name 'Bristol Pullman'. After modification to the engine installation it was purchased by the Instone Air Line on 29 February 1924, together with a spare Jupiter engine and a quantity of spare components. It did not receive a full C. of A. until 16 July 1924, after the Jupiter IV engine had passed its civil type test. By that time Instone's and the other three subsidised air transport companies had been merged to form Imperial Airways Ltd., whose policy was to use only multi-engined aircraft for passenger carrying. Consequently it was refitted as a freighter to carry 1,800 lb. of cargo, and in this form went into service on the London-Cologne route on 22 July. By 23 August it had flown 150 hours

G-EBEV converted for freight-carrying, at Filton in February 1924, with Leitner-Watts airscrew.

without incident, except for a fractured oil pressure gauge pipe. A second Jupiter IV achieved 157 hours without incident and did much to convince Imperial Airways of the suitability of this engine for their fleet. The Express Freight Carrier, as *G-EBEV* had been renamed, continued in the reserve fleet of Imperial Airways until 1926, but suffered from overheating. The fourth Ten-seater, No. 6147, nearly completed in October 1923, was dismantled and sold as spare components along with *G-EBEV*.

The third Ten-seater, No. 6146, was ordered by the Air Council in June 1922 as a result of their trials of the first machine; they required it to be equipped as a troop-carrier and ambulance, and this necessitated a considerable amount of redesign, from which it emerged in July 1923 as the Brandon, *J6997*. After many delays, including sweeping back the wings to compensate for an error in centre of gravity position, the Brandon made its first flight on 19 March 1924, piloted by Uwins, and was delivered to the R.A.F. on 22 May 1925. It differed from the Jupiter Ten-seater principally in having wings of larger chord with Frise ailerons and increased gap; there was accommodation for either two stretchers and four sitting casualties or three stretchers and an attendant. Special attention was paid to ventilation under tropical conditions, and the interior of the cabin was finished throughout in white enamel. The main entrance door was on the starboard side, but there was also a hatch at floor level on the port side for loading stretchers. The engine, at first installed as in the Ten-seater, over-heated to an extent which necessitated a separate oil cooler for the first time. Cooling was later improved by an extended mounting, which also more effectively balanced the rearward shift of the centre of gravity. The Brandon was overweight with full payload and did not go into R.A.F. service overseas, but shared ambulance duties with the Avro Andovers stationed at Halton.

SPECIFICATIONS AND DATA

Type: Ten-seaters and Brandon
Manufacturers: The Bristol Aeroplane Co. Ltd., Filton, Bristol

Type	Ten-seaters		Brandon
Power Plant	450 hp	425 hp	425 hp
	Napier Lion	Bristol Jupiter IV	Bristol Jupiter IV
Span	54 ft 3 in	56 ft	54 ft 1 in
Length	42 ft	40 ft 6 in	42 ft 3 in
Height	11 ft	11 ft	14 ft 4 in
Wing Area	685 sq ft	700 sq ft	890 sq ft
Empty Weight	3,900 lb	4,000 lb	4,370 lb
All-up Weight	6,800 lb	6,755 lb	7,100 lb
Max. Speed	122 mph	110 mph	115 mph
Service Ceiling	14,000 ft	8,500 ft	8,500 ft
Endurance	5½ hours	5½ hours	5½ hours
Accommodation	2 crew 8 pass.	2 crew 8 pass.	2 crew 8 pass.
Production	1	2	1
Sequence Nos.	6124	6145 6147	6146

The Brandon *J6997* as first flown in March 1924.

The Brandon with lengthened engine mounting at Filton in April 1925.

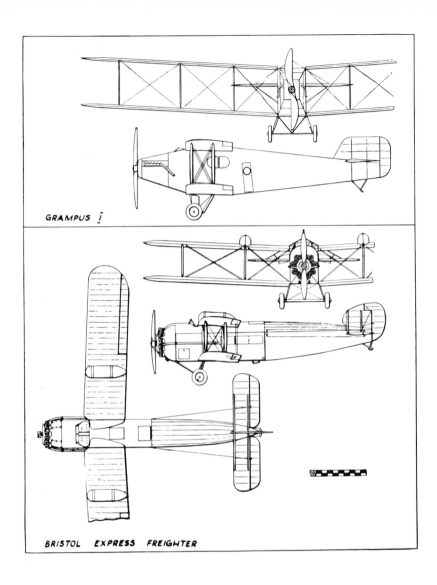

GRAMPUS I

BRISTOL EXPRESS FREIGHTER

160

The second Bullfinch (single-seater) at Farnborough in August 1924. (*Crown copyright.*)

The Bristol Bullfinch

In July 1920, when the Company acquired the Jupiter engine design and manufacturing organisation from the defunct Cosmos Engineering Company, Capt. Barnwell began the design of an all-metal cantilever monoplane single-seater fighter designated the MFA, convertible into a two-seater reconnaissance biplane (MFB), and the new wind-tunnel was used to determine the best wing section and body lines to suit the Jupiter. The Air Ministry promised support for the project and Specification 2/21 covering the design and supply of three prototypes was drafted in April 1921. As originally drawn, the fuselage was faired to a circular section throughout its length and followed very much the pattern of the Bullet, but the tail unit showed a return to the Coanda practice of having a one-piece elevator with the rudder above. At one stage an all-moving tailplane was proposed, as in the Prier monoplane, and the tailplane finally chosen was given a large range of incidence adjustment. The rudder was horn-balanced and hinged to a small triangular fin above the fuselage.

The wing was in two parts, joined at the aircraft centre line to a steel-tube cabane and tapering from maximum thickness at half-span to both root and tip. The aileron hinge line was parallel to the trailing edge and in plan the wing was untapered with rounded tips, with a slight sweep-back to improve the pilot's view. Wind-tunnel tests showed that aileron drag might cause an adverse yaw effect, as in the Badger, and the aileron shape was then changed to a segment of the round tip, with the hinge line inclined at an angle to the trailing edge. This aileron shape was adopted also for the Babe monoplane, whose wing was virtually a model of the outer-semi-span of the MFA wing; had the Babe monoplane flown, some correlation between full-scale and wind-tunnel results on this wing might have been obtained. For the three prototypes, the wing was built in wood, but it was Barnwell's intention to redesign it in metal, and for this each spar would have comprised a side-by-side pair of steel-tube Warren girders.

161

The fuselage was of carbon steel drawn tubing, sweated and pinned into machined end-sockets, built up into a pin-jointed structure braced by tie-rods. Two alternative undercarriages were designed, one having telescopic legs with coil springs and oleo-dampers, while a simpler rubber-cord sprung alternative was intended as an insurance in case of snags with the oleo leg. The front fuselage was carefully faired to match the Jupiter cowling back to the pilot's cockpit, but aft of the bolted joint at this position further fairing was deleted and the four longerons were covered by flat-sided fabric panels, which simplified maintenance. The rudder, as built, became an unshielded balanced oval without any fin above the tailplane, but there were a pair of fins in front of the two steerable tail skids, side-by-side below the bottom longerons. In February 1922 the name Pegasus was proposed for the MFA, but this did not conform to the Air Ministry's naming policy and in March the official name Bullfinch was agreed. Two of the prototypes, Nos. 6125 and 6126 (*J6901* and *J6902*), were completed as single-seater monoplanes and delivered, after delay due to arguments with the Air Ministry over strength

The third Bullfinch (two-seater) at Filton in April 1923.

calculations, in April 1923; the third prototype, No. 6127 (*J6903*), was built as a two-seater biplane with a self-contained gunner's cockpit inserted aft of the pilot and a cantilever bottom wing attached; this brought about a movement of the centre of pressure to compensate that of the centre of gravity, and the only other change necessary was to move the undercarriage back to keep the wheel and tail skid reactions proportionate; it was not delivered until March 1924. All three Bullfinches were flown experimentally by the R.A.F., *J6901* and *J6903* being evaluated at Martlesham Heath and *J6902* being used for engine tests at Farnborough. No production order was given, and, although the single-seater monoplane had a good performance, the two-seater was over-weight and could not carry all the prescribed military load.

SPECIFICATION AND DATA

Type: Bullfinch

Manufacturers: The Bristol Aeroplane Co. Ltd., Filton, Bristol

Power Plant: One 425 hp Bristol Jupiter III or IV

	Monoplane	Biplane
Span	38 ft 5 in	38 ft 5 in
Length	24 ft 5 in	27 ft 6 in
Height	10 ft 9 in	10 ft 9 in
Wing Area	267 sq ft	391 sq ft
Empty Weight	2,175 lb	2,495 lb
All-up Weight	3,205 lb	4,088 lb
Maximum Speed (15,000 ft)	135 mph	120 mph
Service Ceiling	22,000 ft	18,000 ft
Endurance	4 hours	4 hours
Accommodation	Pilot only	2
Production	2	1
Sequence Nos.	6125 6126	6127

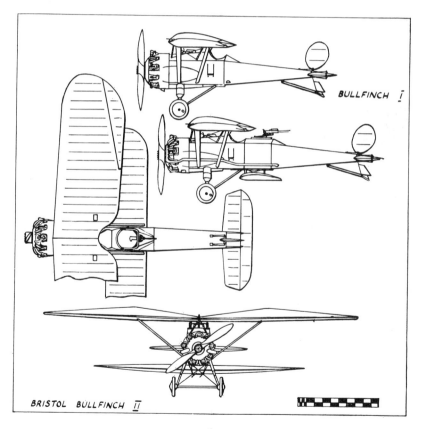

BULLFINCH I

BRISTOL BULLFINCH II

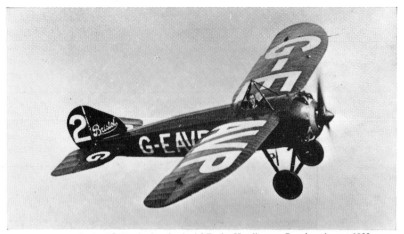

Larry Carter in the M.1D winning the Aerial Derby Handicap at Croydon, August 1922.

The Bristol M.1D Monoplane

Reference has already been made to the three M.1C and one M.1B monoplanes bought back from the Aircraft Disposal Board in 1919 and reconditioned as Nos. 5885 to 5887 and 5888, respectively. Of these No. 5885 was
registered *G-EASR* on 14 April 1920, and Nos. 5887 and 5888, respectively,
G-EAVO and *G-EAVP* on 28 September 1920; No. 5886 was shipped to
the Company's agent in New York in May 1920. Contrary to expectations,
there was no ready market for these sporting single-seaters at home, and it
was not until November 1921 that No. 5887 (*G-EAVO*) was exported to
Senor Juan Pombo as *M-AFAA*, being ferried to Madrid by Larry Carter.
The Company retained *G-EASR* as a demonstrator until the early months of
1925, but in January 1922 converted *G-EAVP* to take the 100 h.p. Bristol
Lucifer three-cylinder air-cooled radial engine; this engine had flown
extensively in an Avro 504K, but needed development at somewhat higher
forward speeds.

In this form, G-EAVP was redesignated M.1D and, painted scarlet with a
black nose and tail and white lettering, made its *debut* at Croydon on 17 April
1922, when Uwins flew into third place in the first race of 16 miles and second
place in the second race of 32 miles, his average speed being just over 100
m.p.h. On 3 June, at the Croydon Whitsun meeting, he won the Handicap
Race at a slightly higher speed. With this early record of success, the M.1D
was entered in the 1922 Aerial Derby Handicap, in which on 7 August Larry
Carter was the winner at an average speed of nearly 108 m.p.h. In the first
King's Cup Race, a month later, it was flown by Rollo de Haga Haig, but he
had to land at Aylesbury with minor engine trouble.

The M.1D's next public appearance was in the Grosvenor Cup Race flown on 23 June 1923, from Lympne via Croydon to Birmingham and Bristol, then back via Croydon to Lympne. On the nine starters, the favourite was the M.1D with a specially tuned Lucifer of 140 h.p. and flown by Major Leslie Foot, who in April had joined the Company as a staff pilot from Handley Page Transport Ltd. Some 25,000 spectators had gathered at Filton to see the race, and Foot had been making exciting progress all round the course after starting as scratch man. When he arrived at Filton he complained of petrol fumes, and the fuel tank was found to be leaking from a crack at one corner. This was patched, but he would not wait for a more thorough inspection to find the source of the defect as he had still a good chance of catching up the leading man and winning the race. Flying low down at full throttle over Fox Hills near Chertsey on the approach to Croydon, the M.1D was seen to dive into the ground and catch fire. The flames were too intense for any attempt at rescue, and it was difficult to ascertain the cause of the disaster from examination of the wreckage, but most probably one of the streamlined bracing wires had become misplaced at an angle which set up flutter, so causing a fracture of the trunnion at the spar attachment; this may have been the cause of the leaking tank also. Leslie Foot was very popular and one of the most competent aerobatic pilots in the country; his death shocked all who had known him, and the Company withdrew their entries from the Aerial Derby and King's Cup races in 1923 as a tribute to him.

SPECIFICATION AND DATA

Type: M.1D

Manufacturers: The Bristol Aeroplane Co. Ltd., Filton, Bristol

Power Plant: One 140 hp Bristol Lucifer

Span: 30 ft 9 in

Length: 20 ft 4 in

Height: 7 ft 9 in

Wing Area: 145 sq ft

Empty Weight: 950 lb

All-up Weight: 1,300 lb

Max. Speed: 125 mph

Ceiling: 22,000 ft

Endurance: $1\frac{3}{4}$ hours

Accommodation: Pilot only

Production: One only

Sequence No.: 5888

The first Taxiplane at Filton in November 1922.

The Bristol Taxiplane and Primary Trainers

Ever since the first appearance of the Cosmos Lucifer engine in 1919 it had been hoped to use it in a light touring aeroplane, and the proposed Colonial three-seater has already been mentioned. Lucifer development proceeded steadily, and in July 1921 Capt. Barnwell completed the layout of a new three-seater biplane for it. Colonel W. A. Bristow of Ogilvie & Partners (aviation consultants) reported favourably on it, but emphasised the importance of keeping down the selling price; it was considered suitable as a trainer with a revised fuselage. In October 1921 Capt. Barnwell emigrated, and the development of the project was left to his successor Wilfred Reid. In February 1922 the Lucifer engine passed its type test and three prototype biplanes, called Taxiplanes, Nos. 6153–6155, were laid down; it was hoped to complete the first in time for the King's Cup Race in September, for which it was to have 5 hours' fuel tankage.

The Taxiplane carried two passengers side-by-side in a cockpit behind the pilot, as in the Tourer, but had a hinged side-door for entry on the port side instead of a ladder. The upper and lower wings were identical, so that a spare could be used in either position, and steel interplane struts of 'N' shape were used to simplify rigging. The Lucifer was installed on a hinged mounting similar to the Jupiter's on the Ten-seater, and the fuselage was a plywood-covered box from the engine bulkhead to the rear cockpit, aft of which were four wire-braced longerons with normal fabric covering. Although not completed in time for the King's Cup Race, the first Taxiplane was inspected by Major Kingsley of the River Plate Trading Company when he visited Filton in September. Interest then switched to a proposed two-seater version with dual control for use as a primary trainer in the Reserve Training Schools to be set up by the Air Ministry in 1923. Attempts to reconcile the two roles in a single design delayed the Taxiplane until, in January 1923, it was decided to design a separate fuselage for the Trainer using the same wings, tail unit and undercarriage; the Trainer had two cockpits in tandem and a plain mounting for the Lucifer to save weight. The Taxiplane was ready for its first flight on 13 February 1923, and had been registered *G-EBEW* on 22 November 1922 in expectation of being shown at the Paris Salon in December. After modifications to the Lucifer and its exhaust system, the first Taxiplane was flown to Martlesham in the second week of April; by then the second Taxiplane was having its engine installed and the third was complete except for its engine. About this time, the Company was asked to lend a Taxiplane to Squadron Leader H. J. L. (Bert) Hinkler to fly from England to Australia in 1,000-mile stages, but Fedden was unwilling to commit the Lucifer to such test at that stage in its development. *G-EBEW* returned from Martlesham in May with approval for certification as a two-seater, but was overloaded with two passengers as well as the pilot. This was a disappointment, but cleared the way for approval of the Trainer, of which six, Nos. 6373–6378, had been laid down for the Reserve Training School in March.

Five of the six P.T.M.'s of the Reserve Flying School at Filton in November 1923.

The first Trainer, *G-EBFZ*, had a better performance than the Taxiplane, due to its narrower fuselage and reduced weight, and the fourth, *G-EBGC*, was entered in the Grosvenor Cup Race on 23 June, but Uwins was forced to retire at Upton-on-Severn with a cracked oil tank. By 2 July four Trainers, *G-EBFZ*, *'GA*, *'GB* and *'GC*, were in use at the Filton Reserve Flying School and the other two, *G-EBGD* and *'GE*, were waiting for engines, those from the second and third Taxiplanes, *G-EBEY* and *G-EBFY*, having already been 'borrowed' for the Trainers. *G-EBFZ* paid a brief visit to Martlesham for formal approval in July, and the test pilots there confirmed that the rough running of the Lucifer, of which Reid had complained to Fedden, was not

The second Taxiplane at Martlesham Heath in January 1924. (*Crown copyright.*)

167

considered serious. The first Taxiplane went to Martlesham in August and the second was also sent there in January 1924, but still failed to gain approval to carry three persons. Meanwhile, six more Trainers were put in hand at the end of October and an enquiry came in March from Canada for a seaplane version, but this was estimated to have a ceiling of only 3,000 ft. The Filton School Trainers survived without a serious crash, and the six new machines laid down were still uncommitted in October 1924, when they were offered to the Bulgarian government, who had bought two Bristol Tourers with Wolseley Viper engines the previous year, and had four more on order. This offer was not at first taken up, but eventually one, No. 6936 (*B-BEPK*), was

B-BEPK, the Bulgarian P.T.M., at Filton in April 1926.

delivered in April 1926. By this time the Lucifer IV engine of 120 h.p. had established its reliability, and its success in various competitions in Europe had led to many enquiries for the Trainer, or P.T.M. (Primary Training Machine) as it was called in its later career. Twelve, Nos. 6924–6935, were sent to Chile in February and March 1926, and five, Nos. 6922 (*G-EBNB*) and 6923 (*G-EBNC*) plus Nos. 6960–6962, to Hungary in April 1926. The first two of the Hungarian batch had been registered in December 1925 for demonstration at Filton to the Chilean and Hungarian purchasing commissions.

All P.T.M.s after the first six were built with larger rudders and elevators, after a modification to this effect, requested by Uwins in December 1924, had been proved satisfactory on *G-EBGD*, concurrently with installation of the Lucifer IV. The original six were modified to the new standard as they fell due for overhaul. In this form all survived until replaced by Tiger Moths in December 1931 except *G-EBGB*, which was destroyed in a collision with the prototype Jupiter Trainer, *G-EBIH*, at Filton on 20 August 1929. The longest lived of all was *G-EBGA*, which, after appearing at the Bristol and Wessex Aeroplane Club's race meeting in September 1931, was flown as a hack until sold in February 1933 to L. G. Anderson at Hanworth. Here the wheel came full circle, for Anderson modified it into a three-seater for joyriding, with two passengers in the rear cockpit, thus reverting to the original Taxiplane concept; in this form it flew throughout the summer with C. W. A.

Scott's British Hospitals Air Pageants, and was finally scrapped in December.

G-EBGA remained airworthy longer than the others because early in 1928 it had been cleaned up for competition work, including fairing out the fuselage sides, re-cowling the engine with a pointed spinner on the airscrew and increasing the chord of the interplane struts. The fin was deleted and a large horn-balanced rudder was fitted; later this was again exchanged for a different fin and rudder. These changes were associated with a strengthened variant of the P.T.M., the Bristol 83E. In April 1928 a test-bed aircraft was required for development of the 250 h.p. five-cylinder Titan engine, and at

G-EBYT with direct-drive Titan, as flown in the King's Cup Race in 1928.

first it was proposed to modify *G-EBGA* for this purpose, but as this was marginal in strength and already tuned for racing, a new and stronger airframe was built for the Titan. This machine, No. 7266, was registered *G-EBYT* on 15 June 1928 and certified on 17 July, three days before the King's Cup Race, in which it was flown by Squadron Leader A. G. Jones-Williams, who averaged over 123 m.p.h. from Renfrew to Lympne on the second day of the race. At first it had a direct-drive Titan, but later it was

G-EBYT with geared Titan at Filton in 1930.

169

flown at Filton with a geared Titan, driving a four-bladed airscrew, whose destabilising effect was compensated by the large horn-balanced rudder from *G-EBGA*; the latter was then fitted with the original fin and rudder from *G-EBYT*, and retained it thereafter, and a similar fin and rudder was later fitted to *G-EBGC*. The sole 83E was scrapped in December 1930, at the conclusion of the Titan development programme.

SPECIFICATIONS AND DATA

Type: Taxiplane and Primary Trainers
Manufacturers: The Bristol Aeroplane Co. Ltd., Filton, Bristol
Power Plants: One 120–140 hp Bristol Lucifer
One 220 hp Bristol Titan

Type	Taxiplane	Lucifer P.T.M.	83E (Titan)
Span	31 ft 1 in	31 ft 1 in	31 ft 1 in
Length	23 ft 3 in	24 ft 4 in	25 ft 6 in
Height	8 ft 10 in	8 ft 10 in	9 ft 3 in
Wing Area	284 sq ft	284 sq ft	291 sq ft
Empty Weight	1,210 lb	1,340 lb	1,400 lb
All-up Weight	1,840 lb	1,900 lb	2,000 lb
Max. Speed	90 mph	96 mph	130 mph
Accommodation	3	2	2
Production	3	24	1
Sequence Nos.	6153–6155	6373–6378 6922–6936 6960–6962	7266

The Racer in its original state without external wing bracing; engine test with spinner removed.

The Bristol Racer

After the engine *débacle* of 1918 in which the Arab and Dragonfly failed in production, due to insufficient development earlier, the Air Board insisted on a most stringent research policy, including a rigorous Type Test, for all new engines before they could be considered for the R.A.F. The Napier Lion, recovering from its teething troubles in 1919, was the first to gain this hallmark and was well-entrenched in the home and export markets by September

1921 when the first Bristol Jupiter type test was completed. Although not an easy engine to install, the Lion was compact and had a very stiff crankshaft which virtually eliminated the torsional vibration which beset other in-line engines; also, being watercooled, it was not given to overheating on large slow aircraft during take-off and climb; consequently it was an obvious choice for transport operators.

Roy Fedden, confident that the Jupiter would surpass the Lion after equal development, was well aware of the Lion's high prestige and most anxious for the Jupiter to miss no opportunity of emulating the Lion's performance. In December 1921 the Lion had added to its laurels by gaining the British speed record in the Gloster Mars I, at 196·4 m.p.h. Fedden had several times urged the Company to build a successor to the Bullet, but Barnwell considered that the Bullet with its reduced wing area was adequate to show the paces of the Jupiter, which he did not think would ever be suitable for really high speed attempts because of cooling problems. Very soon after Barnwell's resignation, however, Fedden and Reid began to investigate a new monoplane with the Jupiter engine completely submerged, and this looked so promising that it was agreed to test a model in the wind-tunnel and not to attempt to improve the Bullet.

The first pencil sketch of the new Racer was shown to the Directors on 7 November 1921; the problems of monocoque construction were discussed on 28 November and authority to go ahead on detail design was given on 5 December. Wind-tunnel results in January indicated that a speed of over 200 m.p.h. was possible without exceeding the maximum landing speed required by the rules of the Coupe Deutsch de la Meurthe race, and an order for one prototype, No. 6148, was issued to the Works Manager on 23 January 1922.

The Jupiter engine was submerged in a circular streamline fuselage which, though of low fineness ratio, was also of low drag. The cylinders of the Jupiter were cooled by air admitted through ducts. At first a tapered wing plan with rounded tips was proposed, with Handley Page slots to reduce landing speed, but finally the wings were untapered both in chord and thickness but had sharply raked tips; the two spars were of a special laminated steel and wood construction, the wings being fabric-covered and without external bracing. They were bolted into root-stubs forming part of the two fuselage main ring frames, between which the fuel tank was installed. The rear fuselage was a true monocoque structure made from three layers of tulip-wood veneer laid diagonally over light circular hoops braced internally by radial steel spokes. The cantilever tail unit was attached by a horizontal hinge about which it could be rotated by a screw-jack for adjustment of tail plane incidence during flight. The engine was mounted on the front of the forward main frame and surrounded by a three-ply outer cowl, within which was the complex array of inter-cylinder baffles and cooling-air ducts. The pilot's cockpit, for which a stream-lined canopy was designed but never made, was just aft of the rear frame. The most striking feature of all was the undercarriage, which the pilot could retract by means of a chain and sprocket gear; when retracted, the wheels lay flush within the lower surface of the wing and the curved chassis tubes were concealed in grooves in the fuselage. The airscrew carried a large-diameter spinner made of three layers of tulip-wood, as in the rear fuselage, and similarly braced by cycle-spokes. A specially tuned Jupiter giving 480 h.p. at 1,850 r.p.m. was installed in June, and cooling on the ground was found to be satisfactory, although oil consumption was at first very high and some airscrew vibration was reported, the spinner being left off for preliminary engine runs.

The Racer, for which the name Blizzard was suggested but not approved, was finished in red and the registration *G-EBDR*, issued on 26 June 1922, was painted on in white. It was expected to attain 220 m.p.h. and its first high-speed test was eagerly awaited. But when Uwins made the first flight early in July, he had hardly left the ground when he found that the full-span ailerons were far too powerful and caused violent wing torsion and lateral instability. He managed to complete a wide circuit, which brought him dangerously low over houses in Bristol, and made a safe landing.

The Racer with bracing wires added, but before the aileron area was reduced, at Filton in August 1922.

The second flight was made after the wing had been braced by external streamline wires. Immediately the Racer became airborne there was a shattering crash in front of the pilot, but the machine continued to climb slowly; Uwins saw that the fabric of the left wing was badly torn and the pitot head had been knocked off; his first impression was that a cylinder had blown off but the engine continued to run satisfactorily. The bracing of the wings had controlled the excessive deflection experienced on the first flight and a slow circuit and safe landing was made. It was then found that the spinner had burst immediately after take-off as the engine revolutions had increased. On the first flight the spinner was unpainted, but during the wing bracing modification several heavy coats of paint had been applied to the spinner by enthusiasts who wished to obtain a superlative finish, and this extra weight was sufficient to result in the disintegration.

In the third flight, without a spinner, the machine behaved fairly normally, but the high drag of the open engine severely limited the speed. The large ailerons, which extended for the full span of the wings and were also some 20% of the chord, still gave serious over-control and it was obvious that changes would have to be made.

The fourth flight was made with a cam device designed to produce small aileron movements for small movements of the stick but progressively larger movements as the angle of displacement of the stick increased. This was achieved by a suitably shaped cam on the foot of the control column, in contact with which were two rollers, connected by cables to the ailerons; there was no direct connection between the control column and the ailerons. This system produced the desired aileron behaviour on the ground, but immediately the machine became airborne the up-load on the ailerons pulled the rollers out of contact with the face of the cam so that virtually there was no lateral control whatsoever; once again Uwins made a precarious circuit and a safe landing. The cam device was then removed and direct control restored, the ailerons being reduced to some 40% of their original area by separating the inner portion and making it part of the fixed wing. While this was being done, a smaller spinner on a hub ahead of the airscrew was designed and made. This spinner acted as a fairing and 'idler' and was intended not to rotate in flight. Three more flights were made and suitably angled vanes were fitted to the surface of the spinner to achieve this, but although the spinner gave no more trouble, it provided a quite inadequate fairing for the front of the aeroplane. During the last two flights, the retractable undercarriage was operated satisfactorily.

Seven flights in all were made on the Racer, which was much in advance of its time, but since it had no prospect of winning a major race while the spinner trouble persisted, and in view of the prolonged period of development necessary to achieve the designed performance, further flying was abandoned. At one time it was suggested that the aircraft might be used as an engine test bed, but Uwins considered its behaviour to be entirely unsuitable for this duty, particularly in the event of engine trouble.

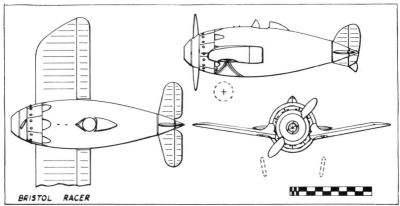

BRISTOL RACER

The special racing Jupiter was sent to the Gnome-Rhône factory and used by them in a French challenger for the Coupe Deutsch in 1923, but the Racer itself languished in a hangar at Filton until scrapped in 1924.

SPECIFICATIONS AND DATA

Type:	Racer
Manufacturers:	The Bristol Aeroplane Co. Ltd., Filton, Bristol
Power Plant:	One 510 hp Bristol Jupiter
Span:	25 ft 2 in
Length:	21 ft 7 in
Height:	8 ft 9 in
Max. Speed:	220 mph (estimated)
Accommodation:	Pilot only
Production:	One only
Sequence No.:	6148

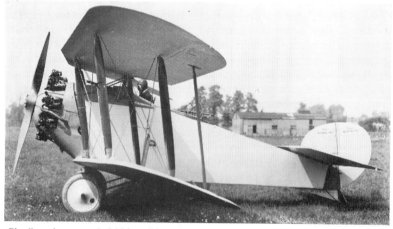

Bloodhound prototype in initial condition with small tail and equal dihedral, at Filton in May 1923.

The Bristol Bloodhound

One aim in designing the Bullfinch was its adoption as a standard reconnaissance-fighter to succeed the F.2B, when the Badger failed to fill that role. In March 1921, Capt. Barnwell doubted that the two-seater Bullfinch could carry the required equipment with a performance equal to the Bristol Fighter's; and after his departure his fears were indeed realised, for the stress levels permitted by the R.A.E. for all-metal construction were reduced and consequently structure weight increased, so that overall performance suffered.

The choice of a Bristol Fighter replacement was still open in October 1921, and although the Company was happy to recondition the Fighter while still in service it was also keen to secure the contract for its successor. Specification 3/21 called for a Napier Lion engine, and two layouts for biplanes and one for a monoplane were submitted by Reid, with opposition from Fedden, who wanted the Air Ministry to admit the Jupiter as an alternative after passing its type test. Sir Henry White-Smith discussed this claim with the Air Council, who agreed to consider a design with the Jupiter if good enough in all other respects. Reid then laid out a biplane and a monoplane for comparison, showing improvements in pilot's view, angle of fire over the tail, front gun installation and overall performance, and a tender was submitted on 23 May 1922. The Air Council rejected it as unsuitable for the reconnaissance role, but issued a new specification (3/22) for a two-seater fighter in June, preferring a supercharged engine. The Armstrong-Siddeley Jaguar was being offered with a geared supercharger, but Fedden contended that equally high power up to 10,000 ft. could be obtained with either alcohol fuel or higher compression. Although willing to collaborate in testing the R.A.E. exhaust-driven supercharger, he felt that the geared supercharger was still too unreliable for squadron service.

The biplane (Fighter 'C') and monoplane (Fighter 'D') designs were tendered in July 1922 and in October the Company decided to build one biplane as a private venture. The Air Council then invited quotations for three prototypes, one to be all-metal and the others to have wooden wings and tailplane, with a supercharged engine, requesting that the biplane should be suitable if possible for metal monoplane wings when developed.

Fedden offered to use the Orion, a derivative of the Jupiter with an R.A.E. exhaust-driven supercharger, giving 400 h.p. at 15,000 ft., and in February 1923 the Fighter 'C' was officially named Bloodhound. The prototype, No. 6222, was surveyed for a civil certificate by Major Mayo in April 1923 and flown at the end of May, the registration *G-EBGG* being issued on 3 May. After preliminary flight trials, the Bloodhound's fin and rudder were enlarged for full load tests in June, instructions to proceed with three R.A.F. Bloodhounds being received later that month, after Capt. Norman Macmillan had reported satisfactory handling with the new tail unit combined with increased stagger and sweep-back. These latter features had been purposely chosen to ensure maximum visibility for both crew members, but posed difficult problems of geometry in design and rigging. The Bloodhound was expected to compete against the Hawker Duiker, Armstrong Whitworth Wolf and de Havilland Dormouse, which it stood a good chance of beating, but Macmillan was not happy about balance and asked for the tail to be lengthened before sending it to Martlesham.

On his return in October 1923, Barnwell solved the Bloodhound's stability problems by increasing dihedral and altering the engine mounting to tilt the thrust line. With these changes, the Bloodhound gave the pilot a better view all round and handled well, attaining a top speed of 130 m.p.h. and a ceiling of 18,000 ft. with full load. It was flown to Martlesham on 21 January 1924, the three Bloodhounds for the Air Ministry being built to the same standard. The first of these, No. 6709 (*J7248*), was all-metal and had a standard Jupiter IV engine; the other two had wooden wings and tail, No. 6710

Bloodhound *J7237* with supercharged Jupiter IV at Farnborough in August 1925.

(*J7236*) having a Jupiter IV engine fitted with variable timing gear to maintain power up to 10,000 ft. and No. 6711 (*J7237*) having a Jupiter IV engine fitted with the R.A.E. supercharger removed from the Jupiter III already tested on the Seely, *J7004*; the Orion engine was not ready and needed much more development before being flown in a Gloster Gamecock in 1928.

The Martlesham test report on *G-EBGG* was less favourable than Macmillan's and showed that the Dormouse had a better performance, although the Bloodhound's handling was superior and it was preferred as a fighting machine. Its steel-tube construction, as in the Bullfinch, was considered unsuitable for production, while the wide centre-planes made it difficult to transport by road or rail. The three service Bloodhounds were delivered in 1925, *J7248* on 3 March, *J7236* on 22 June and *J7237* on 10 September. They were flown for routine testing at Martlesham and Farnborough (*J7237* being based at the R.A.E.) and gave good service, although *J7248* suffered a failure of the metal ribs of the upper centreplane in July 1925.

The prototype was overhauled on its return to Filton and fitted with a Jupiter V; its armament was removed and it received a Certificate of Airworthiness on 30 June 1925, after which it was flown in the King's Cup Race by T. W. Campbell. In October 1925 it was cleaned up further and fitted with long-range tanks; a new Jupiter VI engine, sealed by the A.I.D., was installed, and it was flown intensively between Filton and Croydon by two Imperial Airways pilots, Col. F. F. Minchin and Capt. F. L. Barnard, from 4 January till 8 March 1926, logging 25,074 miles in 225 hours 54 min., with the engine seals unbroken.

This demonstration was enough to convince Imperial Airways that the Jupiter was as good as the Jaguar, while simpler to maintain, subject to proof of its hot-climate reliability, and this was demonstrated by flying *G-EBGG* from Croydon to Cairo and back in 56 hours for the 5,400 miles. There were several delays due to the condition of the desert landing grounds, but none occasioned by failure of the aeroplane or its engine. *G-EBGG* remained in service at Filton until 1928, when, with a four-bladed airscrew and a cockpit

176

enclosure, it was used for endurance testing of the geared Jupiter VIII engine; on completion of this programme it was stored until 1931, and then scrapped.

G-EBGG with long-range tanks as test-bed for Jupiter VIII in March 1928.

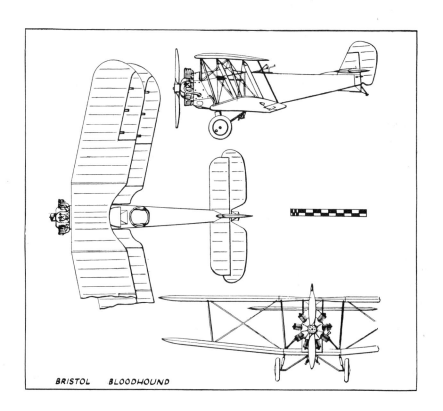

BRISTOL   BLOODHOUND

Type:	Bloodhound		
Manufacturers:	The Bristol Aeroplane Co. Ltd., Filton, Bristol		
Power Plants:	One 425 hp Bristol Jupiter IV, IV (V.T.) or IV (S/c)		
	One 450 hp Bristol Jupiter VI		
	One 485 hp Bristol Jupiter VIII		
Span:	40 ft 2 in	*Max. Speed:*	130 mph
Length:	26 ft 6 in	*Service Ceiling:*	22,000 ft
Height:	10 ft 8 in	*Endurance:*	3 hours
Wing Area:	494 sq ft	*Accommodation:*	2
Empty Weight:	2,515 lb	*Production:*	4
All-up Weight:	4,236 lb	*Sequence Nos.:*	6222 6709 6710 6711

Norman Macmillan with *G-EBGF* at Torslanda on 20 July 1923.

The Bristol Jupiter-Fighter and Advanced Trainers

To demonstrate the Jupiter engine in a cheap airframe the conversion of a spare F.2B was investigated in 1923, and on 22 January W. T. Reid reported that the scheme was feasible, although standard tankage would provide only 2 hours' fuel supply; the speed was expected to be 133 m.p.h., better than the Bloodhound's, and authority was given to build one Jupiter-Fighter, No. 6379, for the Göteborg Aero Show in July. The conversion was simple, since no exhaust manifold was fitted, and the airframe was standard apart from local strengthening and an oleo undercarriage instead of the rubber cord type. The Jupiter-Fighter was completed in April 1923 and a second conversion started. The first was registered *G-EBGF* on 3 May 1923, and two days later it was decided to convert a third, so that while one was at Martlesham the second could be shown at Göteborg while the third was flown at Torslanda. In June, however, it was decided to use the third machine for testing a

Jupiter with alcohol fuel, for comparison with the supercharged Jupiter in the Seely.

G-EBGF was flown by Norman Macmillan early in June 1923 and reached a top speed of 134 m.p.h., at which the slipstream was too rough for the gunner when standing up; with the small fuel capacity and the restricted pilot's view ahead, Macmillan could not recommend it seriously as a fighter, but it was a first-class demonstrator for the Jupiter. The second Jupiter-Fighter, No. 6380, was registered *G-EBHG* and exhibited on the British stand at the Göteborg International Aero Exhibition opened by King Gustav on 20 July. It had no armament, but was equipped with Frise ailerons; *G-EBGF*, flown from London to Göteborg by Macmillan in a single day to take part in the flying contest at Torslanda, covered 755 miles (1,215 kilometres) and was awarded the 'arrival prize' of 1,215 kroner. *G-EBGF* had been fitted with a special climb airscrew and won the altitude prize with an ascent to 26,000 ft., where Macmillan had to break off because he had no oxygen, although the aircraft was still climbing. He also won an aerobatic contest for two-seaters and greatly impressed the Swedish military pilots.

The Swedish government decided to purchase the Jupiter-Fighter, subject to its satisfactory performance in Arctic conditions. *G-EBHG* was therefore equipped with a ski undercarriage and a carburettor heater muff and went north to Kiruna in Lapland in November 1923. It was almost impossible to

Lt. Gardin in *G-EBHG* during Arctic trials at Kiruna in 1924.

operate aircraft at this latitude in winter because even with an aircooled engine the oil froze solid in a few hours. The Jupiter, however, was started repeatedly without trouble after nights in the open at − 20°C, using standard petrol and arctic motor oil. *G-EBHG* was purchased by the Swedish government, and Lt. Gardin flew it back 800 miles from Kiruna to Malmslätt at an average speed of 124 m.p.h. On going into service with the Swedish Air Force in May 1924 it received number *4300*; this was changed in 1926 to *1300*, and again in 1932 to *3667*. It was declared surplus and purchased by Hugo Fredrikson, to whom it was registered *SE-AEE* on 14 February 1935, and he

G-EBHG in service with the Swedish Air Force as *1300* at Malmslätt, 1926.

crashed it at Göteborg in 1936. It was the longest lived of the Jupiter-Fighters, for *G-EBGF* had crashed on 23 November 1923 after engine seizure at 20,000 ft. while being flown by T. W. Campbell. The third machine, No. 6381 (*G-EBHH*), had a high compression engine and a bifuel system with a gravity tank for alcohol above the top centreplane; it took off on alcohol and switched to petrol on reaching an altitude at which detonation would not occur; the Jupiter had two separate carburettors, one for each fuel. *G-EBHH*

G-EBHH with Bi-fuel Jupiter at Filton in June 1924.

began flying in March 1924, but in July the Air Ministry abandoned the bifuel system because of tank corrosion problems and preferred supercharging as a long-term development. So in September 1924 *G-EBHH* was converted into a dual-control trainer, similar to the type already adopted for the Filton Reserve Flying School.

When the school was first established, the surviving Puma-engined Tourer demonstrator, *G-EAXA*, was fitted with Frise ailerons and evaluated as a dual-control advanced trainer. Four more Puma Trainers were built in March 1923, Nos. 6239 to 6242, registered *G-EBFR* to *G-EBFU* on 19 April; they went into service when the school opened on 15 May, but early in June *G-EBFR* was crashed by Arthur Keep, and a replacement, No. 6382, was

Three of the five Reserve Flying School Puma-Trainers developed from the Tourer.

built and registered *G-EBIH* on 15 October. This, like '*FT* and '*FU*, had an oleo undercarriage, which had been adopted in June because of the frequent failures of the rubber-cord type during repeated landings. Before completion of *G-EBIH*, the success of the Jupiter-Fighter had been proved, and it was decided to produce a trainer with a Jupiter, restricted to 290 h.p. because of higher insurance costs if 300 h.p. were exceeded. *G-EBIH*, with a derated

Type 89 prototype (Jupiter III) at Filton in April 1924.

Jupiter III, was ready for flight on 14 April 1924, by which time a second Trainer, No. 6522 (*G-EBJA*), was nearly complete, and two more, Nos. 6523 (*G-EBJB*) and 6524 (*G-EBJC*), were in progress.

The Trainer had Frise ailerons and an enlarged horn-balanced rudder and fin to counteract the torque reaction of the Jupiter, whose rating was later increased to 320 h.p. The Jupiter Trainers were less accident-free than the Lucifer-engined P.T.M.s, and new machines such as Nos. 6918 (*G-EBML*) and 6919 (*G-EBMN*) were built to replace losses from time to time; the type was also adopted by the Beardmore Reserve School at Renfrew, to which Nos. 6963 (*G-EBNZ*) and 6964 (*G-EBOA*) were supplied in June 1926, as the first two of a fleet which remained in service until 1930.

From No. 6965 (*G-EBOC*) for the Filton school in October 1926 the fuselage was strengthened by being covered with plywood instead of braced with tie-rods; it was finished in black Cerric, with silver-doped wings and tail. Ten of this type were built for the Filton school and three for the Renfrew school, who also assembled one final machine, *G-EBWN*, themselves from spares and salvaged components. All the Renfrew aircraft had Jupiter VI engines, but Filton continued to use up surplus Jupiter IVs as a matter of economy, since servicing at the factory was no great problem. The last Jupiter Trainers built were Nos. 7711 and 7712, registered *G-ABPL* and *G-ABPM*

181

Type 89A with Handley-Page auto-slots at Filton in 1930.

on 2 September 1931, and the Filton machines remained in service until superseded by Hart Trainers in April 1933.

Apart from school use, they took their share of experimental work, *G-EBYL* being equipped with Handley Page auto-slots and another with steel wings, which gave so little trouble that their very existence was forgotten by the experimental department; in 1932 *G-ABPM* undertook trials of Dunlop 'doughnut' low-pressure wheels. Five, including '*IH* and '*HH*, met their ends in three mid-air collisions over Filton, the sixth victim being the only P.T.M. to be lost, *G-EBGB*. After withdrawal from school use at Renfrew in 1930 and Filton in 1933, all the survivors were scrapped as unfit for resale to private owners.

SPECIFICATIONS AND DATA

Type:	Jupiter-Fighter and Advanced Trainers
Manufacturers:	The Bristol Aeroplane Co. Ltd., Filton, Bristol
Power Plant:	(Fighter) 425 hp Bristol Jupiter IV
	(Trainer) 320 hp Bristol Jupiter IV (DR) or VI (DR)
Span:	39 ft 3 in
Length:	25 ft
Height:	9 ft 6 in
Wing Area:	405 sq ft
Empty Weight:	(Fighter) 2,190 lb; (Trainer) 2,326 lb
All-up Weight:	(Fighter) 3,080 lb; (Trainer) 3,250 lb
Max. Speed:	(Fighter) 134 mph; (Trainer) 110 mph
Service Ceiling:	(Fighter) 22,150 ft
Range:	(Fighter) 400 miles; (Trainer) 340 miles
Accommodation:	2
Production:	(Fighter) 3 (Trainer-89) 9 (Trainer-89A) 14
Sequence Nos.:	(Fighter) 6379–6381 (Trainer-89) 6382 6522–6525 6918 6919 6963 6964
	(Trainer-89A) 6965–6967 7124 7156 7157 7221 7234 7265 7350–7352 7711 7712

The first Bulgarian Tourer *B-BECA* at Filton in April 1924.

The Bristol Greek and Bulgarian Tourers

In February 1923 Capt. Norman Macmillan flew a reconditioned Bristol Fighter with 300 h.p. Hispano-Suiza engine to Yugoslavia, and in April the same year tenders for two types of aeroplane were invited by the Department of Posts and Telegraphs of the Bulgarian government, one for a five- or six-seater and the other for a two-seater for postal services. Bulgaria, being an ex-enemy country, was prohibited by the Versailles Treaty from operating aircraft with engines of over 200 h.p., so the Company offered a version of the Tourer fitted with a 180 h.p. Wolseley Viper. The Bulgarian government accepted this tender in August 1923 and ordered four aeroplanes, to be delivered by the end of the year. The first two, ready in December, were Nos. 6383 and 6384, registered *B-BECA* and *B-BEHA*, respectively; they were standard Fighters with armament removed and Tourer modifications to the fuselage and rear cockpit, but without the 15-gallon centre-section gravity tank of the Puma-Tourer. Their actual delivery to Bojourishte, near Sofia, was delayed until April 1924, and the order for the other two remained in abeyance while the first two were proved in service.

Improved Bulgarian Tourer *B-BEKA* at Filton in May 1926.

183

For a time it seemed that the Bulgarian government might prefer to accept an alternative offer of Lucifer-engined Primary Trainers, but in the end only one of these and three of an improved type of Tourer were bought, in April 1926. Like the first two, these had Viper engines, but were brought up to date by incorporation of an oleo undercarriage, Frise ailerons and the horn-balanced rudder and large fin designed for the Jupiter-Trainer. These three Tourers, Nos. 6937 to 6939, registered *B-BEBA*, *B-BETO* and *B-BEKA*, respectively, had navigation lights and Holt flares for night operation. A revised radiator, designed by Capt. Barnwell, replaced the earlier Hispano-Suiza type, and, with the rudders painted in white, green and red vertical stripes, the Bulgarian Tourers were very neat machines.

During the period between deliveries of the first and second batches of Tourers to Bulgaria, an order for six Tourers came from the Greek government, who were not restricted in engine power and already operated six

Greek Advanced Trainer (Puma) at Filton before dispatch in May 1925.

standard Bristol F.2B Fighters, which they had bought in 1922. The six new Tourers ordered in 1925, Nos. 6712–6717, were unarmed but convertible into fighters if necessary; they had Marconi radio, oleo landing gear, Frise ailerons and the large fin and rudder. They were flight tested between 24 April and 15 May 1925 using a single Puma engine supplied by the Greek government and then shipped to Phaleron without engines installed, to be fitted with Pumas on arrival.

In 1931 all were converted by the Greek Navy to a new standard, using Rolls-Royce Falcon conversion kits supplied by the Company in March that year. They thus became a modernised version of the original three Falcon-engined Tourers built for the Air Board in July 1919 and, like them, had 15-gallon centre-section gravity tanks, although the rear fuselage decking remained flat, as in the fighter, and a Scarff-ring base was incorporated in the rear cockpit. They wore the Greek national blue-white-blue roundels and rudder stripes, and two of them were numbered *M51* and *M54* and had tropical auxiliary radiators like those on R.A.F. Bristol Fighters in the Middle East and India.

SPECIFICATIONS AND DATA

Type:	Greek and Bulgarian Tourers
Manufacturers:	The Bristol Aeroplane Co. Ltd., Filton, Bristol
Power Plants:	(Greek) One 230 hp Siddeley Puma; One 275 hp Rolls-Royce Falcon
	(Bulgarian) One 180 hp Wolseley Viper
Span:	39 ft 5 in
Length:	(Puma) 26 ft (Falcon) 26 ft (Viper) 24 ft 11 in
Height:	10 ft
Wing Area:	407 sq ft
Empty Weight:	(Puma) 1,750 lb (Falcon) 1,800 lb (Viper) 1,650 lb
All-up Weight:	(Puma) 2,800 lb (Falcon) 3,000 lb (Viper) 2,700 lb
Max. Speed:	(Puma) 120 mph (Falcon) 125 mph (Viper) 120 mph
Endurance:	(Puma) 5 hours (Falcon) 4 hours (Viper) 5½ hours
Accommodation:	2
Production:	(Greek) 6 (Bulgarian) 5
Sequence Nos.:	(Greek) 6712–6717 (Bulgarian) 6383 6384 6937–6939

Greek Advanced Trainer after conversion to Rolls Royce Falcon III in 1931.

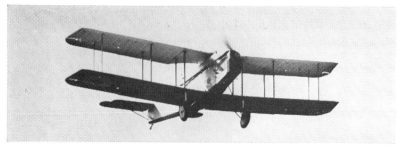

The second Berkeley *J7404* taking-off from Filton in May 1925.

The Bristol Berkeley, Type 90

In August 1923 the Bristol Aeroplane Company was amongst the firms invited to tender for three prototype single-engined two-seater day or night bombers to Air Ministry Specification 26/23. W. T. Reid, who had just been joined by Clifford Tinson from A. V. Roe and Co., produced a layout for an all-metal equal-span biplane having the specified Rolls-Royce Condor engine in the nose, the pilot forward of the centre-plane leading edge, the gunner-observer in a dorsal cockpit with a Scarff-ring and an alternative prone bomb-aimer's station on the fuselage floor. The centre-section span matched the track of the divided oleo landing gear and the outer wings were at first single bay, with Frise ailerons on all four wings; the fin and rudder were of low aspect ratio, similar in shape to the Ten-seater's. The radiator was slung below the engine behind a slanting row of horizontal shutters, and in general appearance the aeroplane was very similar to the Avro Aldershot, on which Tinson had worked two years earlier. Structurally the fuselage was similar to the Bloodhound, having steel tubes with the end sockets bolted together and braced by tie-rods; the wings were of mixed steel and duralumin construction, using the rolled high-tensile steel sections developed by Pollard.

The overall layout was complete when Reid resigned, and the only changes Captain Barnwell made were a longer rear fuselage, a taller fin and rudder and a new location for the radiator, which he divided into two units placed each side of the fuselage between the wings. Tinson, seeking a designation for the bomber, pending choice of name, suggested the Avro system of type numbers; Barnwell agreed and made a retrospective list of Bristol designs, beginning with the Scout C as Type I, and ending with the Jupiter Trainer as Type 89, so the new bomber became Type 90. This system of numbering was approved by the Directors on 7 January 1924, since when all new Bristol projects, except for a few tender designs, have had serial type numbers; meanwhile, Type 90 received the official name Berkeley in October 1923.

At the mock-up inspection on 4 January 1924, the Air Ministry specialists were generally satisfied, but preferred a nose position for the radiator, and this was accordingly transferred to a vertical position under the airscrew shaft. The firm was urged to complete the first Berkeley, No. 6718 (*J7403*), by the end of August, and this and the second machine, No. 6719 (*J7404*), were acceptable with wooden wings and tail plane, provided the third, No. 6720 (*J7405*), was all-metal; metal airscrews were required on both the second and third aircraft in spite of Capt. Barnwell's prediction of a performance penalty. In spite of all efforts, *J7403* was not erected in skeleton form until November 1924; the Air Ministry's revised stress calculations then showed that the rear fuselage longerons were below strength and these had to be changed, so the first Berkeley did not fly until 5 March 1925. It went to Martlesham at the end of that month and was accepted on 22 May 1925. It performed and handled very satisfactorily up to its specified top speed of 120 m.p.h. with a 500 lb. bomb load, but it and the Handley Page Handcross were somewhat larger than the other two competitors, the Hawker Horsley and Westland Yeovil, and were considered better for night-bombing than for day work. Unfortunately the Air Council had already decided, after service trials of a squadron of Avro Aldershots, not to use single-engined bombers for night operations, so the only production contract went to the Horsley. The second Berkeley was delivered in December 1925, but the third, with metal wings, not until 21 June 1926. On completion of its Martlesham trials in November 1925, *J7403* was transferred to the R.A.E. for experimental flying, as were the other two after acceptance. *J7404* was flown for some time with a four-bladed wooden airscrew to compare its efficiency with the metal two-blader. One Berkeley was still in existence in December 1930, when a new radiator was supplied for it.

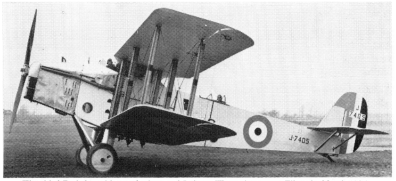

The third Berkeley with metal wings and Leitner-Watts airscrew at Filton in March 1926.

SPECIFICATION AND DATA

Type:	90, Berkeley
Manufacturers:	The Bristol Aeroplane Co. Ltd., Filton, Bristol
Power Plant:	One 650 hp Rolls-Royce Condor III
Span:	57 ft 11 in
Length:	47 ft 6 in
Height:	14 ft
Wing Area:	985 sq ft
Empty Weight:	5,200 lb
All-up Weight:	8,128 lb
Max. Speed:	120 mph
Endurance:	12 hours
Accommodation:	2
Production:	3
Sequence Nos.:	6718–6720

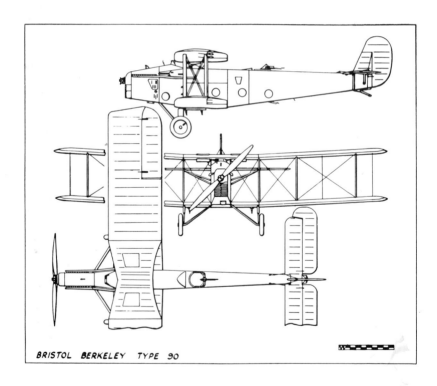

BRISTOL BERKELEY TYPE 90

Brownie *Jill* with Cherub I and large metal wings at Filton in 1925.

The Bristol Brownie, Type 91

In October 1922 the *Daily Mail* sponsored a gliding competition at Itford Hill in Sussex for which prizes totalling £1,000 were offered; the first prize was won by Maneyrol on a tandem monoplane. Shortly afterwards the Aero-engine Department of the Company developed a small flat-twin aircooled engine of 1,095 cubic centimetres capacity giving 18 brake horse power and intended mainly for commercial use in portable generating plants and the like. As there seemed to be some demand for a light aero-engine of this size, a lightened version called the Bristol Cherub, giving 30 h.p., was also produced in small numbers, and in April 1923 Reid suggested that a tandem-winged single-seater with a Cherub should be designed for a competition to be held for a prize of £500 presented by the Duke of Sutherland. Reid was authorised to undertake limited wind-tunnel testing of a tandem-wing model, but soon afterwards the rules for the Duke of Sutherland's prize were announced, limiting the competitors to an engine size of 750 c.c. Fedden considered this too small and continued development of the Cherub, but no work was done on an aeroplane to match it.

The single-seaters flown in the 1923 competition were useless in anything but a dead calm, and in February 1924 the Air Council decided to hold a more realistic competition for two-seaters with engines of up to 1,100 c.c. at Lympne in September, with prizes totalling £3,600. The rules were agreed with the Society of British Aircraft Constructors in December 1923, and Barnwell was ready with alternative monoplane and biplane designs early in the New Year, having satisfied himself that the tandem wing offered no real advantage. After considering rival merits and costs of a wooden biplane and a metal monoplane, the Directors on 4 February 1924 agreed to construct two Type 91 all-steel monoplanes for the competition, with the name Brownie. On 5 May the order was amended to three monoplanes, Nos. 6526–6528, registered *G-EBJK*, *'JL* and *'JM* on 14 July, and promptly christened *Jack*, *Jill* and *Jim* by the Filton pilots. A week later the Cherub passed a 25 hour civil type test at a rating of 32 h.p., and on 6 August 1924, *G-EBJK* was flown first by Cyril Uwins alone, then solo by Barnwell and finally, as a full load test, by both of them together. The handling of the Brownie, especially near the stall, was all that could be desired.

All three Brownies had similar fuselages of thin gauge high-tensile steel tubing with wire bracing. Several types of wing, both wooden and steel, were designed and three versions were built: a wooden one 16 ft. in length and two metal ones of 17 ft. and 14 ft., respectively. For comparative tests the larger metal wings were fitted to *G-EBJL* and the wooden wings to *G-EBJK*. The biconvex wing profile was one of Barnwell's own, developed in the wind-tunnel, and segmental ailerons of the Bullfinch type were adopted. The ailerons were actuated by a single cable acting against rubber cords instead of a return cable; the system was intended to reduce aileron drag, but was unsatisfactory at first because the lack of positive restraint which allowed the down-going aileron to float up also permitted it to flutter near the stall; this was easily cured by a return cable. The larger metal wings were all-steel, having tapered spars comprising upper and lower booms of channel section reinforced by rolled strip formed into a cusped section; the web for most of the span was made from round tube flattened and bent at intervals so as to form a Warren girder. The smaller metal wings, which were intended for speed competition work, had a steel primary structure with duralumin ribs and edge members. The Brownie's undercarriage comprised a pair of vertical tubular struts carrying two light-weight Palmer wheels on a long axle whose deflection provided the only springing.

On 5 September T. W. Campbell had the misfortune to foul some telephone wires with *G-EBJK* and made a crash landing on the airfield at Filton, but the damage was repaired in time for the trials at Lympne between 27 September and 4 October, where Uwins flew it as No. *1*. *G-EBJL* was also there, flown by Campbell as No. *2*, having made its first flight on 22 September, but was withdrawn because of aileron flutter. Campbell then took over the third Brownie *G-EBJM*, which had been flown on 24 September. This had been entered as a single-seater with a long-range tank for the Grosvenor Cup race, in which Campbell gained third place at an average speed of just over 70 m.p.h. In the main trials Uwins took the second prize of £1,000 and also won the Duke of Sutherland's prize of £500 for the best take-off and landing.

Having had its aileron trouble cured, *G-EBJL* went to Martlesham on 28 November for evaluation as a primary trainer, but the Air Council declined to purchase it, and suggested a number of modifications. *G-EBJK* also was tested at Martlesham with wooden wings, and Barnwell suggested that an all-wood version would be cheaper and have a better all-round performance. The Air Council were mildly interested in this proposal but finally turned it down; no prototype was built, nor was Barnwell's proposed wooden single-seat racing version (Brownie III, Type 98), which he estimated would reach 90 m.p.h. with a 36 h.p. Cherub III. The latter engine, which had larger cylinders of 1,228 c.c. capacity, passed its 100 hours type test on 3 December 1925 and was installed in *G-EBJK*, which was considerably modified in November before going again to Martlesham.

Brownie *Jack* modified to Type 91A, with steel wings and increased tankage.

The Cherub III was mounted lower and the top longerons were altered to slope from the rear cockpit to the nose, so as to improve the pilot's view. A revised strut-braced landing gear was fitted, still with axle flexure as the only means of springing, but the axle was streamlined. For its second visit to Martlesham, '*JK* had steel wings and a large fuel tank and, thus modified, was designated Type 91A. Still the Air Council refused it, so after its return from Martlesham in May 1926 it was further improved by a curved decking along the whole length of the fuselage, a still lower thrust-line requiring a re-designed cowling, and an enlarged horn-balanced rudder. The landing gear was altered to a short axle and rubber-in-compression shock absorbers, and a Fairey-Reed duralumin airscrew was fitted.

Brownie II, Type 91B, with Cherub III and Fairey-Reed airscrew; Filton, August 1926.

In this form it was redesignated Type 91B, or Brownie II, and entered in the *Daily Mail* trials for light aeroplanes at Lympne in September 1926, where Uwins won the third prize of £500. He also gained second place in the S.M.M.T. Handicap race on 18 September, while *G-EBJM*, flown by C. T. Holmes as a single-seater with the smaller metal wings, came in third in the Lympne Handicap race on the same day; '*JM* had been flown into second place in the Grosvenor Cup race by Uwins in August the previous year and in 1927 was hired by the London Aeroplane Club at Stag Lane, whence it was flown in several races that year, thereafter continuing as a club hack until it was scrapped in 1930. *G-EBJL* was similarly converted to a single-seater and was sold to the Bristol and Wessex Aeroplane Club in September 1927, continuing in use until the Club moved from Filton to Whitchurch in 1930.

The Brownie II did not survive as long as its sisters, for after being used for Cherub flight-testing at Filton and occasionally raced, as at Hamble in May 1927 by Uwins, it was allotted to Capt. Barnwell for his personal use. Thereafter he was to be seen flying in all weathers and on at least one occasion, on an attempted flight to Farnborough against a strong east wind, was in view from Filton for nearly an hour as he battled across the Cotswold escarpment at Dyrham. The end came on 21 March 1928, when he took-off from Farnborough into severe downwash over trees, and in spite of full throttle crashed in Farnborough Road, almost on the site of his crash nine years earlier in the M.R.1; once again he was unhurt, but *G-EBJK* was a write-off. Although excellently engineered, efficient in performance and economical in fuel, the Brownie was expensive to build and not rugged enough to stand up to normal light aeroplane club treatment, nor was it cheap to maintain and repair. Consequently it stood no chance in an open market against the de Havilland Moth, which, disregarding the rules of the Lympne competition, really brought flying within reach of the man-in-the-street.

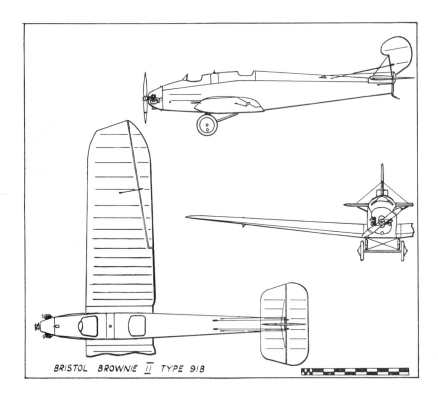

BRISTOL BROWNIE II TYPE 91B

Type:	91, Brownie
Manufacturers:	The Bristol Aeroplane Co. Ltd., Filton, Bristol
Power Plant:	One 32 hp Bristol Cherub I
	One 36 hp Bristol Cherub III
Span:	(91 wood) 34 ft 7 in
	(91 metal) 36 ft 7 in
	(91 single-seat) 30 ft 7 in
	(91A and 91B) 37 ft 7 in
Length:	26 ft 3 in
Height:	6 ft 6 in
Wing Area:	(91 wood) 204 sq ft
	(91 metal) 208 sq ft
	(91 single-seat) 172 sq ft
	(91A and 91B) 210 sq ft
Empty Weight:	(91) 500 lb (91A and 91B) 690 lb
All-up Weight:	(91) 870 lb (91 s/s) 720 lb (91A and 91B) 1,010 lb
Max. Speed:	(91 and 91A) 70 mph (91B) 78 mph
Range:	(91) 100 miles (91A and 91B) 125 miles
Accommodation:	(*'JK* and *'JL*) 2 (*'JM*) 1
Production:	3
Sequence Nos.:	6526–6528

Laboratory Biplane, Type 92, as built in September 1925, with 3 ft. fuselage.

The Bristol Type 92

Probably the least-publicised of all Bristol aeroplanes actually built and flown was the Laboratory biplane, Type 92. Nevertheless, it was flown for research purposes on an Air Ministry contract for nearly three years, always near Filton airfield; for this reason it was never on the civil register. The project originated in 1923, when difficulties with the cooling of Jupiter engines in the Badger, Bullfinch and Ten-seater showed how little was known about cowlings for air-cooled radial engines. It was fairly easy to keep the cylinders from overheating if exposed to the full slipstream, but attempts to reduce drag and regulate the flow of cooling air were singularly unrewarding, and full-scale experience always seemed to disappoint the promise of wind-tunnel tests on models. On the fully-ducted and submerged engine of the Racer reasonable cooling had been obtained with low overall drag, and experiments with a separate helmet on each cylinder had succeeded on the record-breaking Gourdou-Leseurre monoplane which had achieved nearly 224 m.p.h. round a closed circuit, using the same engine as the Racer. The problem was to correlate full-scale and model results, and in January 1924 Barnwell, with Fedden's backing, proposed a biplane scaled-up from a conventionalised wind-tunnel model having a circular section fuselage and no excrescences.

The proposal was put to the Air Ministry, and in April 1924 a fixed-price research contract was awarded to cover the cost of building and testing one full-size aeroplane and all the models. Capt. Barnwell's first general arrangement drawing, dated 17 April 1924, showed a very tall and austere two-bay equal-span biplane with squared-off wing-tips and tail surfaces, a slender fuselage mounted in the gap and a very wide-track landing gear. Structurally

Another view of Type 92 before its Jupiter VI was installed. (*Both photos by the late N. J. Hancock.*)

the fuselage was a square-section plywood-covered box girder 2 ft. wide in plan and of similar depth for half its length, then tapering to a horizontal knife-edge stern as in the F.2B. Two cockpits were located aft of the wings. To this basic structure could be attached circular fairings of various diameters; initially it was proposed to test five fairings ranging from 3 ft. to 5 ft. in diameter, but as model tests proved more costly than expected only the 3 ft. and 5 ft. fairings were actually made and tested in flight. The fairings were of normal wooden frame and stringer construction with fabric covering, and a removable decking carried both cockpit openings complete with low-drag windscreens. The wings were parallel in chord and gap, attached at their roots to upper and lower pylon structures of Tee section, bolted to the plywood fuselage box. Dihedral was constant from centre line to tip and ailerons were provided on the lower wing only. Two gravity fuel tanks each of 17 gallons capacity were suspended between the tops of the inboard wing struts. The wings and tail unit were of high tensile steel strip and tube construction, with fabric covering, and the interplane struts were streamlined steel tubes. The landing gear comprised wheels on rubber-cord sprung half-axles hinged to a centre pylon and was built up from steel tubing; the tail-skid was of the leaf-spring type. The aeroplane was thus both an aerodynamic test vehicle and a useful exercise in combined steel wing and plywood fuselage construction. The very large gap of 9 ft. for a span of 36 ft. and chord of 6 ft. was dictated by the necessity to avoid interference between fuselage and wings, but resulted in an ungainly appearance and sluggish handling characteristics. No official photographs were ever taken, but fortunately two taken by an A.I.D. inspector have survived, showing the 3 ft. fairing before installation of the engine.

At first it seemed that only a Jupiter IV would be available, but in October 1925 the Air Ministry agreed to lend a Jupiter VI, and the completed aircraft, No. 6920, was wheeled out for flight on 13 November 1925. Most of the subsequent two years' flying programme was done with the 3 ft. fuselage, but in 1928 the 5 ft. fairings were installed; soon afterwards the undercarriage collapsed after landing and further flying was discontinued. By then improvements in cylinder design and the invention of the Townend ring had solved many of the cooling and drag problems of air-cooled radial engines.

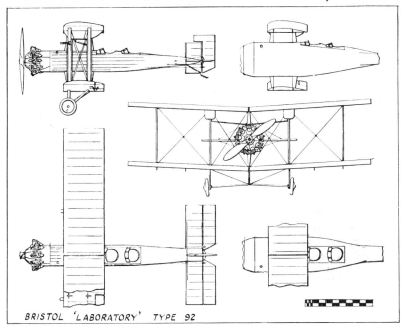

BRISTOL 'LABORATORY' TYPE 92

Type:	92, Laboratory Biplane
Manufacturers:	The Bristol Aeroplane Co. Ltd., Filton, Bristol
Power Plant:	One 450 hp Bristol Jupiter VI
Span:	36 ft
Length:	29 ft 4 in
Height:	13 ft
Wing Area:	432 sq ft
Empty Weight:	2,200 lb
All-up Weight:	3,400 lb
Max. Speed:	132 mph
Ceiling:	26,000 ft
Accommodation:	2
Production:	1
Sequence No.:	6920

Boarhound I with Jupiter VI at Martlesham Heath in November 1925. (*Crown copyright.*)

The Bristol Boarhound and Beaver, Types 93, 93A and 93B

When comments on the Bloodhound came from the test pilots at Martlesham in January 1924, Capt. Barnwell began a free-lance design for a two-seater fighter. He took into account Air Ministry Specification 8/24, calling for a corps-reconnaissance two-seater to replace the Bristol Fighter, and revised the layout at the end of March. This design, Type 93, was of orthodox all-steel construction and had some of the features of the Bloodhound such as the high position of the pilot's cockpit, but avoided the complexities, such as sweep-back, unequal dihedral and wide track, which had made it such a rigger's nightmare. The design was well received by the Air Council, who hinted that enough of the chosen replacement for the Bristol

Fighter would be ordered to re-equip four squadrons, perhaps as many as 90 aircraft. The Bristol 93 with a few alterations seemed better than the Bloodhound, D.H. Dormouse and Vickers Vixen; it would, however, have to carry the comprehensive army co-operation equipment and compete with the new Armstrong Whitworth, D.H. and Vickers prototypes built to the same specification. Thus encouraged, the Directors authorised the detail design and construction of one Type 93 biplane as a private venture and named it the Boarhound.

Capt. Barnwell again revised the design in November 1924, using the system of steel construction developed by Harry Pollard, in which high tensile steel strips were rolled into cusped and flanged sections, which were then riveted together lengthways to form longerons and struts, joints being made by gusset plates instead of machined end fittings. The resulting structure was lighter and stronger than one made from drawn tubes and very much cheaper. The Boarhound was a two-bay staggered unswept biplane, with wings of equal span and unequal chord and Frise ailerons on the lower wing only. The fuselage was ample in depth for the bulky wireless, camera and message gear required in addition to one fixed Vickers gun firing forward and one Lewis gun on a Scarff ring for the observer. The pilot's cockpit was slightly lower than in the Bloodhound, but the Scarff ring was raised to allow the rear gun to be fired on the forward quarters as well as abeam and astern. A simple cross-axle landing gear with long-stroke coil-spring shock struts and a leaf-spring tail skid were fitted. Structurally the fuselage was built up with Warren-girder sides in the forward bays and wire-braced panels elsewhere. A Jupiter IV engine with variable timing gear and a Triplex carburettor was installed for the early flights, with the intention of exchanging it for a Jupiter VI after 50 hours' flying.

The Boarhound, No. 6805, was registered *G-EBLG* on 28 May 1925 and first flown, by C. F. Uwins, on 8 June; it went to Martlesham Heath for official trials on 10 August and was matched against the Armstrong Whitworth Atlas, de Havilland Hyena and Vickers Vespa; its variable timing gear was found to be a disadvantage because, although it maintained power at altitude, it restricted output at ground level. Barnwell went to Martlesham in November to sound the R.A.F. test pilots' opinions and flew it himself while there. He reluctantly concluded that the Atlas was ahead of its rivals on most counts, but came back with the news that the Air Ministry were about to call for tenders for a general-purpose bomber to replace the D.H.9A which, like the Bristol Fighter, was a war veteran in widespread use overseas but long overdue for retirement.

The Air Ministry still clung to the Napier Lion, of which they had several hundred in store, but there seemed a fair chance that the Jupiter would also be considered, so a redesign of the Boarhound to meet the general purpose role was put in hand in December 1925. Concurrently, an enquiry was received from Chile for a two-seater fighter-bomber for which a modified Boarhound design was tendered, under the name Borzoi; some of the improvements therein proposed were incorporated in *G-EBLG* after it returned to Filton from Martlesham in March 1926, including the change to high-compression Jupiter VI engine. It then went back to Martlesham for full load trials and appeared as a 'new type' in the R.A.F. Display at Hendon in July; after this it was passed to the School of Army Co-operation at Old Sarum for operational assessment, still in competition with the Atlas, Hyena and Vespa. At the end of August, when the Atlas had clearly established itself as the winner, all four army co-operation prototypes were handed back to their makers, but meanwhile the Boarhound had crashed at Odiham on 11 August and was rushed back to Filton, where the quite extensive damage was repaired in one week by an all-out effort; it was redelivered to Old Sarum on 20 August. This was striking testimony to the strength and ease of repair of the steel structure developed by Pollard.

When the full requirements for the D.H.9A replacement were issued the Company decided to manufacture three more sets of details and assemble one new machine equipped for general purpose duties. Amongst the various criticisms of the Boarhound had been lateral instability and an ill-defined air

Beaver at Filton in March 1927.

of clumsiness. Barnwell corrected the former fault by modifying the Frise ailerons on the lower wing and adding plain narrow-chord ailerons on the upper wing; he met the latter objection, which was more psychological than real, with improved cowling lines with a pointed spinner, matched by a fin and rudder of approximately D.H.9A shape, together with a long-stroke tail-skid; this slightly increased the ground angle, improving ground handling and take-off, and the general appearance was greatly enhanced. Renamed the Beaver and designated Type 93A, this prototype, No. 7123, was registered *G-EBQF* on 2 February 1927 and first flown by Uwins on 23 February. Like *G-EBLG* it was entirely a private venture. It was flown to Martlesham Heath in April, but its two-bay wing arrangement was liked less than the single-bay layout of the Vickers Valiant, which was at first the favourite in the competition along with the Fairey IIIF, the latter being adopted by the R.A.F. as the best of the Lion-engined competitors.

During the summer the geared Jupiter VIII engine was approved for R.A.F.

service and a revised general-purpose specification was issued based on this engine (which was a substantial victory for Fedden), requiring maximum utilisation, in emergency, of existing D.H.9A wings, tail-surfaces and certain other components. It was not thought worthwhile to re-engine the Beaver with a Jupiter VIII, but a new design, Type 106, was submitted to the Air Ministry; this was similar in many respects to the Gloster Goral and the Westland Wapiti (the eventual winner), but no prototype of it was built.

Meanwhile the Borzoi fighter proposal, although not successful in Chile, chiefly because of the long credit terms expected, had been shown to a Mexican military purchasing commission, which was negotiating for a batch of Bristol Fighters with 300 h.p. Hispano-Suiza engines. In October 1927 a contract was agreed for the supply to Mexico of ten new Bristol Fighters and two Type 93B biplanes equipped as reconnaissance-fighters and named Boarhound II. These two, Nos. 7232 and 7233, were assembled from the

Boarhound II in Mexico in 1929.

remaining sets of details manufactured in 1926; they were almost identical to the Beaver, but without the prone bomb-aiming position on the fuselage floor. They had Jupiter VI engines and minor external differences were a slight reduction in rudder area, further revised ailerons and slight sweepback to compensate for a rearward shift in centre of gravity. They were dispatched to Mexico in January 1928 and gave excellent service for many years in a climate which suited their steel construction. When civil war broke out in Mexico in April 1929, the two Boarhounds took an active part in suppressing the rebel forces.

SPECIFICATION AND DATA

Types:	93, Boarhound I; 93A, Beaver; 93B, Boarhound II
Manufacturers:	The Bristol Aeroplane Co. Ltd., Filton, Bristol
Power Plants:	One 425 hp Bristol Jupiter IV
	One 450 hp Bristol Jupiter VI
Span:	44 ft 9 in
Length:	31 ft 6 in
Height:	11 ft 8 in
Wing Area:	464 sq ft
Empty Weight:	(93) 2,900 lb (93A) 2,906 lb (93B) 3,000 lb
All-up Weight:	(93) 4,460 lb (93A) 4,480 lb (93B) 4,500 lb
Max. Speed:	(93) 135 mph (93A) 142 mph (93B) 140 mph
Service Ceiling:	22,000 ft
Endurance:	3 hours
Accommodation:	2
Production:	(93) 1 (93A) 1 (93B) 2
Sequence Nos.:	6805 7123 7232 7233

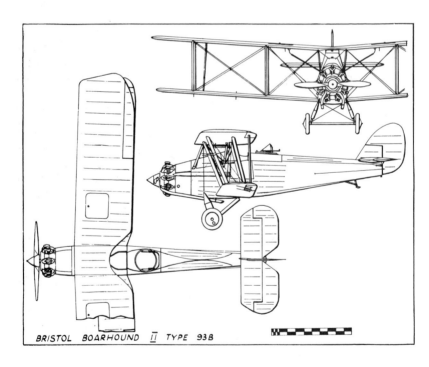

BRISTOL BOARHOUND II TYPE 93B

Bagshot at Filton in July 1927.

The Bristol Bagshot, Type 95

At the end of December 1924, the Company was invited to tender for a large twin-engined two-seater fighter, closely defined by Specification 4/24; a minimum top speed of 125 m.p.h. and maximum landing speed of 50 m.p.h. were required, but details of armament were not disclosed. Barnwell submitted a monoplane having an all-metal semi-cantilever wing which was almost a double-sized version of the Brownie's, with the same planform, profile, thickness and aileron shape. The proposal was accepted and one prototype was ordered in March 1925 at a price of £14,750. The Company suggested the name Bludgeon, but this did not accord with official naming policy and in July the name was changed to Bagshot.

Barnwell's design featured a fuselage of triangular section built up of three longerons with tubular struts, all in steel. The wing had a two-spar steel primary structure with duralumin nose-ribs and edge members and, like the fuselage, was fabric covered. The wide-track landing gear carried aerofoil-section axle fairings which contributed to the overall lift. In September 1925 the Air Ministry amended the specification to call for supercharged engines, increased fuel tankage and a higher top speed at altitude. Fedden attended a conference in London in October to discuss the new demands and was told that the purpose of the aircraft was to carry two 37 mm. shell-firing Coventry Ordnance Works guns, usually called 'Cow-guns', as a night fighter against heavy bombers. On receiving the full list of equipment, Barnwell realised that the machine would be overweight and unable to land more slowly than 57 m.p.h. He suggested making an experimental rolled-strip fuselage, interchangeable with the existing one, which could be tested and if satisfactory would save weight; otherwise he recommended abandoning the project, as it was a waste of time to go on with it. However, at a meeting on 2 February 1926, the Air Ministry declined to cancel the contract and the Bagshot, No. 7018 (*J7767*), was duly completed with Jupiter VI engines, and provisionally accepted by the Air Ministry on 12 May 1927.

Its first flight, by Uwins on 15 July, was uneventful, but later flights were almost disastrous, for at higher speeds the lateral control was ineffective due to wing torsional flexibility causing aileron reversal. Uwins was fortunate in being able to land safely, and the machine was brought back into the factory

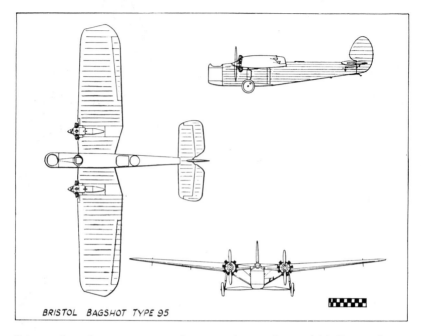

BRISTOL BAGSHOT TYPE 95

for an exhaustive programme of structural tests, from which Barnwell concluded that the only hope was to redesign the Bagshot as a biplane, which virtually meant starting again from scratch.

No further attempt was made to fly the Bagshot until the test results had been examined by the Air Ministry, who, late in 1928, decided to retain it for more extensive research into the torsional stiffness of cantilever wings. This programme continued until 1931, when the Bagshot was scrapped. Concurrently a contract had been awarded for the construction and testing of a new multi-spar wing designed by Pollard, and by January 1929 the results were sufficiently encouraging for this design to be tendered for a three-engined troop-carrier (Type 115), which, although not built, was a step in the direction of the Bombay.

SPECIFICATION AND DATA

Type:	95, Bagshot
Manufacturers:	The Bristol Aeroplane Co. Ltd., Filton, Bristol
Power Plant:	Two 450 hp Bristol Jupiter VI
Span:	70 ft
Length:	44 ft 11 in
Height:	9 ft 6 in
Wing Area:	840 sq ft
Empty Weight:	5,100 lb
All-up Weight:	8,195 lb
Max. Speed:	125 mph

Accommodation:	3
Production:	1
Sequence No.:	7018

Badminton in its original form at Filton in April 1926.

The Bristol Badminton, Type 99

In his struggle to establish the Bristol Jupiter as a more worthy successor to the Napier Lion than the Armstrong Siddeley Jaguar, Roy Fedden had always placed a high value on the prestige gained by record-breaking and racing, and deplored the Directors' decision to discontinue such activities after Leslie Foot's death in 1923. In the following year, the Americans attained very high speeds with watercooled engines of low frontal area, and the Fairey company imported several examples of the Curtiss D-12 engine and were designing the single-seater Firefly and two-seater Fox to suit it. The Air Ministry was interested in high speed aircraft, from which fighters could be derived, to the extent of ordering contenders for the Schneider Trophy seaplane race in 1925, and Fedden feared that the aircooled radial engine's large diameter might lead to its being permanently outclassed for future fighter projects in spite of its many advantages, such as low installed weight and immunity from freezing or boiling.

He pressed Barnwell to design a Jupiter-engined racer and he produced sketches in March 1924, but the project was rejected by the Directors. Fedden returned to the attack in November 1924 with a small-diameter engine proposal, comparable with the Jaguar, and asked for a racing single-seater to suit it to be designed and built for the 1925 and 1926 seasons, at an estimated cost of £10,000. Again the Directors rejected the project, but agreed to the Bloodhound being cleaned-up for competition work in 1925. Fedden then cited the success achieved in France with Gnome-Rhône Jupiters installed with separate helmet fairings for each cylinder, and these were tried out on a Parnall Plover; the Air Ministry became interested and eventually agreed to support a joint effort by Short Brothers and Colonel W. A. Bristow to design and build a Schneider Trophy racing seaplane, the *Crusader*, powered by a much up-rated short-life version of Fedden's new radial, later named Mercury.

203

At last, in September 1925, Barnwell was allowed to design and build a fast biplane, with a landing speed not greater than 60 m.p.h., and an estimated top speed of 170 m.p.h. with a Jupiter VI or 180 m.p.h. with a 510 h.p. supercharged Orion engine which eventually developed into the Jupiter VII; the design, Type 99, was approved on 13 October 1925 and, following Fedden's assurance that a 510 h.p. engine would be available, contruction of one aeroplane, No. 6921, was authorised, named Badminton; it was registered *G-EBMK* on 16 November 1925.

In order to keep cost to a minimum, while ensuring a high strength–weight ratio, the Badminton was built mainly of spruce, with steel tube in highly stressed locations, and the structure was conventional, with tie-rod bracing. Close attention was paid to attaining the best possible streamline shape and comprehensive drag measurements were made on wind-tunnel models. The wings were nearly equal in span and chord and of thin section, with spruce spars formed by two channel sections placed back-to-back, with all attachments located on the neutral axis by means of plates between the channels; ailerons were fitted on the lower wings only. The upper wings were attached to a streamlined pylon structure above the fuselage centre-line, but the lower wings were separated by a centre-section of 4 ft. 6 in. span, equal to the track of the oleo undercarriage. With a wing loading of just over 11 lb. per sq. ft. the Badminton was well adapted for cross-country racing and was entered for the King's Cup Race, to be flown by Captain Frank Barnard of Imperial Airways, who had won the previous year's race on a Jaguar-engined Armstrong Whitworth Siskin.

The Badminton made its first flight on 5 May, piloted by Uwins, with an up-rated 510 h.p. Jupiter VI installed; Barnard was the favourite when the race began on 9 July, and there was great disappointment when he retired after three laps with a faulty fuel feed, which forced him to land at Oxford, nearly in the Thames but fortunately without damage. Although cylinder helmets were normally fitted, they had been removed in the interests of reliability.

Barnard was enthusiastic about the Badminton and agreed to fly it in the 1927 race provided the fuel system had been redesigned and the pilot's view improved. Both these objects were achieved by deleting the upper wing pylon with its associated gravity tank and introducing a 2 ft. 6 in. span upper centre section, supported from the upper longerons by four struts in the orthodox manner; at the same time a new fuel tank and small windscreen were introduced, giving the pilot a clear view forward. This modification increased the span of the top wing to 26 ft. 7 in., the outer wing struts being splayed outwards, and the total wing area was increased by 5%. The Badminton was flown in this form from October 1926 onwards for Orion (Jupiter VII) engine development, both with and without cylinder helmets, the test results being applied to the helmets for the Mercury I in the *Crusader*.

For the 1927 King's Cup Race a formula was used for calculating handicaps, as in previous years. When the entries went in to the Royal Aero Club in April it was known that some handicap advantage would accrue from an increase in span and Barnwell had therefore designed a new top centre section of the same span as the bottom, so increasing the overall span to 28 ft. 6 in. Further examination of the handicap formula in June showed that the Badminton had no chance of winning without a further increase in both span and area, so Barnwell drew and stressed a new set of wings, tapered from root to tip and giving a span of 33 ft. for both upper and lower wings. The original outer struts were replaced by single steel I-struts of wide chord; as before ailerons were fitted only to the lower wing.

The Badminton in this form was redesignated Type 99A and handled quite satisfactorily. A 525 h.p. Jupiter VI engine of reduced diameter was installed for the race and a new Certificate of Airworthiness was issued on 26 July. Two days later, Capt. Barnard took the machine over the speed course to make a final choice between alternative airscrews. Just after take-off the engine suddenly seized at a height of about 200 ft. Barnard was too far outside Filton airfield to risk turning back and could only put the machine into a glide towards a field at Winterbourne; he nearly reached it, but had to turn into wind and stalled; the Badminton dived in from a height of 80 ft. and Barnard was killed outright. On examination of the wrecked engine, it was found that the seizure had been due to insufficient clearance between the cylinder skirts and the crankshaft balance-weights when the latter were sub-

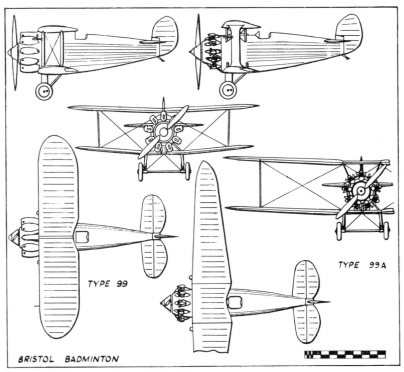

TYPE 99A

TYPE 99

BRISTOL BADMINTON

jected to high centrifugal loading in this specially tuned racing engine. Frank Barnard's death, like Leslie Foot's, was a sad loss to British aviation, for he was one of the country's most experienced transport and test pilots. No doubt the stall would not have been so sudden with less sharply tapered wings, but at that time there was relatively little experience of tip-stalling.

SPECIFICATION AND DATA

Type:	99, Badminton
Manufacturers:	The Bristol Aeroplane Co. Ltd., Filton, Bristol
Power Plant:	(a) One 510 hp Bristol Jupiter VI
	(b) One 440 hp Bristol Jupiter VII
	(c) One 525 hp Bristol Jupiter VI (short-stroke)
Span:	(a) 24 ft 1 in (b) 26 ft 7 in (c) 33 ft
Length:	(a) 21 ft 2 in (b) and (c) 21 ft 5 in
Height:	(a) 9 ft 2 in (b) and (c) 9 ft 6 in
Wing Area:	(a) 210 sq ft (b) 221 sq ft (c) 299 sq ft
Empty Weight:	(a) 1,770 lb (b) and (c) 1,800 lb
All-up Weight:	(a) 2,470 lb (b) and (c) 2,500 lb
Max. Speed:	160 mph
Accommodation:	Pilot only
Production:	1
Sequence No.:	6921

The Badminton with wide-span tapered wings at Filton in July 1927

Type 101 as shown at Copenhagen in August 1927, with full armament.

The Bristol Type 101

During 1924, American success in the Schneider Trophy contest threw into focus the contrast between the performance that could be attained with a really clean aeroplane and that actually achieved by the same machine when forced to carry all the bulky and often obsolete equipment called for in Air Ministry specifications. Mr. C. R. Fairey brought matters to a head by importing the Curtiss D.12 engine and installing it in a very beautifully designed light two-seater bomber called the Fairey Fox, which startled the pundits with its top speed of nearly 160 m.p.h. when it first flew in March 1925.

Both Barnwell and Fedden agreed with Fairey's view that in actual warfare, performance was all-important and that much of the equipment would be jettisoned by squadrons in their efforts to squeeze out the ultimate advantage in speed. By November 1925 Fedden was convinced that the Air Council had taken the point and in only a short time would swing over to high-speed lightly equipped machines; he feared that when this happened all the orders would go to those with watercooled engines of low frontal area, unless the radial engine's capabilities were demonstrated anew. He was developing a long-life military version of the Mercury engine, and Barnwell considered that a biplane with this engine could be designed to carry the same load as the Fox at 160 m.p.h. The Directors agreed to a design being detailed as a private venture in the hope that the Air Ministry might order a prototype; the designer would be free from official interference and there was quite a possibility that as a two-seater fighter the machine might find a market abroad. In January 1926 Barnwell submitted the general arrangement of the new project, Type 101, equipped as a fighter with two front guns, a twin-gun Scarff ring for the rear gunner, 1,200 rounds of ammunition, 70 gallons of fuel, parachutes and oxygen, but no wireless, camera or bomb gear. It had steel wings and tail unit, combined with a plywood monocoque fuselage of great strength, and was expected to reach 160 m.p.h. with a 480 h.p. Mercury. The design was submitted to the Air Ministry in March 1926, but turned down categorically because of its use of wood, so work on it was stopped soon after the prototype, No. 7019, had been registered *G-EBOW* on 17 July 1926. However, in October, interest on the 101 was revived by an enquiry for a high-speed survey aircraft to carry a Williamson Eagle camera, and it was decided to complete one prototype as a private venture, both to demonstrate the Jupiter and Mercury engines and to share their development flying with the Badminton and Bloodhound.

Early in 1927 an International Aero Show to be held at Copenhagen in August was announced and this offered a favourable opportunity to exhibit the 101, in view of the widespread use of plywood construction in Scandinavia and Baltic countries; steel strip construction had been welcomed by Sweden, where the world's best iron ore was an established export, so the 101 was expected to attract attention as a suitable all-purpose fighter for countries with limited budgets. The prototype, with a Jupiter VI, was completed at Filton on 27 July 1927, over a year after its registration. The first flight was made by Uwins on 8 August, and the 101 was then prepared for exhibition and dispatched to Copenhagen on 27 August. There it was examined with interest by King Christian of Denmark and many other visitors, but no sales resulted; some months later an enquiry came from Chile, but once again the credit terms requested were unacceptable. However, *G-EBOW* was kept fully occupied at Filton, having replaced the Badminton as a test-bed aircraft. It was flown with the Scarff ring and guns removed during the winter, and

Type 101 as flown in the King's Cup Race 1928, with armament removed and ailerons on upper wing.

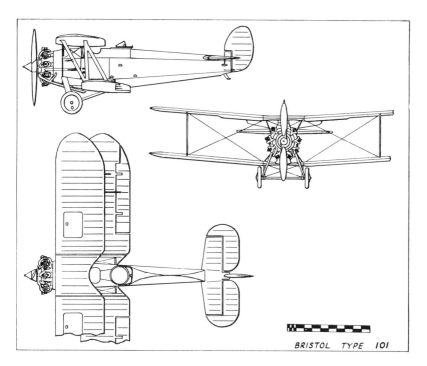

BRISTOL TYPE 101

in April it was decided to incorporate certain drag-reducing modifications and if satisfactory to enter it in the 1928 King's Cup Race. The rear cockpit was faired in, leaving only a small opening, the undercarriage and wing strut fairings were increased in chord and the ailerons were repositioned on the upper wings instead of the lower. A Jupiter VIA engine was installed for the King's Cup Race on 21 July, when Uwins, with Arthur Suddes as passenger, flew round the two-days' circuit of Britain into second place, only $3\frac{3}{4}$ min. behind the winner, at an average speed of 159·9 m.p.h. He would certainly have won had his compass not failed early on the first day, compelling him to rely on landmarks.

After the race, *G-EBOW* was further modified, with new ailerons and a new engine mounting, and became a Company hack, test-bed and demonstrator for the Mercury engine for over a year. While diving steeply in an overspeed test with this engine on 29 November 1929, a fitting in the centre-section failed and the 101 broke up in the air, the pilot, C. R. L. Shaw, escaping by parachute to become the fourth British civilian member of the Caterpillar Club. Ironically the failure occurred in a steel fitting and not in the plywood structure which the Air Ministry had refused to entertain, in spite of its being derived from birch veneer of which plentiful supplies were available. Apart from the specialised High Altitude Monoplane of 1934, the 101 was the last wooden aircraft constructed at Filton.

209

SPECIFICATION AND DATA

Type: 101
Manufacturers: The Bristol Aeroplane Co. Ltd., Filton, Bristol
Power Plant: One 450 hp Bristol Jupiter VI or VIA
One 485 hp Bristol Mercury II
Span: 33 ft 7 in
Length: 27 ft 4 in
Height: 9 ft 6 in
Wing Area: 360 sq ft
Empty Weight: 2,100 lb
All-up Weight: 3,540 lb
Max. Speed: (Fully equipped) 160 mph
(Racing) 170 mph
Service Ceiling: 21,000 ft
Accommodation: 2
Production: 1
Sequence No.: 7019

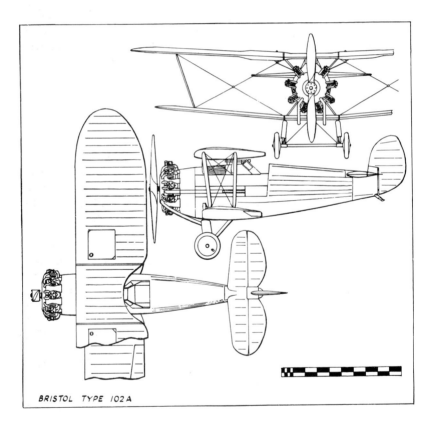

BRISTOL TYPE 102A

Bulldog I prototype with small rudder, at Filton in May 1927.

The Bristol Bulldog and Bullpup,
Types 105 and 107

In 1925 the Fairey Fox revolutionised British thinking on the design of two-seater day bombers, with two results: first, by outpacing contemporary single-seater fighters, it increased the performance required of their successors, and secondly, the renewed threat of the liquid-cooled in-line engine stimulated Fedden and Siddeley to promote radial-engined fighters and bombers, to prevent Napier and Rolls-Royce from regaining the initiative. The ensuing rivalry during a period of extreme government economy led to a succession of fighter specifications, but no promise of production orders until obsolescence of the Siskin forced the Air Staff to decide about its replacement. Lulled into a false sense of security by the low cruising speed of the French bomber fleet, mainly Farman Goliaths, the only potential enemy, the Air Staff concentrated on versatility and serviceability at the expense of performance; not till 1924 did they consider using fast-climbing interceptors instead of standing patrols of radio-equipped fighters. Specification F.17/24 for an interceptor fighter, issued in May, called for the Rolls-Royce Falcon X engine (later developed into the Kestrel) and Barnwell wanted to submit a design, but Fedden naturally objected to using a rival in-line engine. Then the Air Ministry suggested that a light fighter with a supercharged 250 h.p. engine would be adequate, but this view was confuted by Barnwell and Fedden, who stated the case for a 400 h.p. engine convincingly in November

211

1924, but then laid aside the single-seater project to work on the Boarhound and Bagshot.

The Bagshot was an unrealistic fighter concept and the Company would gladly have stopped work on it in April 1926, when Barnwell resumed the single-seater study with a fighter based on the Badminton, which would have met either Specification F.9/26 for a day-and-night fighter or N.21/26 for a Naval fighter, and landplane (Type 102A) and floatplane (Type 102B) versions were proposed. Interest in interceptors revived, and in January 1927 Barnwell submitted general arrangements for a biplane with either a Rolls-Royce F.XI or a Bristol Mercury engine. He had already drawn a revised F.9/26 design with a Mercury engine, designated Type 105, and both seemed so promising that mock-ups were made for Air Ministry inspection in February 1927. In the first layout, dated 13 August 1926, the F.9/26 had wings of equal span, but in November the lower wing was reduced in span as well as chord. The interceptor based on F.17/24 was similar in layout and the Company was invited to revise it to meet the new F.20/27 interceptor specification, with the geared Mercury III engine which Fedden was developing. This new interceptor, Type 107, was accepted and one prototype, No. 7178 (*J9051*), was ordered for competition with four other prototypes, the Gloster and Hawker biplanes and the Vickers and Westland monoplanes. Barnwell also started a monoplane interceptor, Type 103, but this was not completed.

Fedden made it clear that the supply of Mercuries would be very limited at first, but the 105 seemed so promising that the Directors decided to build a private venture prototype, No. 7155, with a Jupiter VII, and in March 1927 offered to build 50 of this type if the Air Ministry would contribute towards the cost of development. This offer was declined, but the Air Ministry agreed to test the prototype at Martlesham Heath. Meanwhile wind-tunnel tests established the advantage of the unequal span arrangement, and in March a third layout of the 105 was drawn conforming more closely to the 107 and differing mainly in size. Both prototypes were detailed and built concurrently and the Company's suggestion to name them Bulldog and Bullpup was readily approved. The Bulldog was completed quickly because its Jupiter engine installation posed no problems and, being a private venture, was not delayed for want of official decisions. The Bullpup was still waiting for its Mercury when the Bulldog took-off on its first flight on 17 May 1927, piloted by Uwins, performing so well in its early handling flights that it went to Martlesham a month later and made its first public appearance in the R.A.F. display at Hendon in July.

Both the Bulldog and Bullpup were of the high-tensile steel strip construction developed by Pollard for the Boarhound, using flat gusset plates instead of bolted joints wherever possible. The upper wings were of the special Bristol 1A section developed by Barnwell and Frise in collaboration with the R.A.E., while the lower wings, of much smaller span and chord, were of Clark YH. Frise ailerons were fitted to the upper wings only and the rudder and elevators had shielded horn-balances. All the fuel was contained in a pair of gravity tanks recessed into the upper wings, a system introduced on the Boarhound and further improved on Type 101. The oil tank, behind the fireproof bulkhead, incorporated a surface oil cooler developed on the Badminton, and the long-stroke undercarriage had oleo-damped rubber-in-compression legs attached to the top longerons. The two Vickers guns were mounted low on each side of the pilot's cockpit and the Bulldog carried a short-wave wireless transmitter-receiver in a compartment just aft of the cockpit, but the Bullpup had no wireless.

Although an interloper in the F.9/26 competition at Martlesham, where it was matched against the Armstrong Whitworth Starling, Boulton-Paul Partridge, Gloster Goldfinch and Hawker Hawfinch, the Bulldog soon gained the lead, with only the Hawfinch as a serious rival. Its manœuvrability and well-harmonised controls were particularly praised by the R.A.F. test pilots, and it could be dived under full control to its terminal velocity of 270 m.p.h. without structural damage. The ease with which local damage to the steel structure could be repaired *in situ* was also appreciated. Its spin recovery was not as good as that of the Hawfinch and a larger fin and rudder were therefore tried; with these spin recovery was excellent, but an increased tendency to weathercock made cross-wind taxying and ground handling more difficult. The only other modifications recommended were some stiffening of the undercarriage and a better seat-adjusting mechanism. After discussion of the spin problem, it was decided to retain the small rudder and lengthen the fuselage, and in November 1927 one Bulldog Mark II, Type 105A, No. 7235 (*J9480*), was ordered by the Air Ministry for extended competition with the Hawfinch.

Bulldog I prototype with high-altitude wings and large rudder, November 1927.

On its return from Martlesham at the end of October the prototype Bulldog, still with the large rudder, was fitted with high aspect-ratio wooden wings of 50 ft. span and 6 ft. gap, with ailerons on the lower wings only, together with cockpit heating from an exhaust-pipe muff, for officially sponsored attempts on the altitude and climb-to-height records. The high altitude Bulldog was first flown by Uwins on 7 November 1927 before going to Farnborough, where Flight-Lt. J. A. Gray was to pilot it in the test programme. The Jupiter VII supercharged engine drove a special climb airscrew and it was hoped that an absolute ceiling of nearly 40,000 ft. would be reached, but in December Donati raised the record to 38,800 ft. for Italy, and the

Bulldog's attempt was postponed until this height could be exceeded by a bigger margin; also stress check showed that aileron stiffness was marginal and four ailerons of reduced span had to be substituted, which delayed the start of the programme. Fuel was carried in a single 71 gallon tank in the top centre-section with a windmill pump to augment gravity flow in extreme nose-up attitudes.

Since the Bulldog I was a private venture there was no restriction on its sale to friendly foreign countries, and in December 1927 the Company offered an export version with wings of Bullpup shape giving a better climb performance, one prototype of which, No. 7267, was built but never flown; it was exhibited at the Paris Salon in June 1928 and again at Olympia in July 1929, with fabric covering and cowling on the port side of the centre-line only, the starboard side being stripped to expose the structure and equipment. At Paris its excellent finish was admired by President Poincaré, and the French Press described it as the 'Cameo of the Show'.

The Bulldog II made its first flight, piloted by Uwins, at Filton on 21 January 1928 and soon afterwards flew to Martlesham Heath, where it was so nearly matched by the Hawfinch that the A. & A.E.E. reserved judgment until both prototypes had been flown by squadron pilots at Kenley, Biggin Hill, Northolt, Upavon and North Weald. The choice had still not been made by 11 June, although the Bulldog was agreed to be slightly faster, and the decision was then taken on ease of maintenance; here the Bulldog scored because it was a single-bay machine, whereas the Hawfinch was two-bay, and the Bulldog's wing tanks could be changed twice as quickly as the fuselage tank of the Hawfinch, an important factor in actual warfare.

The Bulldog II was thus the winner of the F.9/26 competition and was purchased on 21 August 1928 for £4,500; a contract for 25 production aircraft (to Specification F.17/28) followed and a batch of 26 was laid down, comprising Nos. 7322 to 7330 and 7332 to 7347 (*J9567* to *J9591*), for the Air Ministry and No. 7331 reserved as the Company's demonstrator. Deliveries commenced on 8 May 1929 and were completed by 10 October. No. 7331 was fitted with a Jupiter VIA instead of Jupiter VII and registered *G-AAHH* on 15 May, being actually completed on 13 June, finished in silver with green decking and a green stripe along the fuselage side similar to the squadron marking of No. 3 Squadron, to which the first 18 Bulldogs were allotted, the next nine going to No. 17 Squadron; both these units had hitherto flown Woodcocks and specialised in night-fighting. One airframe of the first production batch, No. 7341, was diverted to the Company's agents in Japan, Mitsui and Co., and was replaced on the R.A.F. contract by a new machine, No. 7397, which was completed as *J9591* on 16 October 1929, but retained at Filton as a test-bed for the geared Mercury IV engine.

Bulldogs were an immediate success in squadron service and soon attracted attention overseas, and five (Nos. 7353 to 7357) with Gnome-Rhône Jupiter VI and Oerlikon guns were shipped to Latvia via Hull at the end of September 1929. On 25 October another Bulldog II, No. 7358, with Jupiter VIIF

Bulldog II *J9591* as Mercury test-bed with helmets, September 1930.

engine was shipped to the United States for evaluation at Anacostia Navy Base as a dive-bomber, but during a terminal velocity dive an aileron failed and the Bulldog was wrecked, the pilot, Lt. Cuddihy, being killed. After static tests on a similar wing at Filton, a modification was introduced and a replacement Bulldog II, No. 7398, was dispatched to the U.S.N. on 24 February 1930; this was flown at Anacostia as *A-8607* and was one of a batch

U.S. Navy's second Bulldog *A-8607* at Anacostia D.C. in June 1930. (*Photo via Hal G. Martin.*)

of 40 laid down at Filton, of which 23, Nos. 7364 to 7386 (*K1079* to *K1101*), were delivered to the Air Ministry between March and June 1930, nine to No. 17 Squadron and the remainder to No. 54 Squadron. The next two, Nos. 7387 and 7388, were supplied in January 1930 to the Royal Siamese Air Force, and when Sir Geoffrey Salmond, A.O.C. India, flew from Delhi to Bangkok on a courtesy visit to the King of Siam in November 1930 he was met and escorted to Don Muang airfield by them.

The next eight, Nos. 7389 to 7396 (*A12-1* to *A12-8*), were supplied to the Royal Australian Air Force at the end of January 1930 with Jupiter VIF engines, but were otherwise standard. No. 7399 was completed on 18 January 1930 as a test-bed for the Mercury III and flew with the identification mark *R-1* to continue the test programme frustrated by the loss of the Bristol 101 in November; it had a four-bladed airscrew. On completion of the 50 hours'

Bulldog *R-1* with Mercury III at Filton, May 1930.

Bulldog *R-1* re-engined with Gnome-Rhône Jupiter VI and registered *G-ABAC*; Filton, June 1930.

test schedule, the Mercury was replaced by a Gnome-Rhône Jupiter VI, and on 30 May it was registered *G-ABAC* before going on a European demonstration tour; but on 4 June, while practising flick rolls, T. W. Campbell damaged its rudder bar and baled out rather than risk a landing. Meanwhile, the other Mercury-engined Bulldog, *J9591*, had been loaned to the Company for tests with various engine cowlings, including cylinder helmets, and was registered *G-AATR* on 13 January; it reverted to Air Ministry ownership with its original serial in January 1931 for tests on a Mercury IVA, and a standard Jupiter VIIF engine was substituted when it went into R.A.F. squadron service in September 1931. Three of the last four Bulldogs in stock were sold to the Swedish government in August 1930 after a demonstration by *G-AAHH*; these were Nos. 7400 to 7402 and received Swedish air force serials *1201* to *1203*, for evaluation in competition with the home-produced Jaktfalk fighter, proving superior in all-round performance. The final Bulldog of this batch, No. 7403, was taken as a replacement for *G-ABAC*, for demonstration in Switzerland and Rumania, but these were cancelled because of financial difficulties in Rumania. In September 1930 No. 7403 was taken to Chile by Campbell to compete against the Curtiss Hawk and did so well that the Company was invited to supply 40 Bulldogs, but again the

Chilean government required such extended credit that the Company let the contract go to Curtiss. No. 7403 was shipped back from Santiago after Campbell's return to Filton, but its ultimate fate is uncertain.

Deliveries from a third production batch of 20 Bulldogs commenced with seven more for Latvia, Nos. 7439 to 7445, in July 1930; the first five had Gnome-Rhône Jupiter VI engines and the last two Gnome-Rhône 9ASB supercharged engines, equivalent to the Jupiter VII. Next came No. 7446, built as a second replacement demonstrator and registered *G-ABBB* on 12

Bulldog IIA *G-ABBB* (*R-11*) with Aquila I installed at Filton in September 1935.

June 1930. Intended for European displays, it had a Gnome-Rhône 9ASB engine and, finished in silver with royal blue decking, was exhibited at the Paris Salon on 28 November. Thereafter it was flown regularly until September 1935, when it was modified to take the third Aquila I sleeve-valve engine for 100 hours' endurance flight testing under 'B' conditions, with the identity mark *R-11*. On completion of the Aquila test schedule in 1936, it was stored at Filton until 1939, but saved from the scrap-merchant by the intervention of Herbert Thomas and presented to the Science Museum, London.

G-ABBB rebuilt for the Shuttleworth Trust, about to take off from Filton in July 1961: compare with page 44.

217

On the outbreak of war it was stored until 1957, when, after it had been loaned for the filming of *Reach For The Sky*, it was returned to Filton for reconditioning. By that time it was exceedingly difficult to find a Jupiter engine capable of being made airworthy, but several months of resolute search eventually produced four engines, from which one complete Jupiter VIIFP (no. J7508) was built and tested in May 1961. With this engine, *G-ABBB* was flown again by the Company's Chief Test Pilot, Godfrey Auty, on 22 June 1961, and in July was repainted in No. 56 Squadron's red-and-white chequerboard insignia, with the serial *K2227*, and presented to the Shuttleworth Trust. The remaining 12 Bulldogs of the third production batch (Nos. 7447

Estonian Bulldogs in 1931.

to 7458) were sold to Estonia in August 1930, all with Gnome-Rhône Jupiter VI engines.

The R.A.F. and foreign buyers alike were delighted with their Bulldogs as much for their durability and ease of maintenance as for their lively handling qualities; in particular, freedom from corrosion of the stove-enamelled steel structure, quickly detachable fuel tanks and grouped lubrication points made light work of daily servicing. Improvements, first incorporated in *G-ABBB*, included local strengthening to permit an increased all-up weight of 3,530 lb., revised wing spars and ailerons and many details; with these modifications and a Jupiter VIIF engine, the R.A.F. version was redesignated Bulldog IIA, and a contract for 92 machines was awarded in May 1930, to Specification F.11/29. The Company laid down a hundred Bulldog airframes, assembled in batches of 20 on two parallel production lines, one for 36 complete aircraft and the other for 64 airframes, although all had engines fitted for half an hour's production test flight. The two lines were headed by No. 7459 (*K1603*) and No. 7495 (*K1639*) and deliveries began early in October 1930, *K1603* going to Martlesham as the D.T.D. trial installation aeroplane and most of the others to Nos. 54 and 111 Squadrons at Hornchurch and No. 32 Squadron at Kenley. Deliveries of the whole 92, Nos. 7459 to 7550 (*K1603* to *K1694*), were completed in May 1931, by which time the remainder of the hundred had been purchased as a repeat order by the Royal Swedish Air Force. These

Swedish Air Force Bulldogs on skis at Malmslätt in 1932. (*Photo Flygvapnets.*)

218

eight with Jupiter VIIF engines, Nos. 7582 to 7589 (*5211* to *5218*), were ferried to Malmslätt in two flights of four by Swedish service pilots on 13 and 16 May, respectively. The first three Swedish Bulldogs gave a good account of themselves, although *1202* crashed on 29 January 1931 during trials with ski-landing gear; the other two had longer lives, *1201* being crashed on 30 April 1935 while *1203* survived to be written off as obsolete in May 1937; of the second batch, *5214*, *5215* and *5216* were still serviceable in December 1939, when they were presented to Finland, to be flown for a further year as advanced trainers.

While the hundred Bulldog IIA airframes were in progress the Royal Danish Flying Corps ordered four Bulldogs to their special requirements; designated Type 105D, the Danish Bulldogs, Nos. 7564 to 7567, differed from the Mark IIA in having unsupercharged high compression Jupiter VIF.H. engines with Viet gas starters, and the guns were 0·300 calibre Madsens installed lower in the fuselage side than the Vickers. They were shipped from Filton with engines installed on 25 March 1931, the third and fourth being delivered without fabric covering. They equipped No. 1 Squadron at Kastrup and later at Vaerløse, and were first serialled *J-151* to *J-154*,

Bulldogs (Type 105D) of No. 1 Sqn Danish Royal Army Air Corps in formation over Copenhagen in 1931. ('*Aeroplane*' copyright.)

changed in 1932 to *J-301* to *J-304* and again in 1933 to *J-1* to *J-4*. *J-304* was lent to the Danish Naval Air Service for evaluation in 1932, and negotiations began for the type to be built under licence by the Naval Dockyard. *J-2* was damaged beyond repair at Vaerløse in November 1936, but the other three were still in use as trainers till the German occupation in April 1940 and were not finally scrapped until 1942.

A further order for 100 Bulldogs Mark IIA, Nos. 7590 to 7689 (*K2135* to *K2234*), was placed by the Air Ministry in time to continue the production line, but only 27 of them, *K2155* to *K2169* for No. 19 Squadron, Duxford, and *K2176* to *K2187* for No. 41 Squadron, Northolt, were delivered complete, the other 73 being dispatched, after half an hour's test flight, without engines, except for *K2188*, which was retained at Filton for conversion into a two-seater dual control prototype; deliveries continued from 21 July 1931 till 13 April 1932, when a further 20 airframes, Nos. 7691 to 7710 (*K2476* to *K2495*), occupied the production lines until July, followed by a further 14,

Nos. 7713 to 7726 (*K2859* to *K2872*), until the end of the year. At this period, the Bulldog IIA equipped ten of the 13 fighter squadrons forming the Air Defence of Great Britain.

By December 1932 the two-seater Bulldog T.M., *K2188*, had been evaluated by the Central Flying School and a production version, Type 124,

Bulldog TM prototype *K2188* (Jupiter VIF) at Filton in December 1932.

was ordered to Specification T.12/32. This differed only slightly from the prototype, having increased rudder area and slightly swept-back wings to improve spin recovery. Seventeen two-seaters were ordered in the first batch, Nos. 7727 to 7743 (*K3170* to *K3186*), the first 12 with Jupiter VIF and the last five without engines; they were dispatched between 21 December 1932 and 10 March 1933, three each to the C.F.S. at Wittering and Coastal Area at

Bulldogs IIA of No. 32 Sqn R.A.F. in formation over Northolt in June 1934. (*Charles E. Brown photo.*)

220

Leuchars, one each to Nos. 17, 19, 32, 41, 56 and 111 Squadrons and the five airframes to store at Kenley. Production continued with two batches of Bulldog IIA fighters totalling 28 airframes, Nos. 7746 to 7773 (*K2946* to *K2963* and *K3504* to *K3513*), until 14 November 1933. The last but one, *K3512*, was modified in August 1933 before completion by fitting a wider track undercarriage with Dunlop disc wheels and Bendix brakes. At Martlesham the tail skid was found to be incapable of standing up to fast taxying while the brakes were used for ground steering, so the tail skid was replaced by a castoring tail-wheel and the fin area increased to improve directional stability; this modification permitted a gross weight of 3,660 lb. and was retrospectively applied to all R.A.F. Bulldogs during 1933. The final Air Ministry production order for Bulldogs covered 42 two-seaters, Nos. 7777 to 7807 (*K3923* to *K3953*), of which the first 18 with Jupiter VIF were delivered in November and December 1933 to the R.A.F. College Cranwell and Nos. 3 and 5 F.T.S., while 13 airframes went into store in January 1934, followed by Nos. 7827 to 7837 (*K4566* to *K4576*) between July and December 1934.

Bullpup with Jupiter VI, small rudder and temporary wood interplane struts before first flight at Filton in April 1928.

Unlike the Bulldog, the Bullpup *J9051* failed to gain a production contract, although it performed reasonably well in the F.20/27 interceptor competition at Martlesham in 1929, fitted with a Mercury IIA engine. This was not available for the first flight on 28 April 1928, for which the Jupiter VI originally fitted to the Bristol 101 was used. It did not go to Martlesham until March 1929 because of engine modifications, which in fact bedevilled the other F.20/27 contenders and led to Hawkers submitting a Rolls-Royce Kestrel-engined variant of their biplane which was eventually adopted by the R.A.F. After the Bullpup returned from Martlesham, it was tested with a short-chord Townend ring, then temporarily fitted with a Jupiter VIIF engine for the 1930 R.A.F. Display at Hendon, and in 1931 was used as a test-bed for the 47 in. diameter short-stroke Mercury engine installed in a close-fitting long-chord cowl. In 1934 the Bullpup was again modified to test

221

the second sleeve-valve Aquila I engine for 200 hours' endurance flying concurrently with the 100 hours' test of the third Aquila I engine in Bulldog *G-ABBB*; these were the two civil-rated engines afterwards installed in the Bristol 143 monoplane. With the Aquila, a Dowty undercarriage and low-pressure 'doughnut' wheels, the Bullpup created an excellent impression

Bullpup with Mercury IIA and Townend ring, at Filton in May 1929.

Bullpup with short-stroke Mercury and long-chord cowling at Filton in July 1931.

Bullpup with Aquila I as flown at the S.B.A.C. Show in June 1935.

when flown by C. A. Washer at the 1935 S.B.A.C. Show, after which it was scrapped on completion of the Aquila test programme. The Bullpup was hardly modified during its seven years' life apart from the various engine changes and an increase in rudder area immediately after its first flight.

Reference has already been made to Bulldogs *R-1* and *G-AATR* with experimental Mercury engines. In 1931 an improved 560 h.p. Mercury IV was built, which went into production in 1932 as the Mercury IVS.2, and a new version of the Bulldog was designed to match the Mercury's higher power. Structurally there were few changes apart from a forged steel engine mounting ring in place of the flanged plate formerly used; the stern end of the fuselage was slightly deepened to increase stiffness and heavier gauge steel strip was employed in the longerons. Aerodynamically a great advantage was gained by changing the upper wing profile from Bristol 1A to the biconvex R.A.F.34, which allowed the fuel tanks to lie within the normal profile; the lower wing chord was reduced by 7 in. to improve the pilot's view, and the double Rafwires of the lift bracing were replaced by single lift wires of improved profile. Stiffer ailerons were mounted on self-aligning ball-bearings and the elevator balance area was increased, making the flying controls

Bulldog IIIA *R-5* with Mercury IVS.2 at Filton in June 1932.

lighter at all speeds. Drag was further reduced by fairing the navigation lamps into the wing leading edge and deleting windmill-driven generators in favour of internal engine-driven units. The undercarriage was fitted with wheel brakes and 'spats', while the Mercury had a new exhaust collector ring of very low back-pressure and was enclosed in a short-chord Townend ring which added 12 m.p.h. to top speed without spoiling the pilot's view. The combined effect of all these improvements was to raise the Bulldog's top speed at 15,000 ft. from 175 m.p.h. to 208 m.p.h., with similar increases in rate of climb and service ceiling.

One prototype, Bulldog IIIA, was built as a private venture during the summer of 1931. With R.A.F. roundels, but no serial number apart from the identity mark *R-5*, the Bulldog IIIA, No. 7560, was first flown on 17 September 1931 and went to Martlesham on 7 December with a prototype Mercury

IVA engine. It returned to Filton for installation of a production Mercury IVS.2 and went back to Martlesham for extended trials on 5 March 1932. Throughout the summer it was flown by R.A.F. test pilots against the Gloster S.S.19B, to determine which should be the successor to the Bulldog IIA in the day-and-night fighter squadrons. There was little to choose between them, but the Gloster was slightly superior in climb and went into service later as the Gauntlet. One result of this decision was that a conditional manufacturing licence for the Bulldog III acquired by the Danish government in March 1932 was annulled, the essential condition (that the Bulldog III would be adopted by the R.A.F.) not having been satisfied. The Bulldog IIIA *R-5* was finally written off in a crash at Martlesham on 30 March 1933.

A second Bulldog IIIA was built as a private venture for exhibition at the Paris Salon in November 1932. Although registered *G-ABZW* on 3 October 1932 this machine, No. 7745, never carried civil markings, but like *R-5* was finished in R.A.F. colours with the identity mark *R-7*. No definite orders were forthcoming at Paris on terms that the Company could accept, and further modifications were incorporated to bring it up to full R.A.F. standard before its first flight on 13 April 1933; it went to Martlesham on 12 May to continue the handling trials interrupted by the loss of *R-5*, and returned to Filton in

Bulldog IVA *K4292* (formerly *R-7*) with Mercury VIS.2 and Hamilton v-p airscrew at Filton in July 1934.

March 1934 for conversion to a new standard, Bulldog IVA, to conform with Specification F.7/30 for a four-gun day-and-night fighter. A Mercury VIS.2 engine was installed and high-speed handling was further improved by the addition of ailerons on the lower wings and a slight modification to the fin and rudder. With a top speed of 224 m.p.h., it was hardly a match for the 250 m.p.h. Gloster F.7/30 (later the Gladiator), but the Air Ministry agreed to buy it for flight testing of various long-chord cowlings, with and without controllable gills, for the Mercury VIS.2, and it became *K4292* on 26 July 1934. Endurance trials of the Mercury VIS.2 extended to 100 hours and were very severe because of the prevailing hot weather; climbs to 18,000 ft. at full power were made repeatedly, but the engine showed no loss of power and Uwins reported its behaviour as excellent throughout. A second Bulldog IVA, No. 7808, was built to demonstrate the Mercury VIS.2 engine and was

Bulldog IVA *R-8* with Perseus IA as flown at the S.B.A.C. Show in June 1934.

registered *G-ACJN* on 16 August 1933. It was not at first flown with this engine, however, because after first flights with a Mercury IVS.2 it was urgently needed to test the new sleeve-valve Perseus IA engine in October 1933, being flown with the experimental marking *R-8* until crashed by C. T. Holmes on 17 February 1934. In July it reappeared, with cockpit heating from muffs round the long exhaust pipes and repainted to exhibition standard in pearl and black glossy cellulose, being shown thus in the new type enclosure at the 1934 R.A.F. Display at Hendon, which was followed by the S.B.A.C.'s first annual trade show, where Uwins showed what the Perseus-Bulldog could do in the way of vertical dives and climbs. Later in 1934, *R-8* was at last fitted with a Mercury VIS.2 in a short-chord N.A.C.A. cowl for testing the Hamilton three-bladed variable pitch metal airscrew and appeared in this form at the 1935 S.B.A.C. trade show.

The performance of the Bulldog IVA attracted interest abroad, and in December 1933 the Company was invited to supply a batch to Finland. The Gnome-Rhône Company objected to the export of British-built Mercuries since Finland was in their territory as defined by the original Jupiter licence

Bulldog IVA *BU59* of the Finnish Air Force at Filton in October 1934; this, the first of seventeen, survived both Russo-Finnish wars and is preserved at Vesivehmaa.

225

Bulldog IVA *BU66* of the Finnish Air Force on skis in 1937. (*Photo via C. W. Cain.*)

agreement, but the Bristol Directors were not satisfied with the somewhat half-hearted way in which licence manufacture of the Gnome-Rhône *Mercure* was being conducted. For a time there was deadlock, but in April 1934 the Company signed a contract with the Finnish government for the supply of 17 Bulldog IVA aircraft, with Filton-built Mercury VIS.2 engines, the Gnome-Rhône company's protests were ignored and the licence agreement was terminated soon afterwards. The Finnish Bulldogs, the last to be built, were similar to *R-7* in its final state and had a comprehensive electrical system, including a controllable landing lamp in the port lower wing leading edge for winter work in the Arctic, also electrically heated clothing and gun-heating. These Bulldogs, Nos. 7810 to 7826 (*BU59* to *BU75*), were delivered during January and February 1935 and were the only Bulldogs to see active service, being operated on skis as well as wheels and giving a gallant account of themselves in the early stages of the Winter War of 1939 during the unsuccessful defence of Karelia; *BU59* continued flying until 1944 and is now in the Finnish Air Force historical collection at Vesivehmaa. The Finnish government wished to buy a second batch of Bulldogs in 1935 with a low-drag Dowty undercarriage of the Gladiator type, but the Company had to decline the order, as well as one from the Australian government for 45 Bulldogs in 1936.

The last new experimental Bulldog was No. 7744 (*K4189*), a Bulldog IIA constructed in stainless steel to Specification 11/31, under an Air Ministry contract placed in February 1932. It was flown only for two short acceptance tests by C. T. Holmes on 2 and 4 February 1935 and was thereafter grounded as a static test specimen, the stainless steel structure proving inferior in many respects to the normal stove-enamelled high-tensile steel. A monocoque aluminium alloy fuselage for a Bulldog was also tested as part of Pollard's research programme on stressed-skin construction.

Apart from experimental Bulldogs, several were modified after delivery, some for squadron trials with Townend rings, while various ailerons were tested on Bulldogs at the R.A.E. and *K1653* was fitted with slot-and-interceptor controls linked with the ailerons. The ailerons of Bulldogs in squadron service were sensitive to small rigging errors, and in an attempt to improve this feature *K2475* was fitted with Hartshorn ailerons, which gave more progressive response. Squadron pilots commended the Hartshorn design, particularly at high diving speeds, but Uwins, after comparing it with the

Prototype Bulldog TM *K2188* as a test-bed for Cheetah IX at Farnborough in May 1937. (*Crown copyright.*)

Bulldog TM *K3183* test-bed with Rapier I at Farnborough in April 1937. (*Crown copyright.*)

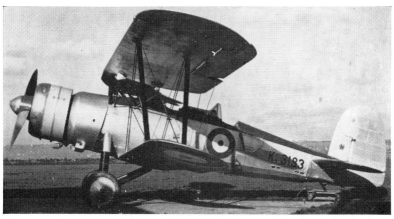

K3183 with Alvis Leonides, flown by G. B. S. Errington at Portsmouth in 1938.

227

standard Frise pattern on *G-ABBB*, considered the improvement to be negligible in equally well-maintained aeroplanes. Bulldog two-seaters were obvious test-beds for engines in the 300–400 h.p. class and two set aside for this purpose were the prototype *K2188*, flown at the R.A.E. with a Cheetah installation for the Avro Anson and Airspeed Queen Wasp, and *K3183*, used for both wind-tunnel and flight development of the Napier Rapier. In 1938 *K3183* was lent to Airspeed Ltd. for flight tests of the prototype Alvis Leonides, for which the pilot was George Errington. Bulldog two-seaters were retained as personal transports by senior R.A.F. officers long after the Bulldog IIA had been superseded in the squadrons and were still in use at Flying Training Schools in 1939, being the only R.A.F. Bulldogs to reach the Middle East, at No. 4 F.T.S., Abu Sueir, Egypt. The last two-seater, *K3932*,

The first J.S.S.F. *701* built by Nakajima at Tokyo in 1930.

The second J.S.S.F. which achieved 196 mph.

was still in existence in 1953, but is believed to have been scrapped since then, leaving *G-ABBB* of the Shuttleworth Trust as the only flying survivor of the 441 Bulldogs built at Filton, for all too short a life.

Two Bulldog variants for Japan, called the J.S.S.F.,* were not built at Filton, but by Nakajima in Tokyo, already making Jupiters under licence. The Bulldog airframe exported in 1929 was successfully flown with a Nakajima Jupiter and followed by a request from the Japanese government for a working party from Filton to supervise the design and manufacture of a similar machine using locally available grades of steel. L. G. Frise and H. W. Dunn went to Tokyo in March 1930 to undertake this design which differed in several respects from the Bulldog IIA, having larger fuel tanks in the upper wing, and a modified undercarriage and tail unit. In the first prototype the Nakajima Jupiter VII was cowled by close-fitting cylinder helmets, and the second had wheel spats and a narrow-chord Townend ring. Both prototypes were very successful in their trials, attaining a top speed of 196 m.p.h., but the Japanese government declined to place a production order and the Bristol party returned home; Bristol features were evident, however, in subsequent Nakajima products, without acknowledgment to the Company.

Pilots who flew the Bulldog regarded it as one of the finest aerobatic biplanes ever produced; others who remembered its spectacular displays at Hendon, whether in squadron evolutions, converging bombing attacks, individual aerobatics or formation manoeuvres with coloured smoke trails were able to enjoy further demonstration flights from 1961 onwards, but in September 1964 the last airworthy Bulldog was regrettably wrecked at Farnborough. Thereafter only *BU-59* survived in Finland, to represent this great fighter in the only arena where it had had an opportunity to win battle honours.

SPECIFICATION AND DATA

Type:	107, Bullpup
Manufacturers:	The Bristol Aeroplane Co. Ltd., Filton, Bristol
Power Plants:	One 480 hp Bristol Mercury IIA
	One 440 hp Bristol Jupiter VIIF
	One 400 hp Bristol Mercury (short-stroke)
	One 500 hp Bristol Aquila I
Span:	30 ft
Length:	23 ft 6 in
Height:	9 ft 5 in
Wing Area:	230 sq ft
Empty Weight:	1,910 lb
All-up Weight:	2,850 lb
Max. Speed:	(Mercury IIA) 190 mph
Accommodation:	Pilot only
Production:	1
Sequence No.:	7178

* Japanese Single-seat Fighter.

SPECIFICATIONS AND DATA

Types: 102, 105, Bulldogs I–IVA, J.S.S.F., Bulldog T.M.

Manufacturers: The Bristol Aeroplane Co. Ltd., Filton, Bristol
The Nakajima Aircraft Works, Tokyo, Japan

Power Plants: One 450 hp Bristol Jupiter VIA and VIFH
One 440 hp Bristol Jupiter VII and VIIF
One 440 hp Nakajima Jupiter VII
One 440 hp Gnome-Rhône Jupiter 9ASB
One 450 hp Bristol Mercury III
One 560 hp Bristol Mercury IVS.2
One 640 hp Bristol Mercury VIS.2
One 500 hp Bristol Aquila I
One 600 hp Bristol Perseus IA

(T.M. only) ⎰ One 450 hp Bristol Jupiter VIFH
One 350 hp Napier Rapier
One 345 hp Armstrong-Siddeley Cheetah IX
One 480 hp Alvis Leonides

Type	102	Bulldog I	Bulldog (H.A.)	Bulldog II	Bulldog IIA
Power Plant	Jupiter VI	Jupiter VII	Jupiter VII	Jupiter VII	Jupiter VIIF
Span	30 ft	34 ft	50 ft	33 ft 10 in	33 ft 10 in
Length	21 ft 7 in	23 ft	24 ft	25 ft 2 in	25 ft 2 in
Height	8 ft 8 in	8 ft 9 in	10 ft	8 ft 9 in	8 ft 9 in
Wing Area	290 sq ft	307 sq ft	480 sq ft	307 sq ft	307 sq ft
Empty Weight	1,815 lb	1,987 lb	2,000 lb	2,200 lb	2,222 lb
All-up Weight	2,720 lb	3,250 lb	3,000 lb	3,490 lb	3,530 lb (later 3,660 lb)
Max. Speed	—	173 mph	150 mph	178 mph	178 mph
Service Ceiling	—	27,000 ft	40,000 ft	29,300 ft	29,300 ft
Accommodation	1	1	1	1	1
Production	nil	2	(1)	92	268
Sequence Nos.	nil	7155 7267	(7155)	7235 7322–7347 7353–7358 7364–7403 7439–7445 7447–7458	7446 7459–7550 7564–7567 7582–7589 7691–7710 7713–7726 7744 7746–7773

Type	Bulldog IIIA	Bulldog IV	Bulldog IVA	J.S.S.F.	Bulldog T.M.
Power Plant	Mercury IVA	Mercury IVS 2	Mercury VIS 2	Nakajima Jupiter VII	Jupiter VIF H
Span	33 ft 8 in	33 ft 8 in	33 ft 8 in	33 ft 8 in	34 ft 2 in
Length	25 ft 4 in	25 ft 4 in	25 ft 4 in	25 ft 6 in	25 ft 3 in
Height	9 ft 1 in	9 ft 1 in	9 ft 1 in	9 ft	8 ft 9 in
Wing Area	294 sq ft	294 sq ft	294 sq ft	300 sq ft	309 sq ft
Empty Weight	2,800 lb	2,810 lb	2,690 lb	2,400 lb	2,200 lb
All-up Weight	4,000 lb	4,100 lb	4,010 lb	3,350 lb	3,300 lb
Max. Speed	208 mph	218 mph	224 mph	196 mph	168 mph
Service Ceiling	31,000 ft	31,700 ft	33,400 ft	30,000 ft	28,000 ft
Accommodation	1	1	1	1	2
Production	2	(1)	18	2	59
Sequence Nos.	7560 7745	(7745)	7808 7810–7826	—	7727–7743 7777–7807 7827–7837

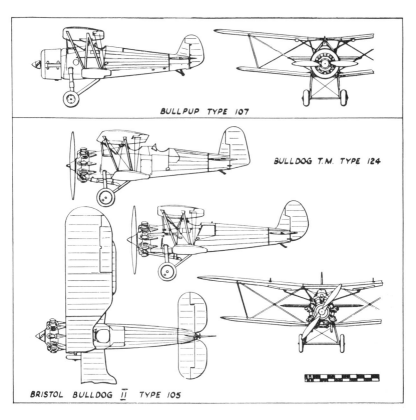

BULLPUP TYPE 107

BULLDOG T.M. TYPE 124

BRISTOL BULLDOG II TYPE 105

Bulldogs of No. 3 Sqn R.A.F. performing formation aerobatics with coloured smoke-trails at Hendon in July 1935. (*Charles E. Brown, photo.*)

231

Type 109 with Jupiter VIII and original tanks at Filton in July 1928.

The Bristol Type 109

Charles Lindbergh's historic solo flight across the Atlantic from New York to Paris on 22 May 1927 narrowly took the world's long-distance record from the R.A.F., who had established it less than a day earlier with a non-stop flight from Cranwell to the Persian Gulf in a Hawker Horsley. This was the first of a series of attempts to fly from England to India without landing to refuel and was an important objective in the development of Imperial air communications. After two more attempts with the Horsley, the Air Ministry decided to order a special long-range aeroplane and invited tenders to which Bristol replied with a biplane and Fairey with a monoplane; the latter was preferred and was successful in flying from Cranwell to Karachi non-stop in April 1929. The Bristol Directors decided in April 1928 to build their biplane as a private venture, because they believed that a long distance flight would be better publicity for the Jupiter than racing, in view of the current interest in such attempts.

One prototype, No. 7268, designated Type 109, was built and registered *G-EBZK* on 4 July 1928. The design originated on Barnwell's drawing board on 27 July 1927 as an all-metal single-bay unstaggered biplane having a span of 49 ft.; it was of classic simplicity with an enclosed cabin and dual controls for two pilots in tandem, a plain cross-axle undercarriage with a low-pressure tailwheel and a geared Jupiter VIII engine tuned for maximum economy, driving a four-bladed airscrew. The designed empty weight of 4,090 lb. was little over half the disposable load which comprised 920 gallons of fuel, 66 gallons of oil and the crew of two. At a maximum take-off weight of 11,900 lb. its wing loading was 17 lb. per sq. ft., its power loading 23·3 lb. per b.h.p. and at an economic cruising speed of 90 m.p.h. its still air range was estimated to be 5,400 statute miles. All the fuel was carried in 13 welded aluminium tanks between the spars within the profile of the upper and lower wings.

Stress checks showed that two-bay wings and a wider track undercarriage with separate axles were necessary, and the wings were given elliptical tips, increasing the span by 26 ins. The design was finished by the end of March, when construction began. It was hoped to begin ground running tests to establish fuel consumption in June; these were scheduled to take six to eight weeks, the objective being to fly to India in October.

No civilian pilot was engaged for the attempt, as it was hoped that the Air Ministry might purchase the machine on completion, or at least take it on loan to be flown by R.A.F. pilots. Roy Fedden had already been approached by the Duchess of Bedford, who was prepared to back a long range record flight provided she could be taken as a passenger, but the Company could not permit any passengers in their aircraft on flights over the sea, because of insurance problems. They were prepared to lend the Duchess a special engine, or even an aircraft and engine, for a specific overland flight if this could be arranged, and in the end the Duchess was lent a Jupiter XI for the Fokker F.VII monoplane *Spider* in which she and Capt. C. D. Barnard made several record-breaking flights to India and Capetown in 1929 and 1930.

When the 109 was finally erected in July 1928, the lower fuel tanks could not stand the internal pressure when the upper tanks were full and the fuel system had to be modified to give separate feeds from the two sets of tanks. Before this was done the world's record had risen to 4,500 miles and it was felt that this left insufficient margin for headwinds, so the distance record was abandoned and it was decided to install a smaller number of steel tanks giving a range of 3,300 miles for long-distance point-to-point flights. Bert Hinkler was interested in using the Bristol 109 for a flight round the world, but even with its gross weight reduced to 9,800 lb. it needed a long take-off run, and it was found impossible to use the large aerodromes required, because of political objections.

Before the aluminium tanks were removed, Uwins made the first flight of *G-EBZK* on 7 September 1928 with only the top centre-section tanks filled. In October the engine mounting was extended 10 in. forward and the fin area slightly reduced to improve stability, the steel tanks being installed at the same time. Fedden wanted Imperial Airways to use the 109 for endurance testing of the Jupiter XF engines ordered for their new Handley Page 42 and Short Kent airliners, and in May 1929 Major Woods Humphery agreed to loan pilots for that purpose. A year later a proposal to fly the 109 to Australia with a Jupiter XIF engine came to nothing and instead the Air Ministry offered a contract for 350 hours' endurance testing of this engine, supplying pilots for 15 hours' daily flying over an inland circuit, with the Shell Company supplying fuel and oil free of charge. Fedden would have preferred a more spectacular demonstration, to appeal to public imagination, but was overruled and the contract was agreed on 3 June 1930.

Wheel brakes were fitted before the flying programme started and the 109 was flown under 'B' conditions with the marking *R-2*. After 37 hours' prior running, the sealed Jupiter XIF commenced its endurance test on 12 September and the 109 was flown from Farnborough under A.I.D. supervision by Squadron Leader W. S. Caster of the R.A.E. After 260 hours a broken valve-rocker tie-rod caused a forced landing at Lympne in January 1931, but the

Type 109 with Jupiter XIF, modified tanks and wheel-brakes, at Filton in September 1930.

test was resumed, with A.I.D. consent, for a further 40 hours, which were completed without incident early in March. Fedden wanted to retain the 109 for a similar endurance test on the Mercury V engine, later renamed Pegasus I, but this was done eventually on the Bristol 118 biplane and the 109 was scrapped late in 1931, having been a familiar landmark at Filton for three years without ever crossing a foreign coastline in pursuit of its intended destiny.

SPECIFICATIONS AND DATA

Type:	109, Long Range Biplane
Manufacturers:	The Bristol Aeroplane Co. Ltd., Filton, Bristol
Power Plants:	One 480 hp Bristol Jupiter VIII
	One 490 hp Bristol Jupiter XIF
Span:	51 ft 2 in
Length:	37 ft 9 in (originally 36 ft 11 in)
Height:	14 ft
Wing Area:	700 sq ft
Empty Weight:	4,600 lb
All-up Weight:	9,800 lb (originally 11,910 lb)
Economic Cruise Speed:	90 mph
Max. Still-air Range:	3,300 miles (originally 5,400 miles)
Accommodation:	2
Production:	1
Sequence No.:	7268

Type 110A with Neptune at Filton in January 1930.

The Bristol Type 110A

Between the wars, the Bristol Aeroplane Company had no more success with civil transports than its rivals, the de Havilland Aircraft Co., with military prototypes; nevertheless Barnwell prepared a succession of designs to Imperial Airways' and similar requirements, none of which were built after the Ten-seater's failure to gain approval. These included the single-Jupiter-engined Type 97 of June 1925, a cabin biplane descendent of the Grampus I to carry five passengers or equivalent cargo on Australian secondary routes and for charter work.

The Jupiter was uneconomically large for small passenger aircraft, while larger machines required multiple engines, and Fedden had taken note of the rising demand for engines in the 250–350 h.p. range, intermediate between the Lucifer and the Jupiter. To meet this need the five-cylinder Titan was introduced at the end of 1927, being followed in September 1928 by the seven-cylinder Neptune, both using many parts common to the Jupiter, which reduced their selling price. Both the Company's engine licensees in Sweden (Nydquist & Holm) and America (E. W. Bliss) were interested in the Titan and Neptune, and in January 1928 Barnwell designed a three-passenger cabin biplane with a Titan, designated Type 110.

The 110 followed Bulldog practice very closely, using many of the same standard sections of rolled strip and the same gusset joints; consequently it could be produced with existing rolls and assembly tools at a relatively low manufacturing cost for a robust and durable airframe. The fuselage was flat-sided and the tubular longerons and struts employed lipped-edge sections which needed very few rivets. The upper wing had fuel tanks of the Bulldog type and Frise ailerons. The lower wing was slightly less in span, but much less in chord, and was braced to the upper by a single V-strut assembly, together with normal flying and landing streamline wires. The undercarriage was a simple cross-axle type employing rubber blocks in compression and oleo dampers. The pilot's cockpit was located high up just below the centre of the upper leading edge and enclosed by Triplex glass panels.

235

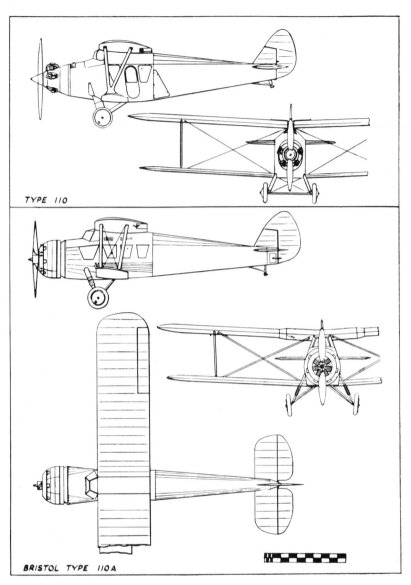

TYPE 110

BRISTOL TYPE 110A

With the introduction of the Neptune in September 1928 Barnwell designed a slightly larger four-passenger version, Type 110A, which could be supplied with either a 220 h.p. Titan or a 315 h.p. Neptune according to the customer's requirements. Without more than 10 in. increase in overall span, the wing area was enlarged by nearly 20% by adopting squarer wing tips and a wider chord for the lower wing, and a divided undercarriage of wider track was adopted. To simplify maintenance, a Warren-girder structure was used throughout the fuselage, thus eliminating truing-up. It was proposed to build three aircraft of this type, one to be specially furnished for the Olympia Show in July 1929, one for the Air Ministry and one spare machine.

When it was seen that the selling price must be kept to £3,000 and that £3,500 was the lowest estimated cost that could be attained in large batch production, the Directors took a second look at the project and in February decided to authorise construction of only two prototypes, Nos. 7348 and 7349. In order to ensure its flying by the end of March, all available effort was concentrated on the first machine, and assembly of the second set of details was postponed until after the Show. The cabin was upholstered in blue leather with a blue carpet to match; special attention was paid to cabin ventilation in the hope that, with the fuel tanks in the wings, the Air Ministry would for the first time permit smoking by passengers. The 110A was not complete for flight as scheduled, although registered *G-AAFG* on 12 March, and a mock-up Neptune was installed for the Olympia Show, which was opened on 16 July by the Prince of Wales. The biplane was admired, but was evidently too much of a luxury for hardworking charter operators struggling along on a shoe-string.

Without firm enquiries and with the project likely to cost £15,000 before the first production model was sold, the Directors postponed indefinitely the assembly of the second prototype and *G-AAFG* was completed with a Titan on 2 September. Uwins made the first flight on 25 October 1929 finding the performance well up to expectations, and hopes began to revive. The Neptune was installed in place of the Titan early in the New Year and flying continued satisfactorily until, after a landing early in February 1930, the machine ran on to a rough part of the airfield which set up 'porpoising' due to under-carriage resonance, the oleo leg top attachments came up through the cockpit and Uwins narrowly escaped injury. This was the final blow to the project and it was scrapped without any attempt at repair, because there were no prospects of selling except at a loss, and the increased demand for Bulldogs taxed the Company's production capacity to the limit.

Concurrently with the completion of detail design of the 110A in September 1929, Barnwell had laid out a larger Jupiter XI-engined cabin biplane of similar appearance, to carry seven passengers or equivalent cargo. No further work was done on this project, Type 114, but in December Barnwell sketched out a sesquiplane version of it, Type 114A, with a Jupiter XIF, intended primarily as a cargo-carrier, but with somewhat austere removable seating for six passengers. The interest in this design lies in the rigid wing bracing, employing a compression lift strut as in the Bristol 118 military biplane.

Types: 110, 110A, 114 and 114A
Manufacturers: The Bristol Aeroplane Co. Ltd., Filton, Bristol
Power Plant: (110) One 220 hp Bristol Titan
(110A) One 220 hp Bristol Titan
One 315 hp Bristol Neptune
(114) One 490 hp Bristol Jupiter XI
(114A) One 490 hp Bristol Jupiter XIF

Type	110	110A	114	114A
Span	39 ft 8 in	40 ft 6 in	50 ft	47 ft 6 in
Length	32 ft 10 in	33 ft 6 in	37 ft 2 in	37 ft 9 in
Height	9 ft 10 in	10 ft 2 in	11 ft 1 in	11 ft
Wing Area	338 sq ft	389 sq ft	613 sq ft	485 sq ft
Empty Weight	1,940 lb	2,330 lb	3,750 lb	3,730 lb
All-up Weight	3,200 lb	4,360 lb	6,760 lb	6,400 lb
Max. Speed	—	125 mph	—	—
Accommodation	Pilot and 3 pass.	Pilot and 4 pass.	Pilot and 7 pass.	Pilot and 6 pass.
Production	nil	2	nil	nil
Sequence Nos.	nil	7348 (7349 not completed)	nil	nil

Type 118 (formerly *R-3*) with Mercury V for tropical trials in June 1932.

The Bristol Types 118 and 120 Biplanes

The success of the Bulldog in 1929, after a succession of prototypes to official requirements, encouraged the Company to consider another private venture which could be offered to foreign air forces. As the initiative in the high speed fighter and light bomber classes had passed for the time being to designs using supercharged watercooled engines, Barnwell recommended a high-performance general purpose two-seater combining all the roles required by a small air force unable to afford many different types of aeroplane. The R.A.F. overseas had always used aircraft in this category, first the veteran D.H.9A and Fairey IIID, then the Westland Wapiti and Fairey Gordon derived from them and originally using their spare components in emergency. The Jupiter XFA engine, with reduction gear and supercharger, had gone into production and combined good take-off efficiency with high power at altitude, so Barnwell sketched a biplane layout with this engine in August 1929, and by February 1930 the design, Type 118, was finalised and two prototypes, Nos. 7561 and 7562, were authorised.

It was intended to exhibit the second 118 at the Paris Salon in 1930, but as development proceeded Fedden asked for this machine to have a Mercury V, because the Jupiter was obsolescent and he did not wish to perpetuate it in production orders for the biplane, which, with the Mercury, became Type 118A. In October the Air Ministry adopted the Mercury V as the Pegasus I, and on this account forbade the Company to exhibit the 118A at Paris, so the Bulldog (No. 7446) was shown instead. Meanwhile work on both prototypes proceeded and the first was registered *G-ABEZ* on 12 September 1930 and flown by Uwins on 22 January 1931.

The Bristol 118 combined high performance with extreme versatility and could fulfil the roles of fighting, bombing, army co-operation, high-level photographic reconnaissance and casualty transport with equal facility. The wings were staggered and unequal in span with a single-bay cellule braced by a single compression lift strut and a drag panel of 'N' formation on each side, so that external bracing wires were eliminated except in the centre section. Like the Bulldog, the forward fuselage was built of round steel tubes bolted to high-tensile steel plates while the aft end was of steel-strip Warren-girder construction. The undercarriage was divided, with long travel Vickers oleo-pneumatic shock legs and hydraulic wheel brakes and a steerable tail wheel. Frise ailerons were fitted to the upper wing only and tailplane incidence was adjustable over a wide range.

The crew comprised pilot and observer, the latter acting as rear gunner, bomb-aimer and wireless-operator. The pilot had an exceptional outlook from a high cockpit and the observer could reach a prone bombing position below him, whence he had an uninterrupted view from above the horizontal forward to aft of the vertical downward. For ambulance work, one stretcher was carried in this position and a second one under the readily detachable decking of the rear fuselage. The pilot had a synchronised Vickers gun on the port side, and the observer a Lewis gun on a Scarff ring mounting. Alternative loads of two 250 lb., four 112 lb. or sixteen 20 lb. bombs could be carried on external racks and released by either crew member. A P.24 camera could be used at the bomb-sight hatch, and R/T for the pilot and W/T for the observer were installed. There were two main tanks of 50 gallons each in the upper wings and two auxiliary tanks of 30 gallons each in the centre-section, with gravity supply throughout, all tanks being of tinned steel. A 10-gallon oil tank in the front fuselage received scavenge oil through a finned cooler on the port side and the Jupiter XFA drove a two-bladed airscrew of 12 ft. diameter.

Flight development, using the experimental marking *R-3*, went on throughout the summer of 1931, and on 30 October the 118 was cleared to go to Martlesham for airworthiness trials, Uwins having dived it to 210 m.p.h. indicated air speed and completed spinning trials at maximum permitted weight. He found it easy to fly and land, cruising steadily with hands and feet off; it was stable at all speeds and stalled gently without wing-drop, due to its relatively thick and efficient wing section. At Martlesham it was well received and a certificate of airworthiness was issued on 24 December, after which it was to go to Scandinavia and the Baltic States on a demonstration tour, enquiries having been received from Estonia and Lithuania. The tour was held up because the Gnome-Rhône firm disputed the Company's right to fit Bristol-built engines for sale in certain territories and, as already mentioned, Fedden was not satisfied that the Gnome-Rhône *Mercure* was yet sufficiently developed to be offered for sale.

Meanwhile the Air Ministry, impressed by reports from Martlesham, asked to hire the 118 for endurance testing the Mercury V, including hot weather trials in Iraq, and in February 1932 it was modified to take this engine, receiving R.A.F. markings and number *K2873*; for this programme a four-bladed airscrew was fitted and armament removed. The desert trials were still in progress at the end of the year, and the R.A.F. unit's reports were taken into account in redesigning the second machine, which had been put on the secret list in January because of an important innovation, a cupola for the rear gunner's cockpit, with a modified Scarff mounting fitted at top longeron level. The cupola, or 'parrot-cage', consisted of transparent panels in a light

Type 120 showing gunner's cupola, at Filton in January 1932.

framework rotating with the mounting and completely shielding the gunner from the slipstream, particularly when standing up to aim downwards, access being via a triangular top-hinged door in the port side of the fuselage. Thus modified, the design became Type 120, and the Air Ministry agreed to test it at Martlesham as a private venture entry in the G.4/31 competition to select a Wapiti and Gordon replacement.

The Bristol 120 made its first flight at Filton on 29 January 1932, carrying the marking *R-6*, with a Mercury V temporarily installed. A production Pegasus I.M.3 was substituted in April and it then went to Martlesham, appearing in the R.A.F. display at Hendon in July. It was unsuccessful in the

G.4/31 competition because in October 1931 the specification had been revised to include the coastal reconnaissance role, including torpedo bombing, as an alternative to the desert role. To meet the considerable increase in equipment weight entailed by this new requirement, Barnwell produced two layouts with increased wing area, Type 121 being similar to Type 120 with larger wings of equal span, while in Type 122 the pilot's cockpit was brought forward of the upper wing to give a better view for torpedo aiming; it was hoped that Type 122 might attract a prototype order, but the Company were not prepared to build it as a private venture. Alternative monoplane versions briefly considered were Type 125 with a low wing and Type 126 with a high wing, using multicellular cantilever stressed-skin construction, of which test specimens had already been tested.

The 120 was nevertheless purchased by the Air Ministry in March 1933 for performance tests with the cupola installed and removed, when it received R.A.F. markings and number *K3587*; the trials continued at Martlesham until October, and useful information on the drag of turrets was obtained for application to later designs. The Spanish government was also interested in purchasing the 120, but the Gnome-Rhône difficulty had still not been resolved in January 1934 when the Spanish tender had to be sent in.

The Bristol 118 was returned to Filton on completion of desert trials in 1933 and was stored until April 1935, when it was modified as a test bed for the Pegasus PE-5SM, a prototype engine with a two-speed supercharger, which was later produced as the Pegasus XVIII for Hampden and Wellington bombers.

Type 120 with cupola removed, at Martlesham Heath in November 1933. (*Crown copyright.*)

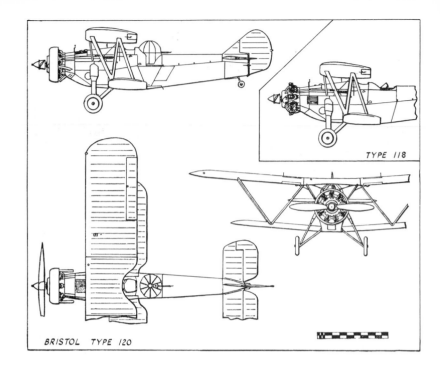

BRISTOL TYPE 120

TYPE 118

SPECIFICATIONS AND DATA

Types:	118, 120 and 122
Manufacturers:	The Bristol Aeroplane Co. Ltd., Filton, Bristol
Power Plants:	(118) One 590 hp Bristol Jupiter XFA
	(118A) One 600 hp Bristol Mercury V
	(120) One 650 hp Bristol Pegasus I.M.3
	(122) One 650 hp Bristol Pegasus I.M.3
Span:	(118 and 120) 40 ft 8 in
	(122) 43 ft
Length:	(118 and 120) 34 ft
	(122) 35 ft 9 in
Height:	12 ft
Wing Area:	(118 and 120) 376 sq ft
	(122) 530 sq ft
Empty Weight:	(118 and 120) 3,632 lb (122) 3,710 lb
All-up Weight:	(118 and 120) 5,200 lb (122) 8,000 lb
Max. Speed:	(118) 165 mph (118A and 120) 175 mph
Service Ceiling:	25,600 ft
Accommodation:	2
Production:	(118) 1, (120) 1, (122) nil
Sequence Nos.:	7561 7562

Type 123 before first flight at Filton, June 1934; note full-span ailerons.

The Bristol Four-gun Fighters, Types 123 and 133

In 1930 the Air Staff, needing a single-seater day-and-night fighter of higher performance and fire-power than ever before, drafted Specification F.7/30; it was issued to the industry late in 1931 with an invitation to tender design studies, the best of which would be ordered as prototypes for competition in 1934, and a promise of substantial production orders for the winner. Firms not selected for prototype construction were encouraged to submit private venture prototypes for the competition.

The specification called for a much better high level performance than in contemporary fighters, exceptional manœuvrability, longer endurance, excellent all-round view and low landing speed and steep initial climb for night operations. With all this it had to combine four synchronised Vickers guns and full two-way radio-telephone equipment. Finally the Air Staff indicated a preference for the evaporative-cooled Rolls-Royce Kestrel IV engine, which had nearly completed flight development and was scheduled for production as the Goshawk.

The Bristol Aeroplane Company, although reluctant to use a rival engine, could not neglect an invitation with so large a prize at stake, and in January 1932 submitted a design for a Goshawk-engined biplane, Type 123, and alternative proposals for monoplanes, two of which were nearly identical low-wing designs, Type 127 having a Goshawk and Type 128 a Mercury, while Type 129 was a high-wing Mercury-engined pusher giving the pilot unobstructed vision and unrestricted fire, with a minimum wetted area in the slipstream. The low-wing monoplanes had monocoque aluminium alloy rear fuselages with a steel-tube forward structure and fabric-covered steel wings braced to a crash pylon above and a fixed undercarriage below by streamline wires as in the Schneider Trophy seaplanes. The Mercury version had a Townend ring, while in the Goshawk version condensers were arranged along the leading edge with supplementary radiators in the undercarriage fairings.

243

The biplane had a tapered cantilever lower wing in one piece, through which loads from the two-piece upper wings were transmitted by a single V-strut on each side, no external bracing being employed; a wide track divided undercarriage was attached to the lower wing, and the upper wing roots were pin-jointed to very slender struts above the centre line of the fuselage, so interfering as little as possible with the pilot's vision and causing minimum drag.

None of these was accepted for prototype ordering, but the Company was invited to build a revised biplane as a private venture, using the latest information available. Drooping ailerons combined with the slot and interceptor controls already tried out on a Bulldog produced a completely new layout for Type 123 in November 1932 and in March 1933 construction of one prototype, No. 7775, as a private venture was approved, the Air Ministry providing a Goshawk III engine, guns and other equipment on embodiment loan. As

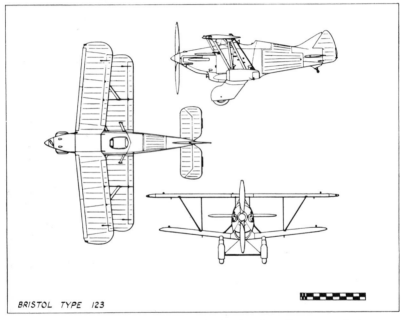

BRISTOL TYPE 123

revised, the wings were nearly rectangular in plan, heavily staggered, the upper being swept back without dihedral and the lower straight but with six degrees dihedral. The undercarriage comprised two rubber-sprung semi-cantilever units enclosed in fairings growing out of the lower wing, with short struts from wing to fuselage. It was hoped to contain the undercarriage units entirely within the fairings, but the base line was too short for lateral stiffness and it became necessary to adopt a cross-axle. The front fuselage and engine mounting formed a fully triangulated framework of high-tensile steel tubes carrying the fuel tanks and two pairs of gun mountings; aft of the pilot's seat the structure was a simple Warren-girder of lipped high-tensile steel rolled strip members faired by light metal formers and stringers. The wing spars had high-tensile steel flanges with light alloy sheet webs, and the upper leading edge, which carried the full span slats in two groups, was a duralumin stressed-skin torsion-box. The whole of the upper trailing edge was occupied by the ailerons, coupled to interceptors and the outer slats for lateral control and arranged to droop symmetrically when the inner slats opened at high angle of attack. The cantilever lower wing was in one piece, with a double-skinned leading edge, forming condensers for the cooling system; these were coupled to a central honeycomb condenser mounted in a tunnel fairing under the fuselage. The fuel tanks, all within the front fuselage, were complex in shape, being readily removable sideways. In all, the design was an extreme exercise in putting a quart into a pint pot.

There was some weeks' delay before the promised engine arrived at Filton and trouble was then experienced with the cooling system before flight tests began on 12 June 1934. When this was partly cured the biplane was found to be laterally unstable because the venting of the inner slats was critical. The inner slats were then clamped shut, the fin and rudder area were increased, but still lateral instability occurred at high speed, apparently due to wing-tip flexure, and Uwins recommended that further development would only be a waste of time and money. Type 123 was the last Bristol biplane built at Filton.

The Air Staff realised that most contractors' interpretations of the specification were too literal, particularly as to the choice of engine, and Fedden persuaded Barnwell to design a revised Mercury-engined monoplane to meet the F.7/30 requirements. In April 1933 Barnwell had laid out a two-seater fighter (Type 132) derived from Type 120, based on the small diameter two-row 16-cylinder Hydra engine, which Fedden was developing as a fighter power plant. Type 132 was a low-wing monoplane with a turret for the rear gunner, a stressed-skin cantilever wing and rear fuselage mono-coque in aluminium alloy, combined with a tubular steel front fuselage structure. The Air Ministry were willing to help the Hydra, which was a private venture, by ordering a prototype for it, and for a time the choice lay between the 132 and a Vickers design. In March the Company received instructions to proceed with a prototype, No. 7774, but on 24 April these were cancelled because of serious difficulties with the Hydra, so work on the 132 stopped before any metal was cut.

Barnwell drafted a Mercury-engined single-seater of similar construction to the 132 and was allowed to complete the design for the F.7/30 competition, one prototype being ordered as a private venture in March 1933, on the strength of an Air Ministry contract just awarded for a large prototype troop-carrier, Type 130. The new fighter, Type 133, made a full use of the recent invention in America of Alclad, coupled with controlled heat-treatment by the salt-bath process and was a cantilever monoplane with fully cowled engine and retractable undercarriage, the first in a prototype for the R.A.F. Its monocoque rear fuselage and girder front fuselage were structural features which reappeared ten years later in the Hawker Typhoon and Tempest. The constant chord wing had round tips, the downswept centre section carrying the undercarriage and fuel tanks and the detachable outer wings. The ailerons, fin, rudder and elevators were the only fabric-covered components and armament comprised two synchronised Vickers guns in the fuselage and a Lewis gun mounted above each undercarriage unit firing clear of the airscrew. The ailerons occupied the full span of the outer wings and were arranged to droop symmetrically to reduce landing speed through a linkage which, like the undercarriage retraction gear, was operated hydraulically by a Dowty hand-pump; hydraulic wheel brakes were also provided.

Type 133 in early condition, showing wide-span drooping ailerons, open cockpit and temporarily enlarged rudder; Filton, July 1934.

With a Mercury VIS.2 installed, the prototype Bristol 133, No. 7776 (*R-10*), was first flown on 8 June 1934 by Uwins, who reported that it was going to be a winner. The wheel brakes were made more effective, the rudder area increased, the original ailerons replaced by short-span ailerons and separate split flaps extending across the centre-section, the tail skid replaced by a castoring tail-wheel and a crash pylon and sliding hood were fitted to the cockpit. Finally an improved low-drag exhaust collector ring and long-chord cowling were installed. By the end of February 1935 all performance and

Type 133 taking off from Filton in September 1934; note reduced ailerons and rudder, and enclosed cockpit. (*'Aeroplane' copyright.*)

Type 133 flying over Filton in September 1934, showing retracted landing gear, split flaps and outer guns. (*'Flight' photo*.)

most of the handling trials had been completed in just under 18 hours' flying by Uwins, and on 8 March only final spinning and diving tests remained before the machine was flown to Martlesham.

On that day Uwins completed the spinning trials and two dives to 310 m.p.h. indicated airspeed. Campbell then took the machine up for a final half-hour's handling and at 14,000 ft. put the machine into a right-hand spin; unfortunately he overlooked the fact that the undercarriage was down and a flat spin developed. He opened the throttle at once but the engine stopped, evidently starved of fuel by centrifugal force. As he had no hope of getting out of the spin and had already lost 8,000 ft. he had to bale out; the cockpit hood opened easily, but as he jumped one foot was trapped by the control column and for some ageless moments he hung head downwards before getting free at about 2,000 ft. His parachute opened quickly and the 133 went on spinning steadily below him, catching fire on impact in a field at Longwell Green, east of Bristol.

This was the end of the Company's hopes in the F.7/30 competition and emphasised the false economy of relying on a single prototype for such a crucial venture. Barnwell was ready to design an improved version of the 133, but time was too short and already Specification F.5/34 was issued, calling for a radial-engined fighter with eight guns in the wings, for which the Company was awarded a prototype contract at the end of March; to meet this requirement a new design (Type 146) was prepared, as described later.

SPECIFICATIONS AND DATA

Types:	123, 127, 128 and 133
Manufacturers:	The Bristol Aeroplane Co. Ltd., Filton, Bristol
Power Plant:	(123 and 127) One 695 hp Rolls-Royce Goshawk III
	(128 and 133) One 640 hp Bristol Mercury VIS.2

Type	123	127	128	133
Span	29 ft 7 in	42 ft 8 in	42 ft 8 in	39 ft
Length	25 ft 2 in	32 ft 2 in	30 ft 8 in	28 ft
Height	9 ft 6 in	9 ft 3 in	9 ft	9 ft 9 in
Wing Area	248 sq ft	285 sq ft	285 sq ft	247 sq ft
Empty Weight	3,300 lb	2,880 lb	2,780 lb	3,322 lb
All-up Weight	4,737 lb	4,300 lb	4,260 lb	4,738 lb
Max. Speed	235 mph	—	—	260 mph
Accommodation	Pilot only	Pilot only	Pilot only	Pilot only
Production	1	nil	nil	1
Sequence Nos.	7775	nil	nil	7776

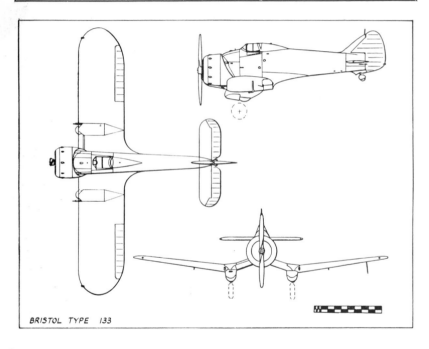

BRISTOL TYPE 133

248

Type 130 prototype at Filton in July 1936.

The Bristol Bombay, Type 130

The aileron-reversal phenomenon encountered with the Bristol Bagshot set in train a long and thorough investigation on the torsional stiffness of cantilever wings, which led to a design using stressed-skin surfaces attached to a multi-cellular structure formed by intersecting multiple spars and ribs with high-tensile booms and sheet webs. A wing of this type was proposed in the Type 115 design tendered to Specification C.16/28 for a three-engined troop-carrier, combined with a fabric-covered fuselage of high-tensile rolled strip construction. Although not ordered as a prototype, this project was followed by a simplified and improved version submitted in response to Specification C.26/31 for a twin-engined monoplane to carry 24 fully-equipped troops or an equivalent load of cargo, including spare engines or bulk fuel; it had also to carry defensive armament and be suitable for operation as a long-range bomber, to replace the Vickers Valentias of the R.A.F. bomber-transport squadrons in Egypt, Iraq and India.

The Bristol project to meet this specification was Type 130, a high-wing monoplane with two Pegasus engines of all-metal construction with an Alclad stressed-skin fuselage developed from recent experimental work by Pollard's structural research department. The cantilever wing had seven spars with high-tensile steel flanges and Alclad sheet webs, pressed Alclad ribs being threaded on and the whole assembly riveted to the Alclad skin, giving a wing of extreme torsional stiffness. A contract for one prototype was awarded in March 1933 and detail design continued throughout the year as construction proceeded, being proved at every stage by tests on representative riveted joints to ensure the lowest possible structure weight compatible with safe stress levels. Pegasus III engines of 750 h.p. were specified; other features included a fixed wide-track undercarriage and castoring tailwheel, a monoplane tail with twin fins and rudders, and an enclosed turret with a Lewis gun in the nose, which was also the bomb-aimer's station. The tail-gunner's position was accessible from the fuselage and at first was an open cockpit with a Scarff ring, but later a cupola was added.

249

The Bristol 130 was the subject of an official contract, so was on the Secret List and no reference to its equipment or performance could be published. Consequently it was impossible to offer a civil version of it when enquiries were received later in 1933 for a commercial transport to carry 14 passengers or equivalent cargo. The Company therefore offered a different design, Type 137, using the same wing as the 130 with a wider and deeper flat-sided fuselage and a single fin and rudder. The nacelles were set lower on the wing than in the 130 and merged into 'trouser' undercarriage fairings; by means of an ingenious jacking system, the undercarriage could be partly retracted into the fairing when standing on the ground to bring the cabin door sill within 14 in. of ground level; valves provided for the automatic extension of the undercarriage while taxying so that it could be fully extended before taking-off. Another feature was a hinged floor section which could be lowered to form a loading ramp for heavy cargo. Although the 137 was not built, it had features which proved their value ten years later in the Hamilcar glider and foreshadowed the Bristol 170 Freighter of 1945, whose wing was derived from the 130.

A further development of the Bristol 130, proposed in July 1934, was Type 144, tendered in response to Specification B.3/34. This employed the same wing and nose and tail fuselage sections as the 130, but the undercarriage was retractable and the centre fuselage was widened, with a raised floor for internal bomb stowage, five 550 lb. bombs being carried below the centre of gravity. There were additional beam gun stations on each side amidships and emergency flotation bags in the bomb compartment and outer wings. With Pegasus IV engines the top speed at a gross weight of 19,000 lb. was estimated at 189 m.p.h., or, with fully supercharged Perseus engines, 202 m.p.h. A supplementary project, Type 144B, proposed a smaller wing and slimmer body to carry 18 troops instead of 24, at a top speed with Perseus engines of 217 m.p.h. Neither design was accepted, the contract going to the Handley Page 54 Harrow, which also had Pegasus engines and in its later career was to outlast the 130 as a transport.

The prototype Bristol 130, No. 7809 (K3583), was first flown on 23 June 1935 by Uwins, and with its span of 96 ft. was the largest aeroplane built at Filton to that date. On completion of maker's trials it went to Martlesham, where its pilot for the official trials was Flight-Lt. A. J. Pegg, who later resigned his commission to join the Company's staff. When Uwins retired from the position of Chief Test Pilot in 1947, his successor was 'Bill' Pegg, whose first new prototype was the Brabazon. Development testing of the 130 went on at Filton and Martlesham until 1936, by which time several improvements had been incorporated, including a change to three-bladed Fairey-Reed metal airscrews and some alteration to the tail surfaces to accommodate the auto-pilot's characteristics, also hydraulic nose and tail turrets of Bristol design, respectively Types B.II and B.III, each carrying a single Vickers 'K' gun. Thus modified, with more powerful Pegasus XXII engines driving Rotol variable pitch airscrews, the design became Type 130 Mark II and, after the

Bombay of No. 216 Sqn over the Egyptian desert in 1941. (*Crown copyright.*)

first proposed name Bedford had been turned down by the Air Ministry, was officially named Bristol Bombay in February 1937. There was no possibility of putting it into production at Filton, because of its size and current preoccupation with the Blenheim, so the contract for 50 Bombays to Specification 47/36 was placed with a new company, Short and Harland Ltd., formed at Belfast by Short Brothers and Harland & Wolff to operate a new government-owned shadow factory on Queen's Island. The first production Bombay, *L5808*, was flown at Belfast in March 1939 and deliveries commenced thereafter to No. 216 Squadron in Egypt, which received them in September 1939. *K3583* was retained for development work at Filton until 1941, wearing camouflage with yellow undersurfaces and the name *Josephine* painted on the nose.

Operationally the Bombay formed the equipment of Nos. 216, 117, 267 and 271 Squadrons. It was used in both transport and night-bomber roles in the Libyan desert campaign, returning to base in Egypt with full loads of casualties on stretchers. A few home-based Bombays were used to ferry supplies to the British forces in France in 1940, and on 18 June 1940 a French intelligence officer attached to No. 1 Squadron found a Bombay abandoned on Chateaudun airfield with a broken tail-wheel. In spite of this damage he took-off successfully with 15 compatriots and flew to England to join the Free French forces, although not a qualified pilot. Bombays of No. 216 Squadron, with full bomb racks and other improvised missiles hurled from the cabin doors, took part in the nightly bombardment of Benghazi in the autumn of 1940. On 2 May 1941 they assisted in the evacuation of Greek refugees (including the Royal Family) from Crete to Egypt, and a week later flew a detachment of the Essex Regiment behind Raschid el Ali's rebel lines at Habbaniyah in Iraq. They were active in the renewed advance into Libya in November 1941 and dropped the first Allied parachute troops on Southern Italy. After being superseded by Lodestars in the later stages of the North African campaign, the surviving Bombays from No. 216 Squadron were transferred to No. 1 Australian Air Ambulance Unit, evacuating over 2,000 casualties from Sicily to North Africa in June 1943 and later carrying nursing sisters to Italy after the Anzio landings. They continued with casualty evacuation from Italy to Sicily, and one Bombay crew alone had carried 6,000 cases before the campaign ended more than ten years after the first Bristol 130 prototype had been ordered.

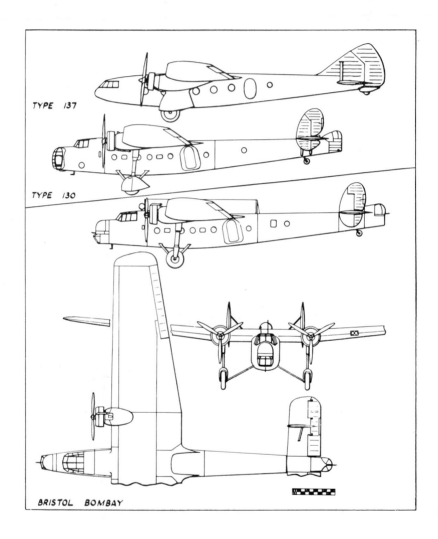

TYPE 137

TYPE 130

BRISTOL BOMBAY

252

Types: 115, 130 and Bombay
Manufacturers: The Bristol Aeroplane Co. Ltd., Filton, Bristol
Power Plants: (115) Three 600 hp Bristol Mercury III
(130) Two 750 hp Bristol Pegasus IIIM 3
(Bombay) Two 1,010 hp Bristol Pegasus XXII

Type	115	130	Bombay
Span	108 ft	96 ft	95 ft 9 in
Length	73 ft 8 in	67 ft 9 in	69 ft 3 in
Height	21 ft	16 ft	19 ft 6 in
Wing Area	1,710 sq ft	1,345 sq ft	1,340 sq ft
Empty Weight	12,910 lb	13,000 lb	13,800 lb
All-up Weight	22,710 lb	18,000 lb	20,000 lb
Max. Speed	—	180 mph	192 mph
Service Ceiling	—	22,000 ft	25,000 ft
Range	—	—	2,230 miles
Accommodation	3 crew and 17 troops	3 crew and 24 troops	3 crew and 24 troops
Production	nil	1	50
Sequence No.	nil	7809	by Short & Harland Ltd. at Belfast

Type 138A during its second record-breaking flight over Farnborough in June 1937.

The Bristol High Altitude Monoplane, Type 138A

In the never-ending rivalry between aero-engine manufacturers, great prestige attached to the making and breaking of the three absolute world's records, for speed, altitude and distance. The speed record had been the one most eagerly striven for in earlier days, because of the political complications of international long-distance flights and the less spectacular nature of altitude records in spite of their technical difficulty. By 1930 absolute speed and distance attempts had passed beyond anything that individual firms could organise without government help, both financial and diplomatic. Engine designers were continually striving to improve high altitude performance, and consequently there was both technical merit and commercial advantage to be gained by the attainment of still greater heights. Fedden was always aware of the value of the altitude record, but even he was caught napping in 1929 by the German Junkers Company, who bought a production Jupiter VII and installed it in a standard W.34 civil monoplane, which their pilot Neuenhofen flew on 26 May to 41,790 ft. This marked the beginning of a series of altitude records made with Bristol engines, built either at Filton or by licensees. A year later, Neuenhofen's record was beaten by Lt. Soucek of the United States Navy with a climb of 43,166 ft., this in turn being surpassed on 16 September 1932 by a flight from Filton by Cyril Uwins to 43,976 ft. in a modified Vickers Vespa biplane powered by a Pegasus S.3 engine; information gained on this flight made possible the flight by two Westland biplanes fitted with similar engines over Everest for the first time on 3 April 1933. A year later the Italian pilot Renato Donati recaptured the world's altitude record by flying a Pegasus-engined Caproni biplane to 47,360 ft. and the physiological problems of attaining even greater heights demanded the full resources of national research establishments.

Air Ministry interest was already evident after the Everest flight, and in November 1933 Barnwell proposed a special high-altitude monoplane for research purposes. This project, Type 138, was a large low-wing single-seater monoplane with a backward-retracting undercarriage, powered by a very highly supercharged Pegasus engine developed from those used in the Everest aircraft. Nothing was done because of the high cost, until Donati's record on 11 April 1934 created a national demand for a new British attempt to be made with government backing. In June the Company was invited to tender for two prototypes to Specification 2/34, and Barnwell revised his project to meet the new requirements, in September 1934 finalising the design as Type 138A. This retained the original size and general layout, but was equipped with a special Pegasus having a two-stage supercharger and capable of routine flights at more than 50,000 ft., carrying an observer in addition to the pilot when necessary.

A thorough preliminary investigation of the problems was made by the R.A.E. and N.P.L., resulting in the establishment of optimum design characteristics for the aircraft and the development of a special pressurised flying suit and breathing apparatus for the crew. It was concluded that the wing-loading should not be greater than 9 lb./sq. ft. and the span-loading not greater than 1·4 lb./sq. ft. To keep the weight to a minimum, the airframe was a wood semi-monocoque except for the tubular engine mounting. As forward speed was not a critical factor, a fixed undercarriage of minimum weight was chosen. A riveted light alloy 70 gallon main fuel tank with a 12 gallon gravity tank built into the top of it was installed in the fuselage fore-end, with a 10 gallon oil tank adjacent, the whole fuel and oil system being kept as simple and light as possible. The pilot's cockpit, just aft of the rear spar, was enclosed by a hinged plastic canopy and was demisted by hot air from muffs round the exhaust-pipes. A second cockpit could be installed ahead of the pilot, also various items of equipment such as guns, cameras and radio sets so that they could be tested at high altitudes and low temperatutes.

The special Pegasus engine incorporated a mechanical supercharger and also drove a separate supercharger mounted on the firewall through a flexible shaft and clutch; on reaching the rated altitude of the normal blower, the pilot clutched-in the auxiliary unit which fed compressed air to the main blower through an intercooler; the rated altitude of the two blowers together was 42,000 ft. The engine installation was thoroughly tested on a dynamometer while the aircraft was being designed and built. Work on the mock-up began in January 1935, detail design being entrusted to Clifford Tinson.

The Bristol 138A, No. 7840 (*K4897*), was completed early in 1936 and on 11 May was flown at Filton by Uwins, with a standard Pegasus IV and three-bladed airscrew. Satisfactory flights were made again on 22 May and 16 July, and early in August it was taken to Farnborough for trials with an oxygen pressure-helmet developed by Sir Robert Davis, head of Siebe Gorman and Co., and Professor J. S. Haldane. On 15 August it returned to Filton for the special Pegasus with its four-bladed airscrew to be installed, and was flown back to Farnborough on completion on 5 September by Sqn.-Ldr. F. R. D. Swain, the pilot chosen for the high-altitude flights. On 28 September Swain took-off from Farnborough at 7.30 a.m. and climbed to about 35,000 ft. where the auxiliary blower was engaged; 40,000 ft. was reached 35 min. after take-off, 45,000 ft. in 50 min. and an indicated 50,000 ft. in 70 min. Swain managed to gain a further 1,000 ft. of indicated height, then throttled back to descend. He became short of oxygen on the way down but obtained relief by breaking the window of his pressure-suit at a safe height and landed at Netheravon 2 hours after take-off. The maximum height attained on this flight was submitted to the Federation Aeronautique Internationale and homologated as a world's altitude record for aeroplanes of 49,967 ft. (15,230 metres). This was the first time 15,000 metres had been exceeded.

After this successful first attempt, various small improvements were made to enable the 138A to reach its designed ceiling of 54,000 ft., including changes in impeller diameter and airscrew pitch and smaller wheels without brakes to save weight. Thus modified, the 138A made six further flights to approximately 50,000 ft. during the early months of 1937 and on 30 June, a few weeks after Italy had again taken the record with a flight to 51,364 ft. and before homologation by the F.A.I., Flt.-Lt. M. J. Adam succeeded in flying the 138A to nearly 54,000 ft. in 95 min., landing at his starting point at Farnborough $2\frac{1}{4}$ hours after take-off. This was homologated as a record in November at 53,937 ft. (16,440 metres).

Research flights continued and the second machine, Type 138B, ordered as a two-seater in 1935, was intended for comparative tests using a similarly supercharged Rolls-Royce liquid-cooled engine. This airframe, No. 8136 (*L7037*), was delivered to Farnborough in 1937, but the engine installation by the R.A.E. was never completed. In the ten years since 1928 the height record had been broken nine times, once by a Jupiter, five times by a Pegasus and only three times by other engines; Fedden had every reason to be pleased with this progress, as a measure not merely of national prestige but of survival in the struggle ahead.

SPECIFICATION AND DATA

Type: 138A and B
Manufacturers: The Bristol Aeroplane Co. Ltd., Filton, Bristol
Power Plant: (A) One 500 hp Bristol Pegasus P.E.6S
(B) One 500 hp Rolls-Royce Kestrel S.

Span:	66 ft	*Speed:*	(A) 123 mph
Length:	44 ft	*Service Ceiling:*	(A) 54,000 ft
Height:	10 ft 3 in	*Duration:*	(A) 2¼ hours
Wing Area:	568 sq ft	*Accommodation:*	(A) Pilot only (B) 2
Empty Weight:	(A) 4,391 lb	*Production:*	(A) 1; (B) 1
All-up Weight:	(A) 5,310 lb	*Sequence Nos.:*	(A) 7840; (B) 8136
Max. Climb:	(A) 1,430 ft/min at 40,000 ft		

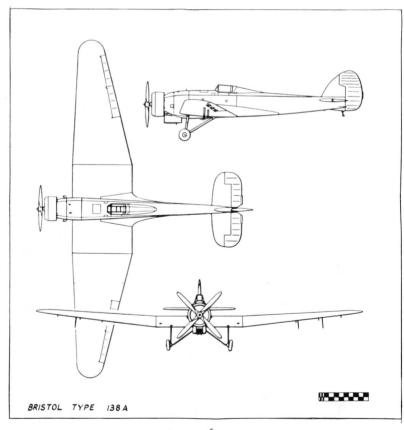

BRISTOL TYPE 138A

Type 142 in its original form with wooden airscrews at Filton in April 1935.

The Bristol Types 142 and 143

On 8 December 1935 the London Chamber of Commerce and the Royal Aeronautical Society joined forces to hold a Conference on Airports, attended by representatives of 124 local authorities in Great Britain. Opening the proceedings at the Mansion House, the Prince of Wales, himself a convinced and regular air traveller, told his audience: "We must think in terms of cruising speeds of 250 miles per hour." Some months earlier the same conclusions had been reached by Frank Barnwell and Roy Fedden, and on 28 July 1933 Barnwell sketched out a twin-engined light transport monoplane with a cabin for six passengers in addition to two pilots, to match the smaller of the two sleeve-valve aircooled radial aero-engines being developed by Fedden. This engine, the Aquila I, was first run in September 1934 and within a month completed a 50 hours' civil type test at a maximum power of 500 h.p.

Barnwell's low-wing layout, Type 135, was compared with a high-wing layout of the same dimensions and estimated to have a lower drag and structure weight, so confirming the findings of Boeing, Lockheed and Douglas in America. No immediate decision was taken to build a private venture prototype but Fedden was authorised in August to build two Aquilas. The 135 was known in the Filton design office as 'the Captain's Gig' and looked so promising that local enthusiasm could not long be confined to those working on it. So when Lord Rothermere, proprietor of the *Daily Mail*, at a luncheon discussion on civil aviation with his editors, declared his intention of having built for him 'the fastest commercial aeroplane in Europe', as a counterblast to American claims for the Douglas DC-1, he was promptly informed of the developments at Filton by Robert T. Lewis, editor of the *Bristol Evening World*. Lewis was told to obtain all particulars of the Bristol 135 within one week, and on 6 March 1934 Barnwell quoted an estimated all-out level speed for a version of the 135 with Mercury engines instead of Aquilas of 240 m.p.h. at 6,500 ft. with moderate supercharging. Lewis passed this information on to Lord Rothermere, and on 26 March telephoned Fedden to say that Lord Rothermere wanted the aircraft built for his private use, to encourage prominent firms and business men to make proper use of civil aviation and, not least, to point out to the Air Ministry how their existing fighters might be no match for a high-speed transport used as a light bomber. The proposition was discussed by the Directors on 27 March with some apprehension; they were unwilling to offend their best customer (the Air Ministry) by becoming a party to press propaganda against official policy; on the other hand the prestige and publicity to be obtained from such a project were too great to be lightly set aside. It was agreed that Sir Stanley White, Barnwell and Fedden should meet Lord Rothermere at Stratton House, London, for lunch on 29 March, and there Lord Rothermere stated his requirements explicitly. He wanted an aeroplane to carry a crew of two and six passengers at the speed already quoted by Barnwell and would pay the estimated cost of £18,500 in two instalments, half immediately and half in a year's time provided the aeroplane was flying by then. The first instalment was not in fact paid until June, which gave the Company two months longer in which to have the machine flying.

The Air Ministry were tactfully approached, but far from objecting, expressed enthusiasm. Thus reassured, the Company decided to build both Lord Rothermere's aeroplane and a twin-Aquila prototype side-by-side, which Barnwell recommended since 70% of the components could easily be made identical for both aircraft; this necessitated some revisions to the 135, which, enlarged to carry eight passengers and crew of two, became Type 143 with Aquilas; the Mercury-engined aircraft, Type 142, had a slimmer fuselage and a more pointed nose. In order to obtain the very latest information on current developments, Barnwell went to America on a brief tour of inspection in May, and by the time he returned enquiries for the Bristol 143 were already coming in. The Finnish government was interested, and the Ethyl Export Corporation wanted to buy the prototype as soon as its tests were finished, if possible at a reduced price in exchange for world-wide publicity. The fuselage of the 143 was shown at the Paris Salon in November and attracted more than ordinary attention because of the interest aroused by the MacRobertson race from London to Australia earlier in the year.

It was fairly obvious that Finland wanted an aeroplane of wide versatility in both civil and military roles, and a brochure was prepared describing a convertible variant, Type 143F, having Mercury VI engines, with interchangeable nose and rear fuselage sections enabling it to perform alternative passenger, freight, postal, ambulance and fighter-bomber duties. In the military version, provision was made for a forward-firing 20 mm. Madsen cannon in addition to a dorsal Lewis gun mounting. In February negotiations began for the supply of nine 143F aircraft, but had not proceeded far before the Air Ministry themselves expressed interest in a possible bomber version, following the first flight of the 142, No. 7838, at Filton on 12 April 1935. For the early flights, which were very successful, fixed-pitch four-bladed wooden airscrews were employed, but these were exchanged for three-bladed two-position Hamilton-Standards before the 142 went to Martlesham in June for airworthiness acceptance trials.

There it created a furore, for it was 50 m.p.h. faster with full load than the winner of the F.7/30 competition, the Gloster Gladiator prototype. All who flew it were so favourably impressed with its performance and handling that the Air Ministry asked to retain it for full evaluation as a potential bomber. Lord Rothermere was so pleased by this easy victory over the pundits that he presented the 142 to the Air Council, having already named it *Britain First*. The 142 was registered *G-ADCZ* as early as 25 February, but never carried this marking and bore only the experimental mark *R-12* when it went to Martlesham; in July it received serial number *K7557* and in October the

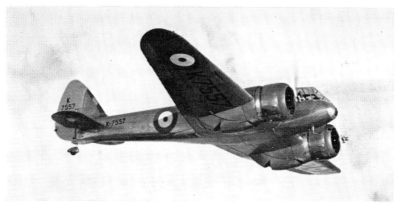

Britain First after presentation to the Air Council, flying at Martlesham Heath in 1936. ('*Flight*' *photo.*)

civil registration was cancelled. Early in July the Company had an enquiry for a replica of *Britain First* from Owen Cathcart Jones, but by then all available production capacity had been promised to the Air Ministry, except for approved foreign government orders, and no private orders could be entertained. Lord Rothermere himself wrote to the Company on 14 February 1936 to order an improved version of *Britain First*, stipulating a cruising speed of 360 m.p.h., but even he had to take 'No' for an answer.

Britain First was damaged at Martlesham in the second week of July, when a cowling panel came adrift, and had to be returned to Filton for repairs. The opportunity was taken to improve the undercarriage fairings and brakes, and after re-delivery and completion of trials at Martlesham it was handed over to the R.A.E., whence it flew on experimental and transport duties until 1942; it was then relegated as an instructional airframe to No. 10 School of Technical Training, Kirkham, Lancashire, with the serial *2211 M*, and was finally scrapped at Morris Motors, Cowley, in 1944.

The Bristol 143 prototype, No. 7839, was registered *G-ADEK* on 22 March 1935, but had to wait until endurance testing of its two Aquila I engines had been completed on the Bullpup and Bulldog *G-ABBB*, so it was not completed until late in 1935 and did not make its first flight until 20 January 1936. Like *Britain First* it never carried its registration mark, but

Type 143 at Filton in July 1936.

flew with the mark *R-14* as a test-bed for the Aquila. Application for a certificate of airworthiness was made on 4 March 1935 but countermanded on 26 June 1936. At one time it was proposed to sell it to Imperial Airways on completion of airworthiness trials, but Fedden secured its retention and it was rarely seen away from Filton; one of its few public appearances was at the Bristol and Wessex Aeroplane Club's Garden Party at Whitchurch on 5

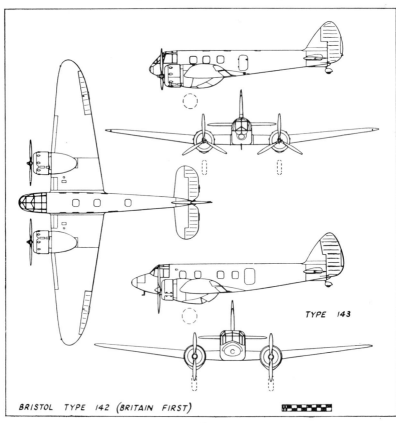

TYPE 143

BRISTOL TYPE 142 (BRITAIN FIRST)

September 1936, when Uwins showed off its paces on a very wet day. The chief obstacle to further development of the 143 was that no variable-pitch air-screws could be obtained in a size to suit the Aquila. It was stored without engines when Aquila production was abandoned in 1938 and scrapped some time after the outbreak of war.

Although Imperial Airways made enquiries for the 143 as late as 1937, any serious intention of producing civil versions of either the 142 or 143 was swept away in August 1935, when the Company received a contract for 150 of the bomber variant, Type 142M, to Specification 28/35. Apart from the 143F enquiry from Finland, the first proposal for a bomber conversion was made on 29 May 1935, when Barnwell estimated a maximum level speed of 262 m.p.h. at 15,000 ft. with fully supercharged Aquilas; the gross weight of 9,600 lb. included a crew of two and 1,000 lb. of bombs. On 20 June this performance was compared with an estimate of 278 m.p.h. with Mercuries at a gross weight of 10,400 lb. Two days later the Director of Technical Development, A.-Comm. Verney, wrote to Barnwell expressing a preference for the Mercury-engined version and calling a design conference in London to discuss it in detail on 9 July. Barnwell there set out his proposals for converting the 142 into a mid-wing bomber with a retractable dorsal turret and internal bomb stowage; this was accepted as the basis for a production contract straight off the drawing board. Thus was born the Bristol Blenheim, the immortal bomber which was ready in quantity when war came.

SPECIFICATION AND DATA

Types:	142 and 143
Manufacturers:	The Bristol Aeroplane Co. Ltd., Filton, Bristol
Power Plants:	(142) Two 650 hp Bristol Mercury VIS 2; (143) Two 500 hp Bristol Aquila I
Span:	56 ft 4 in
Length:	(142) 39 ft 9 in; (143) 43 ft 2 in
Height:	(142) 12 ft 10 in; (143) 12 ft 3in
Wing Area:	469 sq ft
Empty Weight:	(142) 6,822 lb; (143) 7,000 lb
All-up Weight:	(142) 9,357 lb; (143) 11,000 lb
Max. Speed:	(142) 307 mph; (143) 250 mph
Range:	(142) 1,000 miles; (143) 1,250 miles
Accommodation:	(142) 2 crew + 4 passengers; (143) 2 crew + 8 passengers
Production:	(142) 1; (143) 1
Sequence Nos.	(142) 7838; (143) 7839

Type 146 at Filton in February 1938.

The Bristol Types 146, 147 and 148

The loss of the Bristol 133 single-seater fighter on the eve of its departure to Martlesham was a severe disappointment to the Company and underlined the danger of risking so much on a single prototype. Consequently when the Company received a contract for the supply of a prototype eight-gun fighter to Specification F.5/34 at a price of £11,500 it was decided to make details for a second prototype at the same time. The new fighter, Type 146, was the same size as the 133 and embodied all the lessons learned from it. The fuselage was a monocoque throughout, including the engine mounting, and was designed as a 'developable surface', having the maximum area of single curvature. The cockpit was enclosed by a one-piece sliding hood and was protected by a strong crash-pylon. The wing had a wide straight centre section and outer sections with moderate dihedral, the whole being tapered in plan from root to tip. Each outer wing contained a battery of four Browning rifle-calibre guns firing outboard of the airscrew, with integral belt-boxes. The intended engine was a fully supercharged Perseus sleeve-valve radial of 835 h.p. in a long-chord cowling with front exhaust collector ring, but was not available in time for the prototype and a Mercury IX was substituted. The undercarriage was fully retractable, the main oleo-legs folding inboard and the tail unit backwards. The fin and rudder were of generous area and the tailplane was tapered and set low so as to assist spin recovery.

Although it fully met the contract requirements, the prototype Bristol 146, No. 7841 (*K5119*) received only a low priority during manufacture, partly because of the emphasis on the Blenheim, but more because the F.5/34 specification was so soon outdated by the Rolls-Royce Merlin, and the Hurricane and Spitfire fighters designed round it. Nevertheless it was completed, after various delays, in 1937, an order for the second prototype, No. 7842, having been cancelled earlier. It was flown first by Uwins on 11 February 1938, gave no trouble during its makers' trials and went to Martlesham Heath in April. It completed its contract trials satisfactorily, along with the Gloster F.5/34, Martin-Baker M.B.2 and Vickers Venom, but in view of the promise of the Merlin-engined fighters, no F.5/34 competitor was selected for produc-

262

tion and on Empire Air Day 1938 the 146 was flown back to Filton to take part in the local R.A.F. display, only to collide with part of the set-piece on the airfield after landing; it was beyond economical repair and was scrapped forthwith.

In April 1935, soon after ordering the Bristol 146 prototype, the Air Ministry issued Specification A.39/34 for an army co-operation monoplane to replace the Hawker Audax and Hector biplanes. This was a difficult role to fulfil because of the wide speed range and great variety of duties demanded. The Bristol design, Type 148, incorporated many of the same components and details as the 146 and similar monocoque construction was adopted. It was a low-wing monoplane with round-tipped wings of constant chord. At first the tandem cockpits were enclosed by a streamline hood sloping down over the rear cockpit where the gunner was provided with a tilting canopy above a ring mounting for a single Lewis gun; later this mounting was replaced by a B.V. pillar mounting in which the weight of the gun was balanced by that of the gunner in his seat, and this necessitated a sliding hood in place of the tilting section. There was a prone bombing position on the floor, and two forward-firing Browning guns were mounted in the port wing outside the airscrew disc, with bomb-racks below so as to be suitable for dive-bombing. Other equipment comprised radio, a camera and a message pickup hook.

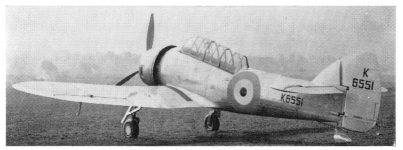

Type 148 (Mercury) at Filton in October 1937.

Although not installed until 1939, provision was made from the first for wing-tip auto-slots, which could be interconnected with the split trailing-edge flaps to improve lateral control at low speed. Two prototypes, Nos. 7843 and 7844 (*K6551* and *K6552*) were ordered in June 1935, and in October the Company proposed that a third should be built and equipped, without armament, for use as a Taurus and Hercules engine test-bed. An order was given for this machine, Type 148A, No. 8167, but cancelled soon afterwards because the Air Ministry preferred to import a Northrop 2-L monoplane for use as the Hercules test-bed. At the same time they agreed that *K6552* should be delivered with a Taurus engine instead of the Perseus specified; this variant was Type 148B. The first 148 was completed with a Mercury IX and was flown on 15 October 1937, achieving the excellent speed range, without slots, of 255 to 62 m.p.h., and after evaluation against the Westland

Type 148B (Taurus) at Filton in May 1938.

Lysander went on to gain satisfactory reports in squadron handling trials, but the Lysander's high wing and fixed undercarriage were preferred and *K6551* came to grief when its undercarriage failed to lock down. When repaired at Filton it was fitted with a Perseus XII engine for endurance testing alongside the 148B, *K6552*, which made its first flight with a Taurus II in May 1938.

The family trio was completed by the Bristol 147, a two-seater night fighter designed, but never built, to meet Specification F.9/35. Type 147 had the same wing, undercarriage and tail unit as Type 148, and the pilot's cockpit was similar, but the gunner had a rotating seat with remote controls for operating a flush-fitting four-gun dorsal turret. The movement of the guns through 90 degrees in elevation and 180 degrees in azimuth was copied mechanically from movement of the gunner's reflector sight which he controlled by two handwheels. A Perseus-engined version of the 147 was tendered in August 1935, with a top speed of 280 m.p.h., and this was followed in September by a Hercules-engined version with a top speed of 315 m.p.h.; both had an estimated service ceiling of 35,000 ft., but neither was accepted, the winner of the F.9/35 competition being the Boulton-Paul Defiant.

The Bristol 146 and 148 were almost the last single-engined aeroplanes to be built at Filton, the only later single-engined Bristol machines being the helicopters and Type 221. After so nearly producing a successor to the Bulldog, the Company was henceforth to make its name with multi-engined aircraft, including some of the largest ever built, while the initiative in single-engined fighters passed to the exponents of in-line liquid-cooled engines, as no doubt it would have done even if the 133 had won the F.7/30 competition, to return only by proxy, as it were, when the Company undertook the production of Hawker Tempests with Bristol Centaurus engines at Banwell in 1944–45.

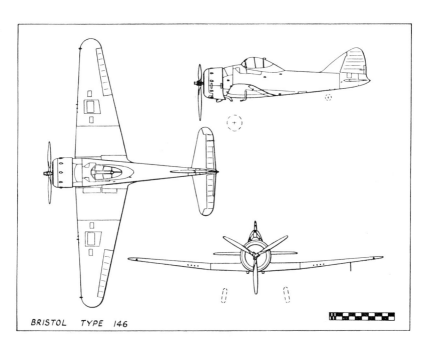

BRISTOL TYPE 146

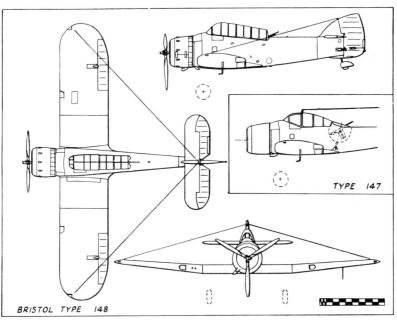

TYPE 147

BRISTOL TYPE 148

265

Types: 146, 147 and 148.
Manufacturers: The Bristol Aeroplane Co. Ltd., Filton, Bristol
Power Plants: (146) One 840 hp Bristol Mercury IX;
(147) One 890 hp Bristol Perseus X;
(148) One 840 hp Bristol Mercury IX;
One 905 hp Bristol Perseus XII;
(148B) One 1,050 hp Bristol Taurus II.

Type	146	147	148	148B
Span	39 ft	40 ft	40 ft	40 ft
Length	27 ft	30 ft	31 ft	31 ft 4 in
Height	10 ft 4 in	10 ft 6 in	10 ft 6 in	10 ft 6 in
Wing Area	220 sq ft	275 sq ft	275 sq ft	275 sq ft
Empty Weight	3,283 lb	—	4,450 lb	4,450 lb
All-up Weight	4,600 lb	—	5,250 lb	5,250 lb
Max. Speed	287 mph	280 mph (est)	255 mph	290 mph
Service Ceiling	38,100 ft	35,000 ft (est)	31,200 ft	—
Accommodation	Pilot only	2	2	2
Production	1	nil	1	1
Sequence Nos.	7841	nil	7843	7844
	(7842 cancelled)			

Blenheim I prototype *K7033* at Filton in June 1936.

The Bristol Blenheim, Bolingbroke and Bisley (Blenheim I, IV and V), Types 142M, 149 and 160

At the first sign of Air Ministry enthusiasm for *Britain First*, Captain Barnwell prepared estimates of the performance of bomber conversions with Aquila or Mercury engines, both being intended to carry a crew of two and a bomb-load of 1,000 lb. over a range of 1,000 miles. The Mercury version was preferred and at the design conference called by A.-Comm. Verney (D.T.D.) on 9 July 1935, Barnwell tabled a layout showing the Company's proposals for converting Type 142 into a three-seater mid-wing medium bomber, Type 142M. His accompanying note described the proposals in these words:

'This machine is a direct development of the Bristol Type 142 twin-engined high-speed transport monoplane. The major alterations in the design are as follows: A Browning gun and a bomber's station have been accommodated in the nose of the body. The wings, complete with engine nacelles and undercarriages, have been raised about 16 ins. This allows for

266

internal bomb-storage inside the body and below the wing spars; it also makes the machine practically a "middle-wing" instead of a "low-wing" monoplane, which should if anything be of aerodynamic advantage. An enclosed rear-gunner's turret, of partially retractable type, is fitted into the body aft of the trailing edge of the wing and projects through the top of the body. The tailplane and elevators have been raised about 8 in. and are of increased span. The tailplane has been altered from "adjustable" to "fixed" type, hence the elevators have been increased somewhat in chord also and have been fitted with tabs (operable in flight by the pilot) to afford pitching trim. As a result the stiffness and strength of body-with-tail anchorage have been somewhat improved and there are gains in cleanness and mechanical simplicity. The structure has now been increased in strength as requisite to allow for the increased weight and for the higher load factors. All passengers' fittings, doors and windows have, of course, been deleted. In all other respects, 142M is of the same overall design as 142, and is of the same structural design except where obvious minor improvements are possible as a result of experience in building and testing 142.'

The outcome of this conference was the issue of Specification 28/35 and instructions to proceed with detail design; a contract for 150 machines followed early in September together with requests from Finland for ten 142M machines and from Lithuania for eight and a manufacturing licence. Since the Air Ministry regarded the 142M as an interim type designed as a private venture, they agreed that the Company could export a limited number to friendly governments after the urgent requirements of the R.A.F. had been met. Eventually contracts were negotiated with Finland for 18 in March 1936 and with Turkey for 12 a month later. On 22 May a Yugoslav government purchasing mission visited the 142M production line, soon after the name Blenheim Mark I had been adopted. The prototype Blenheim, No. 7986 (*K7033*), made its first flight on 25 June 1936 and after completing service trials at Martlesham Heath was cleared for production in December. The chief changes made during this period were the incorporation of controllable gills on the engine cowlings and improved carburettor air-intakes; airscrew spinners were tried, but discarded because they added to maintenance without any useful gain in speed and the tail-wheel, retracted by cables linked to the main landing gear, was locked down permanently for the same reason.

The first production Blenheims, Nos. 7987 to 8135 (*K7034* to *K7182*), were well advanced by the beginning of 1937, and as soon as their dorsal turrets (type B.I Mark I with single Lewis guns) were available, deliveries began to R.A.F. squadrons, in March, the first going to No. 114 (Bomber) Squadron, Wyton. In July 1936, the first order for 150 Blenheims was followed by one for 434 more, Nos. 8380 to 8813 (*L1097* to *L1530*), later increased by 134, Nos. 8816 to 8949 (*L1531* to *L1546* and *L4817* to *L4934*). With R.A.F. requirements met, the Company began limited exports to Finland, Turkey and Yugoslavia. The Finnish contract signed in October

1936 was for 18 Blenheims modified to carry Swedish bombs, Nos. 8137 to 8154 (*BL104* to *BL121*), which were flown away from Filton in small batches from July 1937 onwards. In April 1938 the Finnish Government acquired a licence to manufacture Blenheims in a new factory at Tampere, but none were completed before the Russo-Finnish 'Winter War' broke out in November 1939; during January and February 1940, the original 18 Blenheims, hard-pressed in the defence of Karelia, were reinforced by 24 from R.A.F. stocks, but too late to delay Finland's capitulation in March. After the armistice with Russia, Blenheim production at Tampere continued during the second Russo-Finnish War, until the final armistice in September 1944. The Yugoslav Government acquired a licence to manufacture 50 Blenheims, and bought two sample machines, Nos. 8814 and 8815, ferried in November 1937 by C. F. Uwins and C. A. Washer with British civil marks *G-AFCE* and *G-AFCF*; Yugoslav Blenheims were built by Ikarus A.D. at Zemun and the first was flown ten months after receiving drawings; 16 had been completed and 24 more were well advanced in the spring of 1941 when Germany invaded the Balkans and Yugoslav patriots sabotaged the Zemun factory to prevent its use against the Allies. Early in 1940, 20 Blenheims were diverted from R.A.F. reserves and flown from Aston Down to Zemun (bearing civil marks *YU-BAA* to *YU-BAT*) to supplement those built locally, some being equipped as fighters with two 20 mm. cannon firing forwards.

No licence production was undertaken by the Turkish government, the first two Blenheims, Nos. 8155 and 8156, dispatched by sea in October 1937, being joined between March and June 1938 by ten more (Nos. 8157 to 8166)

Blenheims of the Turkish Air Force in 1938.

The first Finnish Air Force Blenheim *BL104* on skis in 1938.

flown out with British civil marks *G-AFFP* to *G-AFFZ*; a second batch of 12 already ordered was increased to 18 (Nos. 9222 to 9239, *G-AFLA* to *G-AFLS*) and were flown out by a southerly winter route between November 1938 and February 1939. By this time Blenheim production by A. V. Roe and Co. Ltd. at Chadderton and Rootes Securities Ltd. at Speke was in full swing, while the Filton output had reached 24 per month by December 1937 and 700 had been built by March 1939. In November 1939 13 Avro-built Blenheims were flown from Bassingbourn to Rumania in a diplomatic gamble to persuade her into the Allied fold, but a year later she joined the Axis and in June 1941, like Finland, was at war with Russia; both Finnish and Rumanian Blenheims were thus opposed to the Allies in this campaign.

In August 1935 the Air Ministry issued Specification G.24/35 for a general reconnaissance and coastal bomber to replace the Avro Anson, and in November the Company tendered Type 149, differing very little from the Blenheim. The body was wider, the dorsal turret roomier and there was a navigating station amidships, with a separate radio station forward of the turret; supercharged Aquila engines were proposed for maximum range with the existing tankage, the estimated top speed being 254 m.p.h. at 5,000 ft. This tender was not accepted, and the specification was then combined with M.15/35 (for a land-based torpedo-bomber) for which the Company had also tendered. The new specification, 10/36, resulted in Type 152, which was accepted and developed into the Beaufort, but meanwhile the Air Ministry approved an interim general-reconnaissance version of the Blenheim, to which the designation Type 149 was transferred, retaining as many Blenheim components as possible, with the nose extended by 3 ft. to give a navigating and radio station ahead of the pilot. Mercury VIII engines were retained, and the outer wings contained extra fuel tanks for the range specified by G.24/35. These extra tanks were first installed in a short-nosed Blenheim (*L1222*) having a strengthened landing gear to cater for a take-off weight of 14,000 lb.; alternatively external bombs could be carried under the wing inboard of the nacelles, but this variant, Blenheim II, did not go into production because of the concurrent development of the long-nosed version.

An early production Blenheim, *K7072*, became the prototype for Type 149, which was named Bolingbroke I, but a first contract for 134 machines,

269

Blenheim II *L1222* with long-range tanks and external bombs, at Filton, September 1938.

Bolingbroke I prototype *K7072* in its original form at Filton in October 1937.

Nos. 8168 to 8301, was later cancelled to prevent dislocation of Blenheim production and replaced by the same number of Blenheims on the understanding that as many as possible would be delivered to Bolingbroke standard, as defined by Specification 11/36. The prototype Bolingbroke made its first flight on 24 September 1937, but Uwins was dissatisfied with the windscreen position, which was too far from the pilot's eyes. The nose was therefore redesigned to bring the windscreen closer to the pilot, the navigator's station being enclosed in a transparent hooding below the pilot's line of sight. The hooding still interfered with the view for landing, which was then improved by scalloping on the port side only, giving the nose a characteristic asymmetric appearance. The final long-nose modification was accepted for production in the summer of 1938, and *L1222* flew with the outer-wing tanks in September. Although the long-range Blenheim was strong enough to land at its full take-off weight, the landing run was excessive, so jettison valves, with underwing outlet pipes, were installed in the outer tanks.

It was found possible to phase in both the long nose and the extra tankage after 66 of the current batch of Blenheims had been assembled, and to avoid confusion it was decided to use the name Blenheim IV instead of Bolingbroke; the designation Blenheim III was reserved for a putative long-nose short-range variant, no production examples of which were built, because the few long-nosed machines which left the erecting hall without outer tanks had them installed before delivery to the R.A.F. in April 1939. The Blenheim IV was adopted for licence production in Canada, for coastal reconnaissance duties with the R.C.A.F., the name Bolingbroke being retained for the version manufactured by Fairchild Aircraft Ltd. at Longueuil, Quebec. At home, 232

Blenheim IV aircraft, Nos. 9240 to 9471, were ordered in 1938, bringing the total Filton production of Blenheims to 1,000 of both variants; nine of this contract were earmarked for the R.C.A.F., and equipped with direction-finding radio as for the Bolingbroke, but war broke out while this modification was in progress and only four (*P4856* to *P4859*) were delivered, the others reverting to the R.A.F. standard. Twelve others of this batch were ferried unarmed to Greece between October 1939 and February 1940, with British civil marks *G-AFXD* to *G-AFXO*, and were replaced on the Air Ministry contract by a final batch of 12, Nos. 9862 to 9873, after which Blenheim production ceased at Filton. The production jigs were then transferred to the shadow factories and to fringe firms brought in to augment repair capacity after the outbreak of war. Both the Avro and Rootes production contracts were increased several times after the Munich crisis and followed the Filton pattern in switching to Blenheim IV; 250 Blenheim I and 750 Blenheim IV were produced by A. V. Roe at Chadderton, and 422 Blenheim I and 2,060 Blenheim IV by Rootes at Speke and Blythe Bridge, Staffs. All production Blenheim IV aircraft had Mercury XV engines, which were similar to Mercury VIII, but could use 100 octane fuel at 9 lb./sq. in. boost for take-off and combat for a maximum of 5 min. Thus powered, and while unencumbered by later equipment, the Blenheim IV was the fastest bomber in the world. An unpainted, highly polished Blenheim I had been exhibited in flying attitude with undercarriage retracted at the Paris Salon in November 1936, and a similarly presented Blenheim IV at the 1938 Salon was a reminder that in spite of the Munich crisis the R.A.F. was far from being unprepared if war came.

In August 1939, when large-scale air exercises took place, Blenheims (mostly Mk. IV) equipped 16 bomber and two army co-operation squadrons of the R.A.F. at home, while the Blenheim I equipped more than a dozen squadrons in Egypt, Aden, Iraq, India and Singapore. Seven fighter squadrons, previously equipped with biplanes, were being converted to Blenheim IF fighters, adapted from the standard bomber by the addition of four fixed Browning guns in a self-contained battery under the bomb cell. On 3 September 1939, the first aircraft to cross the enemy frontier was a Blenheim IV IV (*N6215*) of No. 139 Squadron at Wyton. After $4\frac{1}{2}$ hours the crew returned with 75 photographs, taken from 24,000 ft., of the German fleet anchored in Schillig Roads; next day, in bad weather, ten Blenheims and eight Wellingtons bombed the pocket battleship *von Scheer* from mast height, four Blenheims being lost during the attack. Thereafter Blenheims made daily reconnaissance flights to bring back information for the Wellington and Hampden squadrons, but failed to provoke enemy retaliation other than minelaying by night. On 25 November, 12 Blenheim IF fighters of Nos. 25 and 601 squadrons attacked the minelayers' base at Borkum; meanwhile a special flight of three Blenheims of No. 600 Squadron operated from Manston with experimental airborne radar equipment (A.I. Mk. III) which had reached operational trial after a long programme of development begun in 1936.

Six Blenheim IV squadrons had accompanied the British Expeditionary Force to France in September; the two army co-operation squadrons (Nos. 53 from Odiham and 59 from Andover) and two bomber squadrons (Nos. 18 and 57 from Upper Heyford) formed part of the Air Component of the B.E.F., while two more bomber squadrons (Nos. 114 and 139 from Wyton) formed the Advanced Air Striking Force in company with eight Fairey Battle squadrons. The long range of the Blenheim IV was exploited by flying round trips over Germany, starting from France and returning direct to England with photographs.

Early operational experience dictated many urgent modifications which R.A.F. ground crews could not cope with unaided, so the Company's Service Department was expanded rapidly to provide skilled working parties at squadron airfields, installing armour plate, self-sealing tanks, reflector gunsights, additional short-wave radio (including I.F.F.) and most important of all, extra fire-power. The early B.I Marks I and II turrets with single Lewis guns were already superseded by the B.I Mark III with a Vickers K gun; these were now modified to mount two K guns, becoming B.I Mark IIIA, which were modified again, as soon as supplies permitted, to B.I Mark IV, carrying two Browning guns with continuous belt feed and a much improved rate of fire, but at first Browning guns were in short supply and reserved for fighters. During this development, the all-up weight of the Blenheim IV had increased to 14,500 lb. in January 1940 and performance and manœuvrability suffered, but the increased fire-power of the Mark IV turret enabled Blenheims to hold their own in many encounters with superior enemy forces, as, for instance, on 19 January 1940, when nine Blenheims were attacked off Borkum by a large number of Me 110 twin-engined fighters and fought them off in a running battle lasting half an hour; several times single Blenheims on patrol fought off four or five Me 109 single-seaters and escaped into cloud cover. Blenheims were the first to spot the enemy fleet leaving Kiel on 7 April under cover of bad weather to invade Denmark and Norway, but were unable to intervene effectively, although for the next fortnight they kept up repeated attacks on Stavanger and Aalborg airports where enemy transport aircraft were concentrated, and their range was not enough for adequate support to the allied landings at Narvik and north of Trondhjem.

Blenheim IF *L1336* of No. 248 Sqn R.A.F. at Northolt in 1940. (*Crown copyright.*)

On 19 May the Netherlands were invaded and Blenheim fighters and bombers attacked enemy transports and gliders as they landed on beaches near the Hague; six Blenheim fighters of No. 600 Squadron made a desperate attack on Waalhaven airport, only one returning to base at Manston. Attacks were kept up all the next day as enemy transport advanced through Belgium, and on 12 May Blenheims destroyed a column 5 miles long between Maastricht and Tongres but failed to breach the key bridges over the Albert Canal. On 17 May 12 Blenheim fighters attacked tanks and troops near Gembloux and were intercepted by a large force of Me 109 fighters; again only one Blenheim returned. The pace was becoming too hot for overtired crews and overtaxed aircraft as enemy fighter cover increased, and on 19 May the A.A.S.F. retired to England, followed two days later by the Air Component, many Blenheims being abandoned with such small but fatal defects as burst tyres, in spite of extraordinary risks being taken by pilots to bring them back to England if they could be flown off. On 5 June the Luftwaffe made its first night raid on London and Blenheim night fighters began patrols; on 18 June they shot down five bombers by moonlight, and on the night of 2–3 July a Blenheim IF of the Fighter Interception Unit at Ford claimed the first kill by means of A.I. Mark III radar.

Blenheim IVF *N6239* of No. 248 Sqn R.A.F. in 1941. (*Crown copyright.*)

By this time a total of 1,375 four-gun fighter conversion sets had been made by the Southern Railway workshops, and Blenheim IVF fighters had gone into service with Coastal Command; these were mainly employed in conjunction with Blenheim IV bombers of No. 2 Group in attacks on the Channel coast harbours from Ostend to Cherbourg where enemy invasion fleets could assemble. On 15 August three Coastal Blenheim IVF fighters intercepted 24 Heinkel bombers returning from a raid and shot down four without loss; three days later a similar patrol intervened in an attack on Portsmouth and shot down two Ju 87 dive bombers. Attacks on harbours and shipping increased in intensity during September, when the enemy day offensive began to give place to night raids. Several attempts were made to increase the fire-power of the Blenheim fighter, one having twin 20 mm. Hispano cannon in place of the four Brownings and two others (*L1290* and *V5427*) having dorsal turrets firing forward (B.I Mark IVF). One attempt was made to achieve maximum speed at low weight for photographic reconnaissance; this was a Blenheim I

Blenheim I *L1348* unarmed, lightened and cleaned-up for high-speed P.R. role; Staverton, 1940.

(*L1348*) with dorsal turret removed and all bomb doors and other joints carefully taped over, finished overall in well-primed smooth sky-blue low-drag paint. Rotol constant speed airscrews were fitted and the nose and wing tips were specially faired, but the result did not warrant further development.

The collapse of France gave Italy an opportunity to emulate in the Eastern Mediterranean the example already set by Germany in Western Europe. From June 1940 Blenheims kept up a ceaseless rearguard action in the Western Desert as Wavell's army withdrew half-way to Alexandria. Other Blenheims in the Sudan, some manned by Free French aircrews escaped from Tunis and Lake Chad, patrolled the frontier with Abyssinia, while a few based on Aden gave unavailing aid to overwhelmed Allied troops in Somaliland. In October Italy declared war on Greece, whose Air Force already included 12 Blenheim IV bombers, but in response to her appeal for help only four R.A.F. squadrons, including two of Blenheim bombers and one of Blenheim fighters, could be spared from Egypt. At first reinforcements of Blenheims were flown from England to Malta, sometimes bombing Turin and Milan en route, and thence, after refuelling, to Egypt to make good the losses, and to compensate for their relatively small numbers in the desert at this period, many Blenheims had 'banshees' consisting of hardwood sirens mounted under the nose which could be turned across the air stream, causing them to emit a blood-curdling wail; these had a useful demoralising effect on inexperienced troops at a critical time, but were of no lasting value. Then Malta had become a target for enemy bombers from North Africa and Sicily, and an alternative ferry route was organised overland from Takoradi on the Gold Coast. The first Blenheims arrived at Khartum in September 1940 along the desert trail from Kano surveyed 16 years earlier by the R.A.F., and the fall of Bardia and Benghazi to Wavell's advance just before Christmas released two more Blenheim squadrons for Greece.

Then the Germans occupied Italian airfields west of Benghazi, forcing the Allies to retreat to Mersa Matruh, and on 6 April poured into Greece and Yugoslavia from Bulgaria. The Yugoslav Blenheims made one raid on Sofia before they were engulfed; the R.A.F., operating on either flank of the Pindus mountains from waterlogged airfields against overwhelming odds, were forced back to Athens after losing most of their Blenheims on the ground. The 24 Blenheims surviving from five bomber squadrons flew back to

Egypt on 22 April while No. 30 Fighter Squadron, assisted by nine Blenheim fighters of No. 203 Squadron flown up from Aden, covered the evacuation of the Allied troops to Crete. In spite of heroic efforts to maintain long range fighter cover from Malta and Egypt after the local landing grounds had been captured, the Blenheim fighters could do little to avert the fall of Crete.

Meanwhile German attacks on Atlantic convoys increased, pocket battleships being replaced by vast numbers of submarines, which were tenaciously attacked by Blenheim bombers of No. 2 Group, usually at mast height, thus exposing their aircrews increasingly to heavy gunfire. A structural limit to the all-up weight at 16,000 lb. precluded the use of front armour-plating with coastal and bomber equipment, so many squadrons improvised a free K-gun in the nose which was so successful that it became an official modification with the gun mounted in a gimbal. Blenheims were usually equipped with single backward-firing guns in blisters under the nose emergency exit hatch, and these were useful against pursuing fighters but ineffective against beam

Blenheim IV *V6083* of No. 18 Sqn R.A.F. in 1941, showing twin under defence guns. (*'Aeroplane'* copyright.)

The first Avro-built Blenheim *L6594* at Boscombe Down before being fitted with downward-firing C.O.W. gun. (*Crown copyright.*)

attacks; later a controllable twin-Browning mounting (Frazer-Nash F.N.54) was adopted by those squadrons of Bomber Command which flew larger formations than No. 2 Group. In the early days of the A.A.S.F. there were many local lash-ups of rear-firing guns, such as the Blenheim with a K-gun in the stern and in each nacelle and an interesting experiment, intended as an anti-submarine weapon, was a 37 mm. C.O.W. gun rigged between the spars of Blenheim I *L6594* to fire vertically downwards. Two other experimental

Blenheim I *L1242* with tricycle landing gear, showing static tests on nose-wheel; Filton, June 1939.

Blenheims deserve mention: the first being Blenheim I *L1242* with a fixed nose-wheel undercarriage; and the other Blenheim IV *L4888* with a hemispherical nose radome for centimetric radar.

When the German invasion of Russia began in June 1941, Bomber Command's attacks on enemy industrial targets were stepped up to prevent Luftwaffe units being released to the eastern front, and Blenheims made massed escorted daylight raids on heavily defended key targets. On 12 August 1941, 54 Blenheims from six squadrons attacked power stations near Cologne, and smaller formations raided shipping at Rotterdam on 26 July and 28 August, and a chemical plant at Mazingarbe on 18 September. More than 300,000 tons of coastal shipping were sunk in three months for the loss of 68 Blenheims.

Then came Pearl Harbour and the Japanese invasion of Malaya, where the 150 aircraft included two squadrons of Blenheim bombers and one of Blenheim IF night fighters, with one more squadron of Blenheim I bombers in Burma. Japanese raids on Rangoon began in December, and early in January No. 113 Squadron arrived there after flying their Blenheims from Egypt; pausing only to refuel and re-arm, they went straight on to bomb the main enemy supply base at Bangkok docks, only then retiring to Lashio for inspections and repairs. Blenheims from Rangoon made daily sorties against Japanese columns advancing across the Salween and Sittang rivers until withdrawn to Magwe on 7 March, whence they bombed Japanese aircraft arriving at Rangoon airport; finally on 21st March they were virtually wiped out on the ground by an attack by 230 enemy bombers lasting 25 hours.

Nearer home, the battle raged in North Africa, with the rival armies and air forces shuttling back and forth between Benghazi and El Alamein. The final phase began on 8 November 1942 when the First Army landed at Casablanca, accompanied by No. 18 Squadron, R.A.F., equipped with the final variant of the Blenheim, the tropicalised Mark V bomber. This had originated from a proposal by the Company in January 1940 for a specialised direct-support bomber derived from the Blenheim with alternative roles as a low-level fighter or a dual-control trainer. In reply, the Air Staff defined the aircraft's functions

Bisley I prototype *AD657* flying near Boscombe Down in 1941. (*Crown copyright.*)

in Specification B.6/40 as 'short range bombing and operations in direct support of an army such as dive-bombing and low level bombing of mechanical transport and troops on the road, supply and ammunition dumps, and rail heads'. The Company proposed a direct modification of the Blenheim IV, Type 160, named Bisley I, and the M.A.P. wished the detail redesign to be undertaken by Rootes, who were to produce the aircraft, but the Company preferred to organise a branch drawing office to supervise Rootes' staff until they had gained experience, and requested that two prototypes should be built at Filton; this was agreed and a contract awarded for Nos. 9874 and 9875 (*AD657* and *AD661*).

The Bisley resembled a Blenheim with a new nose section containing four Browning guns with 1,000 rounds apiece, firing forward. The windscreen was improved and the whole cockpit was protected by about 600 lb. of externally applied detachable armour plate and the dorsal turret (type B.X), carrying two Browning guns and a gyro gun-sight was also heavily armoured and could be continuously rotated through the full circle. The engines were Mercury XVI for maximum power at ground level using 100-octane fuel and drove constant-speed airscrews. There was no possibility of flying the prototypes before autumn, and after Dunkirk there was no urgent need for a dive-bomber, so the specification was revised to include both direct-support and high-level bombing roles to replace the Blenheim IV. The nose was redesigned so that the four-gun battery could be interchanged with a navigating and bomb-aiming station, with an offset aiming window; at the same time a long detachable floor panel on the starboard side was replaced by a 'bath' forming a foot-well for the navigator and a fairing for a twin-Browning F.N.54 rear-defence mounting; in the high-level role the armour plate was removed but oxygen and comprehensive radio equipment took up most of the weight saved thereby. The wing spar webs and undercarriage were strengthened and the familiar undercarriage aprons were replaced by low-drag doors; Mercury 25 or 30 engines were fitted and the name was changed from Bisley to Blenheim V, the first prototype, *AD657*, making its first flight at Filton on 24 February 1941. Although at a maximum all-up weight of 17,000

The first Rootes-built pre-production Blenheim V *DJ702*. (*Crown copyright.*)

lb. the Blenheim V was not as fast as Blenheim IV, it was better protected and 942 of the new variant were ordered to follow the last Blenheim IV at Blythe Bridge off the same assembly jigs.

Deliveries to No. 18 Squadron at West Raynham began in the summer of 1942, a few dual control versions without turrets also being delivered to Fighter Command Operational Training Units at East Fortune, Charterhall, Winfield and Church Fenton. Tropical equipment for operational bomber squadrons required the R.1155 radio to be located at the navigator's station, making a slight bulge in the roof line, and the majority of Blenheim V deliveries were to this standard.

No. 18 Squadron went into action in raids on Bizerta and Sfax in November, and on 4 December 1942 ten aircraft led by W/Cmdr. H. G. Malcolm bombed an enemy airfield at the request of the army and were all shot down by a force of 50 to 60 enemy fighters on their way back, only one crew surviving to tell the tale. For his tenacity and fearless leadership in this and previous raids Malcolm was posthumously awarded the Victoria Cross, but it was realised that the Blenheim V was no match for modern fighters, in spite of its turret, and it was thereafter confined to operations where an adequate escort could be given or enemy fighters were unlikely to be met. The Blenheim V was the product of a school of thought which contended that adequate armour and armament could make up for a deficient performance; the opposite school claimed that speed was in itself sufficient defence and pointed to the Mosquito, which later justified their argument. The Blenheim V did good work in the Malayan campaign, where the climate was unsuitable for the Mosquito because of its wood construction. Some Blenheim Vs were disposed of to the Turkish and Portuguese governments, the latter opting to purchase some of the aircraft which landed in transit to Morocco and would otherwise have been interned, since Portugal was neutral territory.

In Canada, the Fairchild Aircraft Company eventually built 676 Bolingbrokes, the first 18 to Bristol drawings and including components imported from England; they had Mercury VIII engines and were designated Bolingbroke I (R.C.A.F. *702* to *719*). One of them (*705*) crashed during an early test flight and was rebuilt with American equipment and instruments, becoming Bolingbroke II. Another (*717*) was fitted with Edo floats for evaluation as a

278

Bolingbroke III seaplane *717* at Longueuil, Canada, in 1939.

seaplane, Bolingbroke III, but subsequently reconverted to a landplane. Two hundred and one production aircraft which followed were entirely Fairchild-built to American standards developed from Bolingbroke II. These, called Bolingbroke IV (R.C.A.F. *9001* to *9201*), were equipped for general reconnaissance with dinghies, de-icing boots on wings and tail surfaces and interchangeable wheel- and ski-landing gear. As the German submarine offensive in the Atlantic grew in ferocity, with the possibility of Mercury supplies for Canada being interrupted, a successful trial installation was made in *9005* of Pratt and Whitney Twin-Wasp Junior (SB4G) engines, and 14 more (*9010* to *9023*) were completed to the same standard, Bolingbroke IV-W. Mercury supplies did not fail after all, but as there was a shortage of

Bolingbroke IV-C with Cyclone G3B engines at Longueuil in 1941.

100-octane fuel in Canada, an effort was made to improve the Bolingbroke's take-off performance on 93-octane, so *9074* was fitted with Wright Cyclone G3B engines, becoming Bolingbroke IV-C. Its take-off performance was better than with Mercury XVs, but equally good results were obtained with the Mercury XX, which was adopted for future production. The 220th and subsequent Bolingbrokes (*9851* to *10256*) were equipped as navigational and gunnery trainers (Bolingbroke IV-T) and remained in service for Commonwealth aircrew training until the end of the war, a few being used later for forestry patrol and photographic survey. Many were sold as surplus in 1946 including *9892* bought by George Maude of Fulford, B.C., who presented it in 1963 for restoration and preservation in the R.C.A.F. Museum at Ottawa. In 1969 *10001* was restored for the R.A.F. Museum.

Bolingbroke IV *9892* at Rockcliffe Airport, Ottawa, after restoration in 1964. (*R.C.A.F. photo.*)

Production of the Blenheim in Finland amounted to 15 Mk I in 1941, 30 Mk I in 1943 and ten Mk IV in 1944; a further five of the latter were in progress when the armistice was signed on 4 September 1944 and were not completed; about 40 were serviceable in 1945 when the Finnish Air Force was re-established on a peacetime basis. Finnish-built Blenheims were flown until 1956 on forestry and survey duties, and were the latest to remain in service anywhere in the world; the last one (*BL200*) is preserved at the Finnish Air Force base at Luonetjärvi and is now the only European survivor of the 6212 offspring of *Britain First* built over a span of ten years. The sun-bleached wreck of a Blenheim IV (*Z7513*), found in 1959 near the Kufra Oasis, Libya, where it had been abandoned in 1942 with fuel exhausted, was broken up in 1960 by local Bedouin and only the wing spars remained in 1965.

As mentioned in the caption to the frontispiece photo, a Blenheim IV rebuilt by the British Aerial Museum from the remains of an RCAF Bolingbroke was damaged beyond repair in June 1987, only a month after the first flight of the rebuilt aircraft. The accident occurred after a touch-and-go landing during an air display at Denham. The crew suffered minor injuries. An accident investigation report indicated that the cause was rich-mixture cutting of the Mercury engines when the throttles were fully opened more rapidly than advised in the pilot's notes for the type.

The Duxford team which rebuilt this Blenheim has subsequently begun work on restoring another ex-RCAF aircraft to flying condition. This airframe came from the Strathallan Collection in Scotland. Its

Blenheim IV *BL200* built at Tampere in 1944 and now preserved at Luonetjärvi.

280

serial number is 10201 and it was one of the last Blenheims to be built. The target year for the first flight of this reconstructed aircraft is 1992.

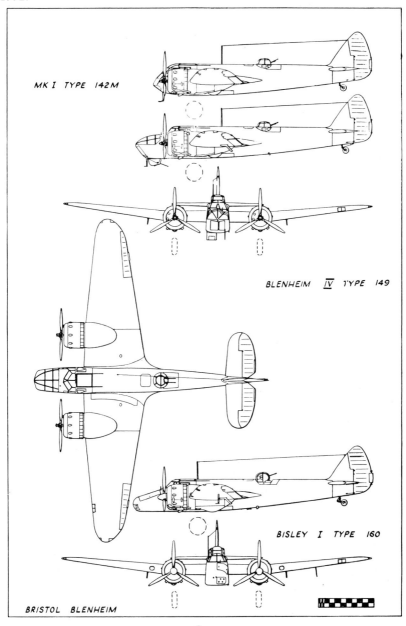

MK I TYPE 142M

BLENHEIM IV TYPE 149

BISLEY I TYPE 160

BRISTOL BLENHEIM

SPECIFICATION AND DATA

Types: 142M, 149 & 160 (Blenheim, Bolingbroke and Bisley)

Manufacturers: The Bristol Aeroplane Co. Ltd., Filton, Bristol ⎫
A. V. Roe & Co. Ltd., Chadderton, Lancs
Rootes Securities Ltd., Speke, Liverpool, Lancs ⎬ (Blenheim I & IV)
Valtion Lentokonetehdas, Tampere, Finland ⎭
Ikarus A.D., Zemun, Beograd, Yugoslavia (Blenheim I only)
Fairchild Aircraft Ltd., Longueuil, P.Q., Canada (Bolingbroke)
The Bristol Aeroplane Co. Ltd., Filton, Bristol ⎫
Rootes Securities Ltd., Blythe Bridge, Staffs ⎬ (Blenheim V)

Power Plants: (Blenheim I, Bolingbroke I & III) Two 840 hp Bristol Mercury VIII
(Blenheim IV, Bolingbroke IV) Two 920 hp Bristol Mercury XV
(Bolingbroke IV & IV-T) Two 920 hp Bristol Mercury XX
(Bolingbroke IV-C) Two 850 hp Wright Cyclone G3B
(Bolingbroke IV-W) Two 750 hp Pratt & Whitney Twin-Wasp Jr SB4G
(Bisley I) Two 950 hp Bristol Mercury XVI
(Blenheim V) Two 950 hp Bristol Mercury 25 or 30

Variant	Blenheim I	Blenheim IV & Bolingbroke I, II, IV	Bolingbroke III	Bisley I	Blenheim V
Span	56 ft 4 in	56 ft 4 in	56 ft 4 in	56 ft 1 in	56 ft 1 in
Length	39 ft 9 in	42 ft 9 in	46 ft 3 in	43 ft 4 in	43 ft 11 in
Height	12 ft 10 in	12 ft 10 in	18 ft	12 ft 10 in	12 ft 10 in
Wing Area	469 sq ft	469 sq ft	469 sq ft	469 sq ft	469 sq ft
Empty Weight	8,100 lb	9,800 lb	8,700 lb	11,000 lb	11,000 lb
All-up Weight	12,250 lb	12,500–14,400 lb	13,400 lb	17,000 lb	17,000 lb
Max. Speed	285 mph	295–260 mph	262 mph	262 mph	260 mph
Service Ceiling	32,000 ft	31,500 ft	26,000 ft	31,000 ft	31,000 ft
Range	1,125 miles	1,950 miles	1,800 miles	1,600 miles	1,600 miles
Accommodation	3	3	3	2	3
Production	1,415	3,853	(1 conv)	2	942
Sequence Nos.	See Appendices B and D		—	9874 9875	—

Beaufort I prototype, showing original nacelle design, at Filton in October 1938.

The Bristol Beaufort, Type 152

In September 1935, the Air Staff issued two Specifications, M.15/35 and G.24/35, for a land-based twin-engined torpedo-bomber and a twin-engined general reconnaissance aeroplane, respectively, and the evolution of the latter into the Bolingbroke has already been described. In the former the torpedo had to be internally stowed, and Type 150 submitted in November was basically a Blenheim with the pilot's cockpit moved forward 54 in. and the dorsal turret moved back to preserve balance, and a radio station between the pilot and the wing, but no navigating station; the fuselage was parallel from nose to turret and 44 ft. 3 in. long, the span being 58 ft. As the weight was higher than the Blenheim's, Perseus VI engines were specified, the estimated top speed being 280 m.p.h. at 5,000 ft.

As the two specifications could be met by aeroplanes directly derived from the Blenheim it seemed possible to combine both roles in a single design, so in April 1936 the Company submitted Type 152, in which the nose extended a further 9 in. to accommodate both a navigation station and torpedo, with the navigator near the pilot, and the radio station and camera side-by-side forward of the turret. The Air Staff accepted a half-exposed position for the torpedo but concluded that a crew of four was essential, so the fuselage was enlarged to raise the pilot's station above the front of the torpedo cell, with a separate radio station close behind him, the raised roof line faired into the top of the dorsal turret and the navigating station combined with the bomb-aiming position in the nose. This layout was satisfactory, providing both pilot and navigator with the best possible view.

Specification 10/36 was drafted to cover the new design, which the Air Staff wished to see in production at Filton as soon as the Blenheim line could be transferred to the shadow factories. Seventy-eight, Nos. 8302 to 8379 (*L4441* to *L4518*), were ordered in September 1936 and named Beaufort in December, with the Duke of Beaufort's consent. It was then found that the Beaufort with the Perseus VI would be slower than the Blenheim, so the two-row Taurus was substituted, although it was not yet cleared for production and for a time there was doubt whether it could be produced in sufficient numbers, but at the end of 1937 the Beaufort was finalised with Taurus III engines and a new dorsal turret, type B.IV Mark I, which the Company wished to equip with twin Browning guns, but these were all earmarked for fighters and only single K-guns were available.

Fedden had developed a special low-drag Taurus cowling, with a standard exhaust ring forward forming the leading edge of the N.A.C.A. cowling, which was of long chord ending in vertical exit slots flanking the nacelle sides under the wing, so eliminating any disturbance of air flow above the wing. The exit slots had controllable flaps, and the bottom of the nacelle was closed by a fairing plate on the rearward retracting undercarriage. Captain Barnwell took a keen personal interest in this installation, but the first Beaufort did not fly until 15 October 1938, eleven weeks after his death, delayed by overheating during ground running, and this necessitated an orthodox cowling with circumferential gills. The undercarriage aprons caused severe yawing when landing gear extension was asymmetric, as often happened, so early flights of *L4441* were undertaken without them until replaced by sideways-opening nacelle doors.

The Australian government chose the Beaufort for manufacture with local resources, and early in 1939 a British Air Mission visited Australia to arrange for production in railway and industrial workshops. About 80 Australian railway engineers and technicians came to Filton for intensive training as key personnel; large sections of the railway shops at Chullora (N.S.W.), Newport (Vic.) and Islington (S.A.) were set aside for aircraft work and construction of two main assembly plants at Mascot (Sydney) and Fishermen's Bend (Melbourne) began. Contracts were placed for 180 Beauforts on 1 July 1939, half of them for the R.A.A.F. and half for R.A.F. squadrons in Malaya. The eighth Filton-built Beaufort (*L4448*) was shipped out as a sample airframe, together with 20 sets of airframe parts; it was agreed that Taurus engines, turrets, instruments, forgings, extrusions and other special materials were to be exported from England until they could be produced locally. In October 1939 the Australian government decided to manufacture Pratt and Whitney Twin-Wasp engines for their own Beauforts, so only the 90 R.A.F. Beauforts would have had imported Taurus, but these were cancelled and Twin Wasps adopted for all Australian-built Beauforts. A twin-float Beaufort was investigated by the Filton project office for use in Australia and Canada, but not built.

The Beaufort was larger than the Blenheim, although only 2 ft. greater in span, but its structure weight was proportionately lower due to refinements in design and the use of high-strength light alloy forgings and extruded sections in place of high-tensile steel plates and angles; the centre-section was inserted into the rear fuselage, and the nacelle structure formed an integral part of the ribs to which the main undercarriages were attached; the front fuselage and the sternframe were detachable at jig-drilled transport joints, as were the outer wings and wing tips; thus it was well adapted for sub-contract manufacture of components which were brought together for final assembly in ordinary road or rail vehicles, no component being of excessive size. The Vickers undercarriage was similar to the Blenheim's, but larger and had hydraulic retraction and a cartridge-operated emergency lowering system; the flap gear was hydraulic and the brakes and gun-firing system pneumatic. In the first nine Beauforts the bomb-aimer's windows were of curved plastic, but were replaced by flat safety-glass panels with better optical properties.

Service trials of the Beaufort were delayed by engine overheating, cured by modified inter-cylinder baffles and cowling and more efficient oil-coolers. Some turbulence over the tail was caused by the turret and cured by alterations to the adjacent rear fuselage shroud. Nearly a year elapsed after the first flight before production Beauforts were cleared for issue to the R.A.F., by which time the Filton contract for Beauforts had been increased to 350 aircraft. The first squadron to be re-equipped was No. 22 at Thorney Island, in January 1940. They began torpedo training a month later and moved to North Coates in April to begin operations as mine-layers in enemy coastal waters, but the teething troubles of the Taurus were not completely cured and several engine failures occurred; in May the C.O. of the squadron, Wing-Cmdr. H. M. Mellor, was lost returning from a mine-laying sortie, because of a fault in the cylinder head relief valve designed to prevent hydraulic locking of the sleeve-valve, and all Beauforts were grounded in June for engine modifications, being cleared again for operations at the end of August. The second Beaufort squadron, No. 42, at Leuchars, re-equipped shortly after No. 22 and undertook 'Rover' raids against shipping in the Skagerrak and bases in Norway, but had insufficient range to support the Trondhjem and Narvik landings, but on 21 June nine Beauforts from Wick bombed the *Scharnhorst* shortly after the aircraft-carrier *Glorious* had been sunk. Nos. 22 and 42 Squadrons were the only operational Beaufort units until the summer of 1941 when two more were re-equipped, No. 86 at North Coates and No. 217 at Thorney Island, to replace No. 22 which had moved to St. Eval during the winter, to concentrate on the German submarine base at l'Orient. Nos. 22 and 42 Squadrons were highly mobile and operated detached flights from whichever base was most suitable for the immediate task. Thus one of No. 22's Beauforts flew from North Coates on 15 September to torpedo the 5,000 ton transport *Ijmuiden* at Flushing, and another from St. Eval on 6 April 1941 scored a direct hit on the battleship *Gneisenau* in Brest harbour which nearly sank her and kept her out of commission until the end of the year; in this gallant attack from a height of only 30 ft., the Beaufort was destroyed by a withering barrage after her pilot, F/O Kenneth Campbell, had released his torpedo, and he was posthumously awarded the Victoria Cross. To give the aircrews a better chance of survival in low-level attacks, many Beauforts were armed with two K-guns on gimbals in the extreme nose, and single K-guns were installed on pivots to fire on the beam against enemy fighters; there were the same backward-firing under-defence Browning guns on the Beaufort as the Blenheim, but they were not very useful and most units discarded them; an experimental twin-Browning nose mounting was tested on a Beaufort, but not adopted. The Air Staff were anxious to increase Beaufort production, and urgently wanted a better single-engine performance, but there was little hope of increasing Taurus output and still less of developing the improved Taurus XX, with two-speed blower and fully-feathering airscrew, to production standard. In the summer of 1940 there were proposals for the Beaufort II with Pratt and Whitney Twin-Wasps and Beaufort III with Merlin XX; the latter was not built, but as the Australian sample Beaufort (*L4448*) had been successfully modified to take Twin-Wasps and the Australian Government had adopted Twin-Wasps for all their Beauforts, the Air Ministry decided to specify these engines for a new batch of Beauforts to be built at Filton. Beaufort I (*N1110*) was converted and flown at Filton in November 1940 and the engine change was approved for production; *L4448* made its first flight at Mascot in May 1941, and the first production Beaufort II (AW 244) flew at Filton in September 1941, a month after the first Australian Beaufort V (*T9540*), the first of 90 ordered for re-equipment of Nos. 36 and 100 Squadrons at Singapore. The Beaufort II and V had Twin-Wasp S3C4G engines and fully-feathering Curtiss electric airscrews, which gave them an excellent single-engine performance as well as improved take-off; they had B.IV Mark IE turrets with two K-guns at first, but some Beaufort IIs had B.IV Mark II with twin Brownings; later still these were superseded by a modified Blenheim turret, the B.I Mark V with fixed cupola and twin Brownings. The Beaufort V retained the original folding D.F. loop of the Beaufort I, but in the Beaufort II this was replaced by a small low-drag fixed loop in a plastic fairing. The Beaufort II was more stable than the Beaufort I, which was improved to a similar standard by small local extensions of the trailing edge behind the nacelles. After the fall of Singapore, all Beaufort V production was transferred to the R.A.A.F. and those ordered for the R.A.F. were replaced by an additional 90 from Filton, comprising 85 Mark I and five Mark II; soon afterwards a new contract for 150 Mark II was

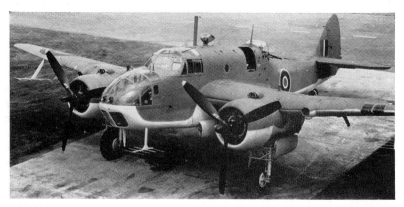

Beaufort II *DD930* with Yagi A.S.V. aerials, gimbal nose-guns and B.I Mk V turret at Filton in 1942.

Late series Beaufort I *EK982* with Taurus XVIs and Youngman dive-brakes, at Filton in 1942.

placed; this was subsequently increased to 690, of which the final 500 were intended as Beaufort IV with Taurus XX and B.XV four-gun turrets, one prototype of which was converted from Beaufort II *AW372*, but not cleared for production; it was then hoped to continue with the Beaufort II; but supplies of Twin Wasps were limited because of enemy attacks on Atlantic convoys, and after the 165th Beaufort II production was switched back to the Mark I with improved Taurus XII or XVI engines, strengthened structure, B.I Mark V turret and A.S.V. radar with Yagi aerials. Some of these were fitted with Youngman pneumatic dive-brakes, which were not liked by squadron pilots and so were locked up after a short time and removed later. Later Beauforts were fully tropicalised and equipped No. 39 Squadron at Alexandria and Malta, which was joined in June 1942 by No. 217, equipped, like No. 86, with the Beaufort II. No. 86 was the last Beaufort squadron operating in home waters and, although unable to stop the *Scharnhorst* and *Gneisenau* from escaping through the Straits of Dover on 12 February 1942, co-operated in the attack on the *Prinz Eugen* off Haugesund on 17 May 1942, when three torpedo hits were scored. No. 86 Squadron moved to Malta in July 1942 to replace No. 217, which went to Burma later in the year.

The supply of Twin Wasps for Australian Beauforts never failed because most of them were manufactured locally by General Motors-Holdens Ltd., but after the first 50 Beaufort Vs a shortage of home-built Twin Wasp S3C4G engines had to be filled by imported S1C3G engines in the next 100 aircraft, which were known as Beaufort VI with Curtiss airscrews; after 40 of these had been completed no more Curtiss airscrews were available, so Hamilton bracket-type had to be fitted instead, and with these and S1C3G engines the aircraft was called Beaufort VII, while the subsequent 30 with S3C4G engines became Beaufort VA. By the end of the first 180 aircraft the anomalies had been resolved, and a new contract was placed for the revised Beaufort VIII to bring the total Australian production up to 700 Beauforts; these had B.I Mark V turrets as in the later Beaufort II, with additonal tankage and Loran radar equipment, and the last 140 Beaufort VIIIs had Australian-made Mark VE turrets with 0·5 in. calibre Browning guns. Production of the Beaufort VIII began in November 1942 and continued at the rate of 30 per month until August 1944.

Australian Beauforts played an important part in the campaign against the Japanese. The first six were flown to Singapore before the Japanese invasion,

The last Australian-built Beaufort VIII *A9-700* flying near Sydney in 1944.

but five returned to Australia because they were not fully operational and the sixth was retained for photographic reconnaissance. By the summer of 1942 Beauforts had taken their place in the battle and had used their torpedoes effectively against the Japanese invasion fleet at Normanby Island. Later they took part in long-range attacks on Japanese shipping from the Solomans to Northern New Guinea and Timor. After Beaufort production ceased in Australia, 46 of the final production batch were converted into unarmed transports with a faired-in turret position, as Beaufort IX; one of these

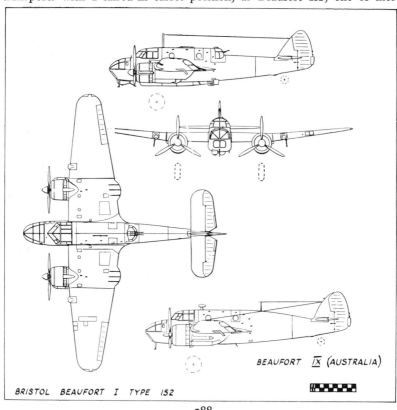

BEAUFORT IX (AUSTRALIA)

BRISTOL BEAUFORT I TYPE 152

288

(*A9-201*) was further modified with a large under-belly compartment for four passengers or cargo, but this conversion was rejected and subsequently restored to Beaufort IX standard. A distinctive feature of the Australian Beaufort was the large fin introduced on the ninety-first aircraft and made retrospective on all, including *L4448*. A similar fin was tested at Filton on a Beaufort II (*AW304*) and the Beaufort IV (*AW372*) and considered an advantage in single-engined cruising flight, but by then the Beaufort line at Filton had ended, and a final batch of 250 Beaufort IIs was being built from sub-contracted components at Banwell; the last 121 machines of this batch were supplied as dual-control trainers, with turret positions faired over, for twin-engined instruction at O.T.U.s and many earlier Beauforts were similarly modified by the R.A.F.

Beauforts were taken out of R.A.F. service at the end of 1944, and none survived the end of the war except in Australia, where some remained stored in the open, but were not flown again by the R.A.A.F. apart from two to spray insecticide on a plague of grasshoppers in 1946, when crops were threatened over a wide area. No Beauforts were ever flown by civil operators, and only one or two were exported outside the British Commonwealth (to Turkey as trainers for Beaufighter pilots); a few Beaufort trainers transferred to the R.C.A.F. found their way as far west as Patricia Bay, British Columbia. Altogether 1,429 Beauforts were built by the Company at Filton and Banwell, in addition to the 700 built in Australia.

SPECIFICATION AND DATA

Type: 152, Beaufort I–IX

Manufacturers: The Bristol Aeroplane Co. Ltd., Filton, Bristol and Banwell, Somerset

Beaufort Division, Dept. of Aircraft Production, Mascot (N.S.W.) and Fishermen's Bend (Vic.) Australia

Power Plants: (Mk I) Two 1,130 hp Bristol Taurus VI, XII or XVI

(Mks II, V, VA, VIII & IX) Two 1,200 hp Pratt & Whitney Twin-Wasp S3C4G

(Mks VI & VII) Two 1,200 hp Pratt & Whitney Twin-Wasp S1C3G

(Mk III) Two 1,250 hp Rolls Royce Merlin XX

(Mk IV) Two 1,250 hp Bristol Taurus XX

Mark	I	II, V–VIII	IX
Span	57 ft 10 in	57 ft 10 in	57 ft 10 in
Length	44 ft 3 in	44 ft 3 in	44 ft 3 in
Height	14 ft 3 in	14 ft 3 in	14 ft 3 in
Wing Area	503 sq ft	503 sq ft	503 sq ft
Empty Weight	13,100 lb	14,070 lb	13,000 lb
All-up Weight	21,230 lb	22,500 lb	20,000 lb
Max. Speed	260 mph	265 mph	250 mph
Service Ceiling	16,500 ft	22,500 ft	23,000 ft
Range	1,600 miles	1,450 miles	1,500 miles
Accommodation	4	4	7
Production	1,014	1,115	(46 conversions)
Sequence Nos.			—
	See Appendices B and D		

The Bristol Beaufighter, Type 156

The Beaufort was quicker to build than the Blenheim because of its well-planned unit construction and formed the basis of a fast well-armed day bomber, Type 155, projected at Filton in the summer of 1938. This was a mid-wing monoplane with two Taurus engines, but differed from the Beaufort in having a nose-wheel landing gear, twin rudders and dorsal and ventral hydraulic turrets each mounting two 20 mm. cannon; these turrets (types B.VI and B.VII) were designed and a Lockheed nose oleo-leg was being tested on a modified Blenheim when the Air Ministry ruled that high-grade aluminium alloys must be conserved in new designs, and issued Specification B.18/38 calling for a bomber like Type 155, but with a composite structure of welded steel tube and plywood, so as to make full use of the light engineering and woodworking industries in time of war. The Company completed wind-tunnel tests on a model of Type 155; but after Capt. Barnwell's death, work was discontinued in favour of an Armstrong Whitworth design which finally became the Albemarle.

The Company had also tendered for a cannon-armed fighter monoplane to meet Specification F.37/35, derived from a single Hercules-engined unarmed high-speed mid-wing design study (Type 151, to Specification 35/35); this was the low-wing Type 153, with four 20 mm. Hispano cannon in the wing. The 151 in racing trim was estimated to be capable of 440 m.p.h. on 100-octane fuel, or 395 m.p.h. on 87-octane. The 153 with a military load required an increase in wing area from 170 to 204 sq. ft., reducing its estimated top speed to 357 m.p.h. at 12,500 ft. but giving an initial rate of climb of 3,580 ft./min. and a service ceiling of 33,200 ft. Barnwell and Frise were doubtful about the wisdom of mounting large weapons outboard and proposed an alternative design (Type 153A) with guns in the centre and two Aquila engines in underslung nacelles, the span remaining the same but the area and weight being slightly greater. The fuselage was extremely slim, having no nose forward of the wing, with a one-piece sliding cockpit canopy and a high tailplane with small end-plate fins and rudders. The 153A was expected to be faster than the 153, with 370 m.p.h. at 15,000 ft., but neither of these designs, tendered in May 1936, was accepted by the Air Ministry, although the Westland Whirlwind I chosen for production was similar in layout to Type 153A.

A year later the Company tendered for two further specifications for cannon-armed fighters; these were the F.11/37 twin-Hercules design, with a dorsal turret mounting four cannon, and the single-engined F.18/37 with four cannon submerged in the wing, to be powered by a new large sleeve-valve engine, the Centaurus, of over 2,000 h.p., with provision for the Rolls-Royce Vulture and Napier Sabre as alternatives; an advanced version of the F.11/37 with two Centaurus was also proposed. Neither tender was accepted, nor was a radical proposal by Fedden for a thick-winged version of Type 153A with flat horizontally opposed sleeve-valve engines submerged in the wing profile; although aerodynamically efficient, such an arrangement posed unacceptable transmission and accessibility problems. Prototype orders were placed with Hawkers for the F.18/37, and Boulton-Paul for the F.11/37, but the Munich crisis found the R.A.F. dangerously short of modern fighters and entirely without cannon-armed aircraft for long-range escort and night defence duties.

At this point the Bristol design team under Frise came to the rescue with an inspired stop-gap—a twin-Hercules two-seater armed with four cannon and using the existing wings, tail unit and landing gear of the Beaufort, assembled on the existing jigs so that priority for bomber and fighter production could be switched at short notice as dictated by events. The first layout was submitted a few days after the first flight of the prototype Beaufort and received

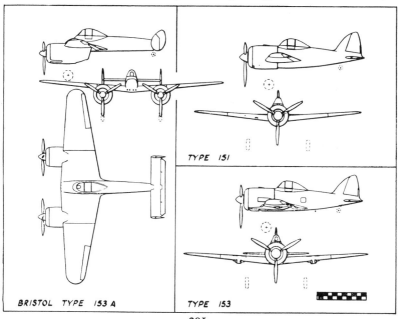

BRISTOL TYPE 153 A

TYPE 151

TYPE 153

291

by the Air Staff with enthusiasm, although it was felt that so large a fighter might be lacking in manœuvrability. Nevertheless immediate instructions were given to proceed with four prototypes, whose preliminary weight estimate of 16,000 lb. was stated on 16 November, when detail design began. The Company also looked into further developments, and on 4 January 1939 suggested a three-seater bomber version with Hercules engines and a dorsal turret, and an improved fighter version with a slimmer fuselage (the so-called 'sports-model') on which some development began later. The three designs were recorded as Types 156, 157 and 158, and in March the name Beaufighter for Type 156 was agreed.

Enthusiastic co-operation between the Air Ministry and the Company resulted in the first Beaufighter prototype being completed six months after the first layout was drawn, only 2,100 drawings being required to convert Beaufort to Beaufighter at the time of its first flight on 17 July 1939. More than twice as many drawings were needed to make it fully operational, and although the design staff, through its earlier cannon-fighter studies, was not held up for information on the gun installation, another year passed before deliveries to the R.A.F. commenced. The first two prototypes had 13 ft. de Havilland airscrews, but Rotol constant-speed fully feathering airscrews were proposed for subsequent machines, so as to give a maximum speed of 360 m.p.h. at 15,000 ft. with Hercules VI engines, which Fedden hoped to provide, but their speedy development was incompatible with a production programme already agreed for the new Hercules shadow factory at Accrington, and in June it was decided to begin Beaufighter production with Hercules III engines, with which the maximum speed at 13,500 ft. was estimated at 335 m.p.h., the same as the Hawker Hurricane. In July the Air Ministry issued Specification F.17/39 to cover an initial contract for 300 Beaufighters, Nos. 9562 to 9861, including the four prototypes, stipulating that D.H. non-feathering bracket-type airscrews should be installed and also requiring the design to accommodate the Rolls-Royce Griffon as an alternative to the Hercules, with maximum interchangeability between these engines as removable power-plant installations.

The handling of the first Beaufighter prototype was generally satisfactory after minor changes had been made to stiffen the elevator control circuit and increase the fin area; the Beaufort's Vickers main oleo-leg assembly was changed to a longer-stroke Lockheed unit, to cater for future weight increases and heavy landings at night and this required the airscrew diameter to be cropped from 13 ft. to 12 ft. 9 in. for adequate ground clearance. The clean lines of the first two prototypes (*R2052* and *R2053*) were somewhat marred on subsequent aircraft by cannon blast tubes and a bullet-proof windscreen, together with a camera-gun on top of the fuselage behind the cockpit and a radio mast nearby. Internally, armour plate was fitted in front of the pilot's cockpit and as doors at the rear spar; the four cannon were mounted accessibly at floor level, and the oxygen crate was stowed behind the observer's seat. These features were embodied in the third prototype (*R2054*), and the first two were brought up to the full standard before delivery to the R.A.F. in April 1940. In its clean state, *R2052* achieved its estimated top speed of 335 m.p.h. at 16,800 ft., with Hercules I-SM engines (similar to Hercules III), but *R2053* with Hercules I-M (similar to Hercules II) was limited to 310 m.p.h. by its low-altitude rating of 4,000 ft.; Hercules II engines were fitted also to the fourth prototype (*R2055*), which was reserved for armament development and firing trials at surface targets. But when *R2054* with full operational equipment began acceptance trials at Boscombe Down in June 1940 its top speed with Hercules III engines was only 309 m.p.h. at 15,000 ft.; official preference veered at once towards the Griffon, in reply to which Fedden proposed a close-cowled Hercules VI power plant with reverse flow cooling, but this was not far enough advanced for serious consideration. It had already been decided in February to continue development of the 'sports model' version (Type 158), named Beaufighter III with Hercules engines and Beaufighter IV with Griffons, and the first of these was pro- grammed to fly by the end of the year; then the Battle of Britain began and refinements were shelved to ensure maximum production.

Certain improvements were already adopted for production machines, whose nacelle drag was lessened by lengthening the part above the wing, reducing the cross-section below the wing and fitting doors which completely enclosed the wheel; at the same time the outer tank fuel jettison pipe, in- herited from the Blenheim IV, was deleted and a combined inner and outer tank jettison chute located in the tail of the nacelle, also the oil coolers, installed below the power plant on the first prototype, were moved back to the leading-edge, as on the Beaufort. All Beaufighters normally had flush-riveted fuselages, although one front and rear fuselage was made with mushroom- headed rivets for comparison of drag and strength. To find out the ultimate gain in speed obtainable by improving workmanship in manufacture, *R2060* was specially finished with smooth filler over all rivets and panel joints and all leaks sealed with tape, but the top speed rose only to 319 m.p.h. at 16,000 ft., showing that stricter quality control could not greatly enhance perfor- mance.

Meanwhile the Luftwaffe intensified its night raids, and initial disappoint- ment with the Beaufighter's performance was dispelled when it proved to be such an excellent vehicle for the early airborne interception radar, which was too bulky for smaller aircraft. The Fighter Interception Unit at Ford and Shoreham had already gained practice successes with A.I. Mark III in their Blenheim fighters, and an early production Beaufighter was sent there for trial installation of A.I. Mark IV, which was forthwith adopted as standard equipment for Fighter Command Beaufighters. Hercules VI production was still postponed and all available Griffons were reserved for Admiralty con- tracts, so it was decided to install Rolls-Royce Merlin XX engines in 450 of the Beaufighters on the line at Filton. These were available as power plants developed for the outboard nacelles of the Lancaster bomber, but needed a wedge-shaped intermediate bay carrying the fire wall and throttle connections

Beaufighter IIF *T3019* with A.I.Mk IV at Filton in 1940.

to pick up on the Beaufighter nacelle; this bay was designed by Rolls-Royce at Hucknall and manufactured by Morris Motors at Cowley, who were also responsible for production of the whole power plant, which contained complete coolant and oil systems; the Merlin XX variant was named Beaufighter II. Three airframes (*R2058*, *R2061* and *R2062*) were reserved as Beaufighter II prototypes, but no Merlin XX engines were yet available, so Merlin X were temporarily fitted in *R2058*, which was flown at Hucknall in July 1940. The long power plants increased the tendency to swing on take-off, and a special tall fin and rudder were fitted, but without significant improvement; Rotol airscrews with Schwartz wooden blades were standardised for Beaufighter II, but were not fully feathering. On 26 July 1940 the Beaufighter I was cleared for R.A.F. squadron service and next day the first five production aircraft were dispatched; the tenth followed on 3 August, and from then on production machines came off the line in rapid sequence. The number on order at Filton was increased by a new contract for 918, and 500 each were also ordered from two new shadow factories, just completed, one at Stockport managed by Fairey and the other at Weston-super-Mare by Bristol; the latter site had been chosen after alternative sites near Warwick, Exeter and Taunton had been considered.

The first 50 Beaufighters from Filton were armed only with four cannon, but later machines, including the 1,000 ordered from the shadow factories, had six additional Browning guns installed in the outer wings, two on the port side and four on the starboard. The cannon installation on the Beaufighter was the subject of much intensive development at Filton, because when first adopted the Hispano was fed by spring-loaded drums of 60 rounds capacity which had to be changed by hand. Although the Beaufighter provided relatively good facilities for storing and handling these bulky magazines, a continuous feed was urgently needed, and the first proposal by the Company for a recoil-driven barrel sprocket was rejected by M.A.P. armament specialists on the grounds that any recoil-operated feed would either jam the gun or be wrecked after a short period in service, so a completely different Bristol servofeed was proposed, comprising a compressed air motor driving a continuous belt by which loose rounds were fed into the gun. This feed was installed on *R2055* for comparison with the 60-round drums on *R2054*, and both were inspected by M.A.P. specialists on 6 May 1940; the drum feed was accepted as a temporary measure for the first 50 aircraft, and the servo feed was to be manufactured and introduced on the 51st aircraft, subject to its satisfactory performance in air-firing trials and to an increase in capacity from 120 to 240 rounds. Both aircraft cleared their gunnery trials satisfactorily and the servo feed was considered better than two other types submitted by A. V. Roe and Co. and Hydran Products.

Meanwhile Free French officers, escaping just before the capitulation of France, brought samples and details of the Chatellerault recoil-operated feed and demonstrated it at Boscombe Down, whereupon M.A.P. standardised it for all cannon installations as the 'Mark I Feed'. Only when drawings reached Filton was it realised that the Chatellerault design was almost identical to the original Bristol recoil feed, except that it extracted by pushing the shell nose instead of the rims of the case, later found to be a disadvantage with pointed armour-piercing rounds. The unfortunate effect of these changes of official policy was that the Mark I feed only went into service on the 401st Beaufighter in September 1941, a year later than either Bristol feed could have done, while magazines had to be hand-changed on 350 more Beaufighters than originally intended. With its four cannon and six Brownings, the Beaufighter was the most heavily-armed fighter in the world, but alternative

Beaufighter V *R2274* at Boscombe Down in May 1941. (*Crown copyright.*)

armament was tried out on two Merlin-engined Beaufighters (*R2274* and *R2306*) converted on the line at Filton in March 1941 and tested in May by several R.A.F. squadrons; in this variant, Beaufighter V, the six wing guns and two inboard cannon were removed and a four-Browning Boulton-Paul BPA.I dorsal turret (Defiant-type) installed immediately aft of the pilot (the observer's cockpit hood being replaced by a flush panel), but rejected because the turret obstructed the pilot's parachute exit. This device, a feature of all Beaufighters, comprised a balanced floor hatch pivoted horizontally so that the leading edge could be instantly unlocked in emergency. The hatch was then swung by the airstream into a vertical position where it locked and formed a wind shield for the crew who could drop straight through the hatch from handrails above. The pilot's seat had a spring-loaded folding back which, when released, enabled him to slide back, grasp the handrails and lift his feet over the front spar in an easy and natural movement. There was a similar hatch for the observer, and the effect of one flying open inadvertently in

Beaufighter IF *R2268* with wide tailplane and twin rudders at Filton in 1940.

flight was somewhat alarming at first experience, but the device was an effective life-saver and did not impair stability. The Beaufighter always suffered from low frequency longitudinal instability, particularly on the climb; it was more pronounced on the Beaufighter II which was slightly tail heavy and various remedies were tried, including a wide tail-plane with end-plate fins and rudders on *R2268* and a twelve-degree dihedral tail-plane on *R2057*. The latter was effective, but made the Beaufighter rather too stable for night-fighting, so Fighter Command squadrons generally preferred the flat tail-plane in spite of its discomforts.

The first fighter squadrons to re-equip with Beaufighters were No. 29 at Digby and No. 25 at Debden in September 1940. Soon afterwards No. 25 was bombed out of Debden and moved to Wittering, and in November Nos. 219, 600 and 604 Squadrons (at Catterick, Manston and Middle Wallop) also received Beaufighters; these five were the only units so equipped during the winter blitz of 1940–1. The first operational success was scored by S/Ldr. John Cunningham and Sgt. J. Phillipson of No. 604 Squadron on 19 November 1940 during a heavy raid on Birmingham when they damaged a Ju 88 over Oxfordshire which crashed later in Norfolk. Their success was isolated and during the next two months only three more raiders were shot down by fighters, none of them by means of A.I., mainly because of the short range imposed by radar ground return. The position improved rapidly after the introduction of G.C.I. in January 1941, which enabled controllers to see both fighter and quarry on a plan position indicator; by March, half of the 22 kills claimed by fighters were due to Beaufighters, and in the heavy night raids on London on 19 May 1941, 24 of the enemy were shot down by fighters compared with only two by anti-aircraft guns.

Production at Filton mounted steadily after the slight set-back caused by the daylight raid on 25 September 1940, when eight of 50 completed aircraft in the works were damaged beyond repair, one of them being the third Rolls-Royce prototype *R2062*. The 100th Beaufighter was dispatched on 7 December 1940 and the 200th on 10 May 1941. Fairey's first Beaufighter was flown on 7 February 1941, and the first from Weston on 20 February, followed by *R2270*, the first production Beaufighter II, from Filton on 22 March. By this time a Beaufighter (*R2130*) with Hercules VI engines was flying satisfactorily after installation of larger oil coolers. Fedden was keen to try a high-altitude version of the Beaufighter with the Hercules VIII engines with two-stage blowers developed for the Wellington V. Rolls-Royce had similar versions of their engines (Merlin 61 and Griffon 61) under development, and for a time a high-altitude Beaufighter project seemed promising, but its aileron response was marginal above 30,000 ft. and it was not practicable to make extensive modifications in an aeroplane which could not easily be pressurised. Nevertheless the two Beaufighter II prototypes at Hucknall became test-beds for the Merlin 61, and a production Beaufighter II (*T3177*) was allocated to Rolls-Royce Ltd. as a Griffon IIB test-bed; for a time both *R2061* and *T3177* had long-tailed nacelles, and the former was used for aerodynamic tests of cowlings modified to represent Rolls-Royce Exe power plants.

Beaufighter IIF *T3177* with Griffon IIB installation at Hucknall in 1941.

Early in April the German invasion of Greece emphasised the need for long-range fighters in Coastal Command, and a modified type was proposed with guns replaced by fuel tanks, a navigator's table and instruments for the observer and a D.F. loop in the former camera-gun position on the fuselage. After a satisfactory trial installation on *R2152*, a batch of 80 coastal Beaufighters was completed with the utmost urgency; but it was impossible to incorporate the extra wing tanks on the production line and 50-gallon Wellington tanks were temporarily mounted on the floor between the cannon bays. These Beaufighters were issued to No. 252 Squadron, based on Chivenor and Aldergrove, whence flights were detached to Gibraltar, Malta and Cyprus; they arrived too late to help in the defence of Crete, but operated from Cyprus against enemy shipping during the brief campaign which drove the Germans out of Syria. Coastal Command thereafter made increasing demands for Beaufighters, and the Fairey and Weston production lines turned

Beaufighter IC *T3318* of No. 252 Sqn R.A.F. over Malta in 1940. (*Crown copyright.*)

over entirely to coastal machines, with alternative desert equipment, whilst Filton went back to building only night fighters; in view of the increasing divergence of the fighter and coastal roles two distinct airframes were standardised having fixed fittings appropriate to either Fighter Command (suffix F) or Coastal Command (suffix C). All Merlin-engined Beaufighters were Mark IIF and were flown by Nos. 255, 207, 406 and 410 Squadrons, but they were not popular because, although faster at altitude, they lacked the punch of the Hercules for a short take-off at night. While Beaufighter II production proceeded, the volume of Lancaster production also grew, resulting in a shortage of Merlin XX power plants at Filton, and many airframes had to be dispatched by road without engines to avoid congestion at the works, being later completed at Whitchurch and Colerne. It had been hoped to introduce Hercules VI engines at Filton when the last Beaufighter II left the line and two Weston-built machines (*X7542* and *X7543*) were converted for Hercules VI endurance testing, but 120 more Beaufighters had to be delivered with Hercules XI, which used 100-octane fuel and replaced Hercules III early in 1941.

Beaufighter VIF with A.I.Mk IV at Filton in 1942.

During the summer of 1941 no fewer than 20 Beaufighters were reserved for various trial installations; they included *R2057* and *R2270* with dihedral tailplanes, and the former was also testing the Fairey-Youngman bellows-type dive-brake, originally proposed for night fighter use to permit rapid overtaking of a target without risk of collision at the last moment; flight tests showed that flaps were necessary above the wing as well as below to avoid a change of trim, and it was some time before reliable operation was achieved; the bellows were held shut by suction from a venturi below the wing and could be inflated very quickly by a valve which closed the venturi outlet and so applied ram pressure. Both the dihedral tailplane and dive brakes were adopted for Coastal Command Beaufighters and proved particularly valuable on the later torpedo variant. Another trial installation was of 40 mm. heavy guns, three types of which were considered for aircraft use, the 2-pounder anti-tank field gun, the 2-pounder tank-turret gun, and the much larger 40 mm. Bofors anti-aircraft gun, the last being preferred because of its automatic loading hopper. Then two new 40 mm. aircraft guns were offered, one

Fourth prototype Beaufighter *R2055* with Vickers S and Rolls-Royce 40 mm. guns, at Duxford in 1941.

by Vickers and the other by Rolls-Royce, so the Bofors scheme was dropped and both new guns installed, the Vickers on the starboard side and the Rolls-Royce on the port side of the fourth prototype *R2055*. Trials at Duxford showed the Vickers gun to be the better for service use, and it was put into production for the anti-tank Hurricanes for desert warfare.

As soon as Germany invaded Russia in June 1941, Beaufighters began intruder raids over France and Belgium and increasing numbers were deployed in the Mediterranean theatre, where in July alone No. 272 Squadron, based on Malta, destroyed 49 enemy aircraft which attacked convoys passing through 'bomb alley' and damaged 42 more. In November they accompanied the desert army into Libya and shot down many dive-bombers as well as harassing tanks and transport. By the spring of 1942 many coastal squadrons had re-equipped with the Hercules VI-engined Beaufighter VIC, and these were active against Doenitz's submarines supported by four-engined Focke Wulf Kuriers. They began to replace Beauforts in operations over the North Sea, and on 17 May backed up No. 86 Squadron's Beauforts' attempt to sink the *Prinz Eugen* off Haugesund. On 12 June 1942 Ft./Lt. Gatward and Sgt. Fern of No. 236 Squadron dashed across Normandy at tree-top height in a single Beaufighter to plant a *tricouleur* on the Arc de Triomphe, after which they shot up the German Admiralty headquarters in Paris and dropped a second flag across its doorstep; but the limit of the Beaufighter's versatility and striking power was still to be reached.

Before Christmas 1941 the Air Staff requested a successor to the Beaufort, suggesting a Beaufort body with Hercules engines and Beaufighter wings, but the Company preferred the idea of carrying a torpedo externally beneath a coastal Beaufighter; using aerodynamic tails, torpedoes could be dropped from a considerable height without diving or porpoising, the air tail breaking off on contact with the water and in March the Company submitted a torpedo-carrying scheme for the Beaufighter VIC, receiving permission on 13 April to make a trial installation, provided that it did not interfere with other priorities and could cater for both British 18-in. and American 22½-in. torpedoes. Four days later *X8065* arrived at Filton from Weston, and on 24 April the modified Beaufighter was ready for inspection by M.A.P. Flight trials at Filton were completed by 8 May, and *X8065* then went to the Torpedo Development Unit, Gosport, for weapon trials, where it crashed due to engine failure, killing its pilot, W/Cdr. Shaw, C.O. of the Unit, but not before its value had been assessed, and at Whitsun the Company was instructed to convert 16 more aircraft with all possible speed, to equip a trial squadron. By the end of the year this squadron (No. 254) completed training, and Weston's 1000th Beaufighter rolled off the production line complete with torpedo gear. The first successful action with the new weapon was the sinking of two supply ships off Norway on 4 April 1943.

Prior to the fitting of torpedo gear, Coastal Command pilots complained that the Beaufighter VI was not so fast at sea level as the earlier version, because the Hercules VI was rated at a higher altitude than the Hercules XI,

Beaufighter IF with prototype A.I.Mk VII installation at Filton in 1940.

to suit the Beaufighter VIF with centimetric A.I. Mark VII which had re-equipped Nos. 68 and 604 Squadrons of Fighter Command in the spring of 1942. For Coastal Command, Hercules VI engines were modified by cropping the impellers and locking the blowers in 'M' gear and then became Hercules XVII, with a combat rating of 1,735 h.p. at 500 ft. Beaufighters with Hercules XVII were designated Mark X with torpedo gear and Mark XIC without, but the first 60 torpedo fighters had Hercules VI or XVI engines and were Beaufighter VI (I.T.F.), becoming Beaufighter X after engine change to Hercules XVII. From this point onward, the Beaufighter X replaced the Beaufort in Coastal Command. All production Beaufighter X and XIC were fitted with a rear-firing Browning gun for the observer, and many squadrons fitted K-guns to earlier models. A final 250 Beaufighter VIF were ordered from Filton for Fighter Command, and a further batch replaced Blenheims in the Rootes factory at Blythe Bridge; all had A.I. Mark VIII installed in a nose radome, and this was adapted for A.S.V. purposes, U-boats having been equipped to detect 1½ metre radar; later Rootes and Weston Beaufighters were delivered as Mark X with both nose scanner and torpedo gear, also

Beaufighter X *LZ114* flying with full load on one engine at Old Mixon in 1943.

gyro-angling equipment and so much additional radio and navigational gear that the increasing weight began to affect stability in spite of the dihedral tailplane. This was restored by enlarging the elevator area and fitting a long dorsal fin of a type first tried on a Beaufighter IIF (*T3032*) and found effective in curing swing on take-off; a similar fin was fitted later to the Griffon-Beaufighter (*T3177*) to balance the effect of its four-bladed airscrews.

In the spring of 1943 many of Fighter Command's Beaufighter VIF squadrons, including Nos. 255 and 600, moved to North Africa, where they wrought havoc among German transports hurrying back to Europe, as on 30 April when Ft./Sgt. Downing and Sgt. Lyons of No. 600 Squadron shot down five Ju 52 troop-carriers near Setif in 10 min. Later the night fighter squadrons followed the enemy retreat to Sicily and gave night air cover to the army landings at Anzio and Salerno; in this campaign Beaufighters were operated by the United States First Tactical Air Command while waiting for Black Widows. Beaufighter VIF squadrons were also active from home bases on intruder patrols into France against railways and shipping, an outstanding exponent of intruder tactics being W/Cdr. J. R. D. Braham of No. 219 Squadron, who, after achieving a record score on home defence operations, developed the art of flying among enemy night fighters while escorting R.A.F. bombers. Using both backward and forward scanning radar, he would entice an enemy night fighter to follow him, waiting until the last possible moment before executing a rapid turn which brought him behind his quarry. These tactics were later employed by the Bomber Support Group flying Mosquitos, but some Beaufighters remained in this role until the end of 1944. In Burma Beaufighters of Nos. 176 and 217 Squadrons went into action against the Japanese and earned the soubriquet of 'Whispering Death' from a surprise attack on troops parading at Myitkyina on the Mikado's birthday. In their sorties against railways and river boats Beaufighter pilots often flew so low that the enemy retaliated by arranging trip-wires above dummy targets in the valleys.

Early in 1944 still more Beaufighters went into action on all fronts, and Weston shadow factory maintained a steady output of 87 per month. Only the Beaufighter X remained in production at Weston and Blythe Bridge, with a new and powerful weapon added to its armoury, the rocket projectile, designed in 1939 as an anti-aircraft weapon and later proved effective against tank armour and shipping, including submarines. A trial installation of eight

Beaufighter X *LZ293* with rocket projectiles; No. 236 Sqn R.A.F., 1944. (*Crown copyright.*)

rockets was tested on a Beaufighter VIC (*EL329*) in September 1942, and by April 1943 special Beaufighter Strike Wings of Coastal Command were being trained, using both rocket and torpedo aircraft. In an attack on a convoy, by this time always heavily defended by anti-aircraft vessels, the rocket aircraft went in first to sweep the decks and silence the guns; then the second wave launched torpedoes, and after hits had been observed the enemy's confusion was completed by the whole formation attacking with more rockets and cannon-fire. The Strike Wings (Nos. 143, 144, 235, 236 and 254 Squadrons R.A.F., No. 404 Squadron R.C.A.F., No. 455 Squadron R.A.A.F. and No. 489 Squadron R.N.Z.A.F.) began operation from Scottish bases against shipping off the Norwegian coast in March 1944, concentrating on convoys carrying supplies to the *Tirpitz* and returning with Swedish iron ore.

As D-Day approached, enemy E-boats became more active and the Strike Wings moved south to North Coates and Strubby in Lincolnshire, Langham in Norfolk and Manston in Kent. Pairs of Beaufighters reconnoitred the enemy coastline, and when a target was spotted the rest of the Wing went out at wave-top level to attack, one of the biggest of these strikes being made by 75 escorted Beaufighters on 25 September 1944 against shipping at Den Helder. Similar tactics were employed in the Mediterranean, and on 8 September Beaufighters sank the 51,000 ton liner *Rex* in daylight near Trieste with 55 rocket hits below the water line. Both gyro-angling gear and radio altimeters

Beaufighter X *NE355* with R.P. and Fairchild camera; No. 404 Sqn R.C.A.F., 1944. (*Crown copyright.*)

302

were used to achieve surprise, and thus equipped the Beaufighter X had a take-off weight of 25,400 lb., made tolerable by strengthened nacelle and main undercarriage fittings and the B.L.G. tail-wheel, which for the first time eliminated the shimmy trouble for which the Marstrand tyre offered only a partial cure; a third crew member behind the pilot helped him to aim the torpedo by means of the gyro-angling device.

There was an urgent demand for Beaufighters in the Australian battle against the Japanese shipping and strongholds, and in January 1944 a switch to Beaufighter production followed completion of the Beaufort programme at Fishermen's Bend. At first a version of the Beaufighter VIC with Hercules 26 engines (Bendix carburettors) was chosen, designated Beaufighter VII. Fifty-four Fairey-built Beaufighter IC were already in service with the R.A.A.F., and one of these, *A19-2*, was modified to take Wright Double

Fairey-built Beaufighter IC *A19-2* with Australian installation of Cyclones, 1943.

Cyclone GR 2600-A5B engines installed in long nacelles as the prototype for proposed production variants Beaufighter VIII and IX. Then, as Hercules supplies were not interrupted, it was decided to adopt a version of the Beaufighter X, having 0·5 in. calibre wing guns, a Sperry auto-pilot and Hercules XVIII engines with both blower gears fully operative. The engines were shipped as power plants from Accrington, but otherwise the aircraft were built entirely from local resources, 55,000 microfilm negatives of drawings being sent from Filton by the Airgraph service. The first Beaufighter 21 (*A8-1*) was test flown on 26 May 1944, and from August onwards Australian-

Beaufighter 21 *A8-99* flying over Melbourne in 1945.

303

Beaufighter X *NE343* with 200-gallon drop-tank on torpedo-rack, 1944. (*Crown copyright.*)

built Beaufighters took a prominent part in the Allied advance towards the Netherlands East Indies, one of their longest missions being to escort bombers covering the landings at Tarakan on 2 May 1945. Out of the original contract for 450 Beaufighter 21s, 364 were completed before production ceased after VJ-Day.

The final war-time development of the Beaufighter was a strengthened version, Beaufighter XII, intended to carry one 1,000 lb. bomb outboard of each nacelle. This variant was cancelled because Bendix carburettors for its Hercules 27 engines were not available, but the same wing was put into production for the final series of Beaufighter X and external fuel tanks could be carried on the torpedo and bomb racks. Many earlier Beaufighters were also modified just before D-Day to carry two 500 lb. bombs under the fuselage and one 250 lb. bomb under each wing, with which they operated against enemy E- and R-boats trying to interfere with the Mulberry Harbour installations. Both rockets and bombs were also used by Beaufighters of the R.A.F. and S.A.A.F. operating in the Aegean Sea, and with the Balkan Air Force in support of Marshal Tito.

When the war ended in Europe, most of the Beaufighter squadrons moved

Beaufighter X *NT921* bomber version, June 1944. (*Crown copyright.*)

304

east, leaving only a few strike squadrons at home bases. Many squadrons were either disbanded or re-equipped by 1946, but No. 84 Squadron retained their Beaufighters until 1949 and No. 45 until 1950, both being finally based at Kuala Lumpur. Surplus Beaufighters were exported, and 20 Mark X were sold to Turkey and two to Portugal in 1946; in 1948 ten more were specially modified from Mark X to Mark VI standard at Filton and sold to the Republic of Dominica. Although no genuine civilian application of the Beau-

Beaufighter X modified at Filton to Mk VIF for Dominican Republic, 1948.

fighter was envisaged, six surplus Mark X machines were overhauled by the Fairey Aviation Co. at Ringway in 1947, and five of these were sold to a film company the following year; one crashed at Thame while being ferried and the other four were flown on to Palestine in August 1948, bearing civil marks *G-AJMB*, '*C*, '*D* and '*G*, but whether their ultimate use was strictly legal is not known. One Beaufighter VIC was flown at Filton in 1946 as a test-bed with Hercules 130 power plants and four-bladed airscrews, later becoming an instructional airframe at Halton.

Production of Beaufighters ended at Filton early in 1944 and at Weston and Blythe Bridge in September 1945, when a total of 5,564 Beaufighters had been built in England and 364 in Australia. In November 1947, a minor revival occurred when a target-tug conversion was approved and named Beaufighter T.T.10, the prototype conversion (*NT913*) being flown in May 1948 equipped with a standard windmill winch. This role was first suggested in 1942, as an alternative to the Miles Monitor. Thirty-five Beaufighters were converted into target-tugs at Filton and delivered during 1948, 1949 and 1950 to R.A.F. co-operation units for gunnery practice, notably in Gibraltar, Malta,

Prototype Beaufighter T.T.10 at Filton in 1948.

Cyprus, Ceylon and Malaya. The last one in service (*RD761*) ceased flying and was scrapped at Seletar, Singapore, on 16 May 1960, nearly twenty-one years after the first flight of the first Beaufighter; the airframe of *RD867* was retrieved from Malta in 1963 for restoration, and in 1969 went to the R.C.A.F. Museum at Ottawa in exchange for Bolingbroke *10001*; meanwhile *RD253*, one of the two sold to Portugal, had been retrieved and restored for the R.A.F. Museum at Hendon, while in Australia *A8-186* of No. 22 Squadron, R.A.A.F., was preserved at the Camden Museum of Aviation.

In early 1988 the restoration of some ten Beaufighter airframes was under way in England, Australia and Canada, according to Skysport Engineering Ltd of Hatch, Bedfordshire. This company specialises in the manufacture and restoration of old types of aircraft. It is working on a Beaufighter 1F (*X7688*) which saw service with Nos. 29 and 154 Squadrons, R.A.F. After the war a large part of this airframe had been used to train R.A.F. Halton apprentices in the operation of piston engines. The Skysport rebuild is a long-term programme and this aircraft is not expected to fly until well into the 1990s.

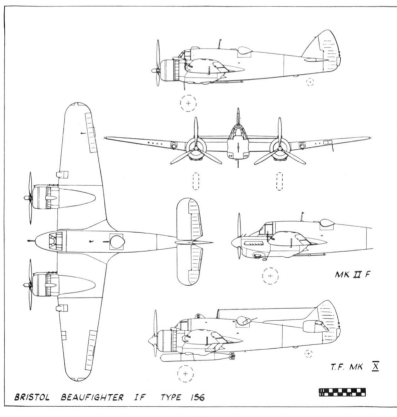

BRISTOL BEAUFIGHTER IF TYPE 156

MK II F

T.F. MK X

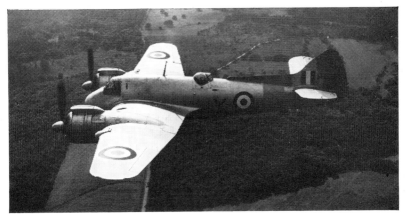

Beaufighter T.T. 10 *SR914* flying in 1960.

SPECIFICATIONS AND DATA

Type: 156, Beaufighter

Manufacturers: (I, II, V, VIF) The Bristol Aeroplane Co. Ltd., Filton and Whitchurch, Bristol

(I, VIC) The Fairey Aviation Co. Ltd., Stockport, Cheshire

(I, VIF, VIC, X, XIC) Ministry of Aircraft Production Shadow Factory, Old Mixon, Weston-super-Mare, Somerset

(VIF, X) Rootes Securities Ltd., Blythe Bridge, Staffs

(21) Beaufort Division, Department of Aircraft Production, Fishermen's Bend, Vic., Australia

Power Plants: (I) Two 1,400 hp Bristol Hercules III, X or XI

(II, V) Two 1,250 hp Rolls-Royce Merlin XX

(VIF, VIC) Two 1,600 hp Bristol Hercules VI or XVI

(X, XIC) Two 1,735 hp Bristol Hercules XVII

(21) Two 1,735 hp Bristol Hercules XVIII

Span: 57 ft 10 in

Length: (I, VI, XI & 21) 41 ft 4 in; (II) 42 ft 9 in; (X) 42 ft 6 in

Height: 15 ft 10 in

Wing Area: 503 sq ft

Empty Weight: (I, II) 13,800 lb; (VI, XI) 14,900 lb; (X, 21) 15,600 lb

All-up Weight: (I, II, V, VI, XI) 21,000 lb; (X, 21) 25,400 lb

Max. Speed: 330 mph

Service Ceiling: 29,000 ft

Range: 1,500 miles (1,750 miles with extra wing tanks)

Accommodation: 2 or 3

Production:
Sequence Nos.: } see Appendices B and D

307

Mock-ups of Type 159 and Type 162 (in front) at Filton in January 1941.

The Bristol Type 159 Heavy Bomber

The successful modification of *Britain First* into the Blenheim encouraged Capt. Barnwell to investigate other lines of development by making use of geometric similarity, which he considered a reliable design philosophy as his experience of stressed-skin construction grew. So in December 1935 the Company submitted a four-engined long-range high-speed bomber design, whose estimated performance was well in advance of the requirements of the current specification, B.1/35. Barnwell's aim was to take advantage of all the experience gained in developing the Blenheim and in particular the drag and performance data obtained from the wind-tunnel and flight tests of *Britain First* together with information obtained on stiffness, weight estimation and the reliability and efficiency of retractable landing gear, landing flaps, variable-pitch airscrews and hydraulic turrets.

Barnwell expected the proposed bomber to show as big an advance on official requirements as *Britain First* on its contemporaries and laid out a low-wing monoplane of 96 ft. span and 68 ft. long aerodynamically similar to the Blenheim, but with areas and profiles scaled-up to appropriate dimensions. Structural design followed the Blenheim's, but with flush riveting. The front fuselage was exactly the same as the Blenheim's, with pilot and navigator side-by-side and a bomb-aiming station in the extreme nose. The centre fuselage was parallel for most of its length and only half as deep again as the inner wing, whose spars passed through it, with a retractable 'dust-bin'-type under-defence turret between the pilot's station and the front spar, and a radio-station, near a retractable dorsal turret, behind the rear spar. The single fin and rudder were exactly the same shape as the Blenheim's, but 15 ft. tall; the wing had constant dihedral and taper from root to tip, with a straight trailing edge and swept-back leading edge, the four engine nacelles, similar to the Blenheim's, being all mounted on the inner wing. All bombs were stowed between the spars in the inner wing, with the longest bombs nearest the centre-line, and the fuel tanks were located outboard of the bomb compartments. There was a choice of Mercury IX or Taurus engines, the top speed, carrying 4,000 lb. of bombs and a crew of four, being 275 m.p.h. with Mercuries or 300 m.p.h. with Taurus, with a range of 2,000 miles when cruising at 225 m.p.h. The all-up weight was 38,500 lb. with Taurus or 37,500 lb. with Mercuries. This design study was received with interest by the Air Staff, but the only immediate response was an invitation to tender for the B.12/36 and P.13/36 specifications; the Company submitted designs for both these, powered by four and two Hercules engines, respectively, early in 1937, but neither was adopted.

In October 1938, Frise submitted concurrently with the first Beaufighter proposal a larger four-engined bomber design incorporating Beaufort components, cannon armament and Hercules engines. The Air Staff replied with Specification B.1/39, formulating their requirements for an 'ideal' four-engined bomber, which they proposed to develop as a standard replacement for the Stirling, Manchester and Halifax, which had just begun flight testing. The aim was to achieve the highest possible ratio of bomb-load to supporting manpower, both in operation and manufacture. In January 1939 the Company

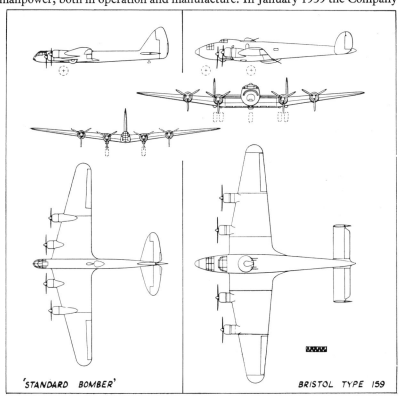

'STANDARD BOMBER'   BRISTOL TYPE 159

tendered to the new specification Type 159, a low-wing monoplane with a nose-wheel landing gear, carrying its entire bomb-load of 15,000 lb. within the inner wing between the spars. Hercules engines were preferred but, in deference to Air Staff policy, Rolls-Royce Griffons were provided for as alternatives, the aim being to develop interchangeable Hercules and Griffon power plants. The middle portion of the fuselage, containing all the crew stations except the bomb-aimer's nose position, was designed as an armoured monocoque structure, with low-drag dorsal (B.VIII) and ventral (B.IX) 'mushroom' turrets, each with four 20 mm. cannon. Many other firms also tendered, and in face of strong competition the Bristol and Handley Page designs were accepted, but in view of the heavy production programmes already under way, the Air Ministry postponed any B.1/39 production contracts, limiting themselves in September 1939 to an intention to order two prototypes from each firm for evaluation, on condition that the under-carriages and other components using large forgings or castings should be common for both companies' prototypes. In the Bristol design all the oleo-units and wheels were identical, being used singly for the nose unit and in pairs for the main undercarriages; the fuel tanks, also, were all one size, eight being installed permanently, with provision for carrying four more on the bomb racks.

The wind-tunnel tests of the Bristol 159 were very satisfactory, promising excellent stability and low drag, and the structural design was well advanced by the spring of 1940, when a full-scale mock-up had been built and a rear fuselage section completed for mechanical testing. At one point it was proposed to build a half-scale flight-test aeroplane, but no decision was taken to do so before the formation of the Ministry of Aircraft Production in May 1940 (and the over-riding priority for fighter production on which Lord Beaverbrook insisted) stopped further work on the 'Beaubomber', and the mock-up was finally dismantled in January 1941. No prototype contract had been agreed and no sequence number was allotted. Little over a year later the R.A.F. turned from defence to attack and the Company was asked to con-sider designing an enormously larger aircraft to carry a bomb-load of 80,000 lb.—a load rather more than the total all-up weight of the 159 which in 1939 was intended as the ideal bomber.

SPECIFICATION AND DATA

Type:	159, Heavy Bomber		
Manufacturers:	The Bristol Aeroplane Co. Ltd., Filton, Bristol		
Power Plant:	Four 1,550 hp Bristol Hercules VII		
Span:	114 ft		
Length:	80 ft 3 in		
Height:	20 ft 3 in		
Wing Area:	1,800 sq ft		
Empty Weight:	37,350 lb	*Range:*	3,500 miles at 280 mph
All-up Weight:	71,000 lb	*Accommodation:*	7
Max. Speed:	302 mph	*Production:*	Prototype cancelled
Service Ceiling:	25,300 ft	*Sequence No.:*	Nil

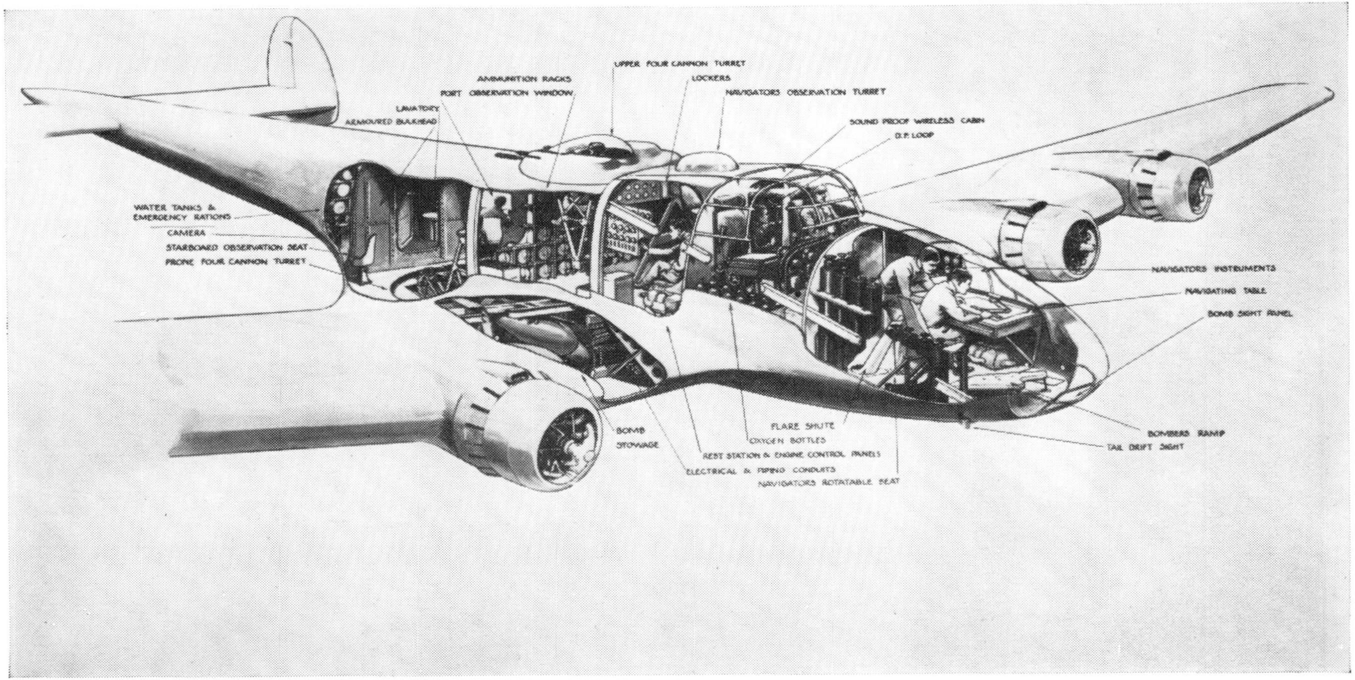

NAVIGATORS INSTRUMENTS
PLANISTATING TABLE
BOMBS SIGHT PANEL
BOMBER RAMP
TAIL DRIFT SIGHT

SOUND PROOF WIRELESS CABIN
D.F. LOOP
NAVIGATORS OBSERVATION TURRET

UPPER FOUR CANNON TURRET
LOCKERS

AMMUNITION RACKS
PORT OBSERVATION WINDOW

LAVATORY
ARMOURED BULKHEAD

WATER TANKS &
EMERGENCY RATIONS
CAMERA
STARBOARD OBSERVATION SEAT
PRONE FOUR CANNON TURRET

FLARE SHUTE
OXYGEN BOTTLES
REST STATION & ENGINE CONTROL PANELS
ELECTRICAL & PIPING CONDUITS
NAVIGATORS ROTATABLE SEAT

BOMB
STOWAGE

Artist's impression of Type 159.

311

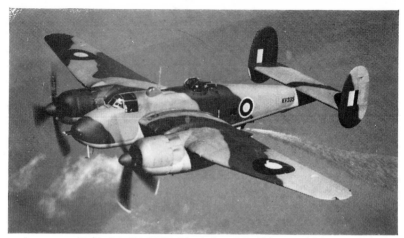

Buckingham B.1 *KV335* flying in June 1947. (*Crown copyright*.)

The Bristol Buckingham, Brigand and Buckmaster, Types 163, 164 and 166

Although the suggested Beaufighter bomber version (Type 157) was not pursued in 1939, the Air Staff in April 1940 issued Specification B.7/40 for a two-seater light bomber derived from the Beaufighter, to be used in the alternative roles of close-support fighter dive-bomber and high level bomber to replace the Blenheim. Initial B.7/40 layouts, for either Hercules or Merlin engines, designated Type 161, showed a small four-Browning dorsal turret (B.XI) and either two forward-firing 20 mm. cannon or twin rear-firing under-defence Brownings, according to role. Requirements changed rapidly during the summer of 1940 and soon included night-fighting (F.18/40) as well, and in October Frise evolved a new design, Type 162, provisionally named Beaumont. In March 1941 the Air Staff issued Specification B.2/41 for the Beaumont, but called for a crew of three, and attempts to stretch the project to the new requirement raised its weight too high for Hercules engines to reach the specified performance, so in April the design was again revised with a bigger wing for Centaurus engines and submitted as Type 163.

Specification B.2/41 required a range of 1,000 miles with a bomb load of at least 2,000 lb., or 2,000 miles with no bomb load, when cruising at 300 m.p.h. at 15,000 ft.; the top speed was to be 370 m.p.h. and the single-engine ceiling at least 15,000 ft. in any climatic conditions. The armament specified was a Boulton-Paul BPA.I four-Browning dorsal turret, a twin-Browning F.N.64 under-defence mounting and two fixed front guns of 0·5 in. calibre; a single 4,000 lb. bomb or two 2,000 lb. or six 500 lb. bombs were to be internally stowed and full de-icing, barrage protection and oxygen were required. The crew of three comprised pilot, observer and wireless-operator/air-gunner, with pilot and observer having the best possible view. At the advisory design conference on 17 July, soon after the type had been named Buckingham, its purpose was summarised as 'a fast medium day or night bomber carrying the maximum defensive armament compatible with high speed'; maximum flexibility between bomb load and range was desired, but not the former ground attack role, although with a torpedo the type might be considered for a Beaufort replacement. The Company pressed strongly the use of their new B.XII dorsal turret and B.XIII under-turret instead of those specified, and this was conceded. Fedden recommended reverse-flow engine cooling, and a first-flight date for the prototype was targeted for February 1942. Specification B.2/41 was revised on 26 July 1941, when a contract was awarded for four prototypes, and in the third issue of the specification on 11 August the secondary role had to cater for a toraplane, but without fuel jettisoning. Soon afterwards the torpedo requirement was dropped and N.A.C.A. cowling with gills was agreed for the prototype because of adverse stability effects with the reversed flow ventral exit. Mock-up conferences were held in October from which it was found impracticable to combine the functions of wireless operator and rear gunner, so necessitating a crew of four. Then the Air Staff called for a range of 1,600 miles, which raised the normal all-up weight to 34,000 lb. and required a new landing gear; at the overload weight of 36,000 lb. take-off performance became marginal in spite of increased span and wing area. To resolve this impasse a new specification (Buckingham I/P.1) was issued on 16 March 1942, cancelling B.2/41, and calling for a top speed of 355 m.p.h. at 20,000 ft., a range of 1,600 miles at 15,000 ft. with 2,000 lb. of bombs, a crew of four with the dorsal gunner as fighting controller and a B.XIV four-gun nose mounting remotely controlled by the bomb-aimer from a prone position. The prototypes and 400 production aircraft were to be built to this standard and a normal all-up weight of 34,000 lb. was agreed. The Company was somewhat reluctant to transfer Beaufort assembly to Banwell and terminate Beaufighter production at Filton to make room for the Buckingham, but Sir Henry Tizard made a personal appeal for this programme to be followed and emphasised the R.A.F.'s real need to have the Buckingham in service as soon as possible.

Buckingham first prototype *DX249* at Filton in January 1943.

Production was well under way by the time the first prototype, No. 11332 (*DX249*), was flown by C. F. Uwins on 4 February 1943, without armament or the bomb aimer's ventral 'bath'. The Buckingham was designed for dispersed manufacture of completely fitted-out components, which were brought together at Filton on specially designed final assembly jigs and handling trolleys. The output available from this production line was very rapid for so large an aeroplane, but this achievement was wasted because the R.A.F.'s night bombing offensive became more effective than expected after adopting radar and Pathfinder techniques, and day bombing by unarmed Mosquitos was also more successful than foreseen. So after all its birth-pangs the Buckingham was unwanted, in Europe at any rate, and likely to be useful only in the campaign against the Japanese, for which purpose full tropicalisation was ordered, resulting in a severe reduction of output for several months; at the same time, the number on order was reduced to 300.

The second prototype, No. 11333 (*DX255*), flew soon after the first and was fully armed and equipped, as were the third and fourth prototypes, Nos. 11334 and 11335 (*DX259* and *DX266*). All four had Centaurus IV engines of high altitude rating, but production Buckinghams had Centaurus VII or XI rated for moderate altitude. Handling tests of the first two prototypes showed the need for revised spring tabs on the control surfaces, which were fitted in May 1943 and eventually cleared for production. The first production Buckingham, No. 11905 (*KV301*), flew on 12 February 1944, and nine others had been completed when it became necessary to modify the tail unit to improve stability, particularly with one engine dead; after tests on *DX266* with an enlarged rectangular tailplane in conjunction with fins of various areas, a revised fin shape was cleared in May 1944 for production Buckinghams, 54 being delivered as bombers by the end of the year. In its final form the Buckingham B.1 bomber had a top speed of 330 m.p.h., 25 m.p.h. below specification, but was nevertheless the fastest fully armed bomber of its day. A faster version with remotely controlled nacelle-mounted turrets instead of the dorsal turret was proposed in August 1943, but not approved. Yet the early promise of the two-seater Type 161, so similar in line to the Mosquito but all-metal in structure, was redeemed by a completely independent project, evolved concurrently with the Buckingham.

The somewhat makeshift adaptation of the Beaufighter as a torpedo-bomber to replace the Beaufort had met with such success that in July 1942 a Buckingham II project to carry two torpedoes was discussed, but found too heavy for adequate performance low down with Centaurus engines. It was therefore dropped in favour of a proposal by C. W. Tinson for a smaller Beaufighter derivative with a single torpedo, in which the crew of three were concentrated in a single cabin amidships, so overcoming the principal disadvantage of the Beaufighter in the torpedo role, which demanded very close co-ordination between the crew; this project was expected to attain 330 m.p.h. at sea level with Hercules XVII engines in low-drag cowlings, and a mock-up was inspected on 21 August; five days later Specification S.7/42

Mock-up of original H.7/42 project at Filton in November 1942. (*Crown copyright.*)

was reserved (changed to H.7/42 on 15 September) and the Company suggested the name Buccaneer, estimating that the first prototype might fly in November 1943. Specification H.7/42 was drafted on 4 October and finalised on 13 November, calling for a still air range of 1,500 nautical miles, a top speed of 300 knots at sea level and ability to climb to 5,000 ft. on one engine. The design submitted on 16 December was similar to the Beaufighter but had the engines 10 in. further forward in pointed nacelles and oval cowlings with rear-swept exhaust stubs and individual cooling ducts to each cylinder. The fuselage was slimmer than the Beaufighter's and the tailplane was raised 20 in. above the pointed stern. The all-up weight was estimated at 26,150 lb. on 21 December, when the official name Brigand T.F.Mk.I was given. It soon appeared that 300 knots could not be realised with Hercules XVII engines, so an alternative small-bodied version of the Buckingham was drawn for comparison; this was expected to weigh 33,900 lb but could reach 310 knots at sea level with derated Centaurus IV s, and climb to 12,000 ft. on one engine. The installation of A.I. Mark VIII, adapted as A.S.V., increased the weight by 550 lb., leaving the Hercules version with virtually no single-engined climb, so on 11 March 1943 it was agreed to combine the Brigand body with Buckingham wings and tail, in which form the design was recorded on 12 April as Type 164, four prototypes being formally ordered.

In the specification, the Air Staff called for provision, to special order, for a dual control variant, and a layout for this version, Type 165 (Brigand II) was drawn, but the Company was anxious not to complicate Brigand development with a trainer variant and in August 1943 suggested a dual-control version of the Buckingham instead. This was readily contrived by substituting a wide front fuselage with side-by-side pilots' stations and a radio-operator behind them, all armament, armour and other military equipment being removed. Two partly completed Buckinghams, Nos. 12024 and 12025, were converted to become the prototypes of Type 166, the Buckmaster (*TJ714* and *TJ717*), to Specification T.13/43, and Uwins flew *TJ714* on 27 October 1944.

With the end of the war with Japan in sight there was no need for the Buckingham even in the Far East, and the total number on order was cut to 119; fifty-four of these had already been delivered as bombers and the remainder were converted to fast courier transports, stripped of all armament and armour, with Christie-Tyler seats for four passengers, a crew of three and extra tankage for a range of 3,000 miles; without turrets the Buckingham C.1 was 6 m.p.h. faster. A further 150 sets of Buckingham components already manufactured were used in Buckmaster production, 110 Buckmasters being assembled and dispatched during 1945 and 1946. A photographic reconnaissance variant of the Buckingham, Type 169, briefly investigated in 1945, was not proceeded with. Both the Buckingham C.1 and Buckmaster had Centaurus VII or XI engines. The 54 bombers already delivered returned to Filton for conversion to transports, but most of them remained in storage after redelivery and were eventually scrapped after very short flying lives. The relatively small number operated on courier services to Malta and Egypt by the Transport Command Development Unit performed well and

Buckingham C.1 *KV405* at Filton in 1946.

Buckingham C.2 *KV365*, one of two conversions by T.C.D.U. in March 1946. (*Crown copyright.*)

amassed a great deal of valuable operational data, but were obviously uneconomical as load carriers. Two of them, *KV365* and *KV369*, were adapted by T.C.D.U. in March 1946 to accommodate seven passengers, with the bomb-aimer's 'bath' deleted; these had a higher cruising speed, but the modification was too costly for general application. One Buckingham, *KV322*, was fitted with a central dorsal fin for stability tests, and the last survivor, *KV419*, remained at Patchway until 1950 as a ground rig, with only the starboard engine installed, to provide a slipstream for Hercules power-plant fire tests on a Halifax VII similarly rigged behind it.

Buckmaster T.1 *RP179* at Filton in 1949.

Buckmasters were mainly used by Operational Conversion Units training Brigand pilots, although a few were employed on communications duties at Aden by No. 8 Squadron. The last four in R.A.F. Training Command service were still flying at No. 238 O.C.U., Colerne, in 1956, while two were retained at Filton for experimental work; one of these was modified to test the Burney recoilless gun and the other, *RP164*, carried out flight tests with combustion heaters for the Brabazon wing de-icing system, later becoming an instructional airframe at Halton, where it was scrapped in 1958.

Of the three related types, only the Brigand saw operational service with the R.A.F. The first prototype, No. 12455 (*MX988*), was flown by Uwins on 4 December 1944, with Centaurus VII engines, which were also installed in the three subsequent prototypes Nos. 12456, 12457 and 12629 (*MX991, MX994* and *TX374*). After early handling tests Centaurus XVIIs were substituted and these in turn gave way to Centaurus 57s with methanol-water injection on production aircraft. The Brigand was similar in construction to the Buckingham and finally assembled on the same jigs, but differed in detail apart from the fuselage shape. The tail unit was stronger and the wing centre-section 6 in. wider, resulting in a similar increase in span. The Brigand had larger ailerons than the Buckingham, also Fairey-Youngman pneumatic dive-brakes operated from a venturi in the wing leading edge outboard of

Brigand T.F.1 *RH742* with long-range drop-tanks, at Filton in 1948.

each engine, and the wing tips were of bonded wood, so as to act as dielectric fairings for the A.S.V. transmitting antennae. The main undercarriage units were the same, but the Brigand had a Messier tail wheel, with spring emergency extension instead of the Turner unit of the Buckingham.

The first 11 production Brigands, Nos. 12630 to 12640 (*RH742* to *RH752*), were delivered as torpedo-fighters to Nos. 36 and 42 Squadrons and the Air/Sea Weapons Development Unit of R.A.F. Coastal Command in 1946, but by that time the Air Staff requirement for a coastal strike aircraft was obsolescent and they were returned to Filton for conversion into light bombers for tropical duty in Burma and Malaya. This variant, Brigand B.Mk.I, retained the four cannon armament (with modified blast tubes) but not the rear gun. The cockpit enclosure was redesigned as a one-piece moulded

Brigand B.1 *N1125* for Pakistan Air Force about to leave Filton in 1949.

Brigand Met. 3 *VS819* at Filton in 1948.

transparency, giving an improved view and rapid hood jettisoning. Armour plate was retained and external bomb racks and rocket rails were fitted. In addition to the 11 Brigand T.F.I conversions, 69, Nos. 12641 to 12709 (*RH753-777, 792-832, 850-852*), were built as the Brigand B.1, followed by 16 of an unarmed meteorological reconnaissance version, Brigand Met. 3, Nos. 12710 to 12725 (*VS812-827*), and finally four Brigand B.1, Nos. 12726 to 12729 (*VS828-831*), completed the initial production batch of 100. All were delivered from Filton during 1948 and production continued with a second batch of 32 bombers, Nos. 12837 to 12868 (*VS832-839, VS854-877*), into the spring of 1949. During 1948 *RH820* and *RH821* were delivered to the Pakistan Air Force for evaluation, as *N1125* and *N1126*; the latter went back to the R.A.F. after major overhaul in 1950 as *WA560*, but the former crashed in Pakistan and a final new Brigand B.1, No. 12901 (*WB236*) replaced it.

Brigands went into service early in 1949 with No. 84 Squadron, Habbaniyah, and No. 8 Squadron, Aden, and in 1950 replaced the last armed Beaufighters of the R.A.F. in No. 45 Squadron at Kuala Lumpur, where they were joined by No. 84 Squadron when terrorist activities broke out in the Malayan jungle; Brigands operated continuously in Malaya from 1950 to 1954, using both bombs and rockets. The Brigand Met. 3 was used mainly by No. 1301 Meteorological Flight, F.E.A.F., at Negombo, Ceylon, with long-range tanks, wing, tail and airscrew de-icing equipment and special instruments, including a hand-camera for recording cloud formations; they made daily sorties over the Indian Ocean up to 25,000 ft. and collected valuable information on turbulence under monsoon conditions. Two experimental Brigands were

Brigand *RH748* modified for catapult proving trials, 1949.

No. 12636 (*RH748*), specially prepared in 1949 by Folland Aircraft Ltd., with reinforced fuselage skin, catapult points and inner fuel tanks replaced by water-ballast tanks as a test-vehicle for the Royal Navy's steam catapult development programme, and No. 12657 (*RH763*), flown until 1959 at Boscombe Down for parachute recovery tests of the D.H. Spectre rocket-assisted take-off unit. One other Brigand, No. 12633 (*RH745*), was partially converted in 1950 as a test-bed for the Centaurus 663 engine which was at first proposed for the Britannia; large long-tailed nacelles were built and a dorsal fin as on Buckingham *KV322* was added, but the conversion was abandoned when it was decided to install Proteus engines in the first Britannia.

A late variant of the Brigand was a radar trainer, Brigand T.4, of which nine, Nos. 12877 to 12885 (*WA561–569*), were delivered new from Filton in 1950. With blacked-out rear cockpit hooding, these were used to train A.I. operators at No. 228 O.C.U., Leeming, from July 1951 until June 1952, when the unit reformed at Colerne as No. 238 O.C.U. After three years the final variant, Brigand T.5, appeared with a different A.I. installation in a slightly longer nose radome; these were at first converted from B.1s by the R.A.F., but late in 1956 all T.4s still in service were flown to Cambridge for conversion by Marshalls to T.5 standard. In January 1957, No. 238 O.C.U. moved

Brigand T.4 prototype *RH798* converted from B.1 in 1949.

to North Luffenham, where it was finally disbanded in March 1958, after training some 600 radar navigators on Brigands.

The total number of Brigands built was 147; they were the last piston-engined attack aircraft in service with the R.A.F. and held the fort in tropical climates, for which wooden aircraft were unsuitable, until the Canberra jet-bomber arrived.

SPECIFICATIONS AND DATA

Types: 163, Buckingham; 164, Brigand; 166, Buckmaster
Manufacturers: The Bristol Aeroplane Co. Ltd., Filton, Bristol
Power Plants: (163) Two 2,400 hp Bristol Centaurus IV, VII or XI
(164) Two 2,500 hp Bristol Centaurus 57
(166) Two 2,400 hp Bristol Centaurus VII

Type	163	164	166
Span	71 ft 10 in	72 ft 4 in	71 ft 10 in
Length	46 ft 10 in	46 ft 5 in	46 ft 10 in
Height	17 ft 7 in	17 ft 6 in	17 ft 7 in
Wing Area	708 sq ft	718 sq ft	708 sq ft
Empty Weight	24,040 lb	25,600 lb	23,000 lb
All-up Weight	36,900 lb	39,000 lb	33,700 lb
Max. Speed	335 mph	360 mph	352 mph
Service Ceiling	25,000 ft	26,000 ft	30,000 ft
Range	2,200 miles	2,000 miles (2,800 miles with drop tanks)	2,000 miles
Accommodation	4	3	3
Production	123	147	112
Sequence Nos.	11332–11335 11905–12023	12455–12457 12629–12709 12710–12729 12837–12868 12876–12885 12901	12024–12135

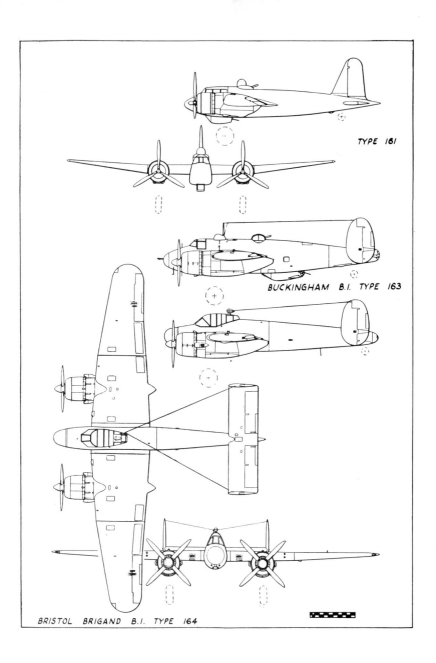

TYPE 161

BUCKINGHAM B.I. TYPE 163

BRISTOL BRIGAND B.I. TYPE 164

Brabazon taking off on its second flight from Filton on 7 September 1949.

The Bristol Brabazon I, Type 167

When the Air Staff drafted Specification B.1/39, the R.A.F. had not had any practical experience with four-engined bombers, but early operations with Stirlings and Halifaxes in 1941 soon showed how valuable the Bristol 159 would have been for long-range strategic attacks. No question of reviving it arose in 1941 when the Air Staff issued Specification B.8/41, for a heavy bomber to carry a bomb load of 10,000 lb. at 300 m.p.h. over a range of 4,000 miles, and the Company was neither invited to tender to this specification nor informed of its existence until 1942, when it was asked to submit a study for a larger bomber of 100,000 lb. all-up weight, with four Centaurus or six Hercules engines. It was soon evident that to meet the specified range and speed, with an adequate margin of drag for two or three gun-turrets, a substantial reduction in overall drag was essential. Analysis of the best existing designs showed that conventional wing-mounted engines accounted for 30% of the total drag, although only 5% was needed for cooling. Power plants completely submerged in the wing were thus likely to reduce total drag by 25%, if technically feasible.

Obviously the wing would have to be at least as thick as the height of the engine, and coupling several engines side-by-side to a single airscrew unit located well inboard would leave the outer wing free from interference and available for fuel storage. Investigations in September 1942 indicated that still larger aircraft could achieve ranges between 4,500 and 5,000 miles. German penetration into Russia and Japanese gains in the Pacific emphasised the need for a really long-range bomber, and the Company's proposal for a large 5,000-mile aircraft met with some interest from the Air Staff. Outlines were studied with six Centaurus, eight Griffons and, eventually, eight Centaurus, and the last of these in November 1942 showed a mid-wing monoplane of 225,000 lb. all-up, 225 ft. span, 5,000 sq. ft. wing area and aspect ratio 10, the limit imposed by structural considerations. The depth of the inner wing was then just adequate to submerge a Centaurus without excessive thickness/chord ratio, but only if the engines were closely pitched in a coupled power-plant arrangement. The final Bristol '100-ton bomber' had a very slender fuselage and a 'butterfly' tail, close to the ideal minimum drag

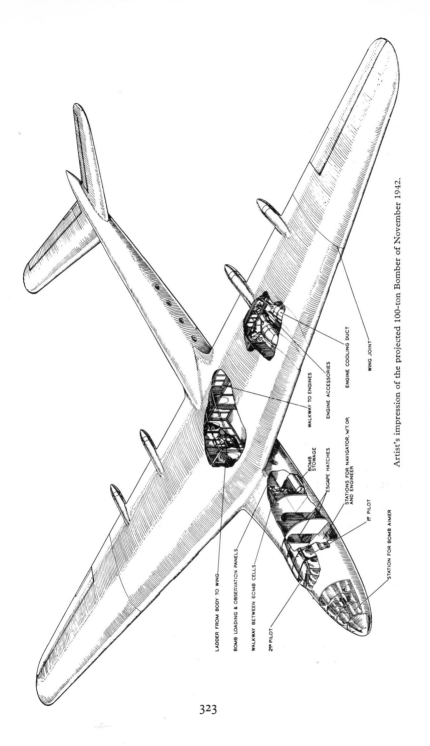

LADDER FROM BODY TO WING

BOMB LOADING & OBSERVATION PANELS

WALKWAY BETWEEN BOMB CELLS

2ND PILOT

WALKWAY TO ENGINES

ENGINE ACCESSORIES

ENGINE COOLING DUCT

WING JOINT

BOMB STOWAGE

ESCAPE HATCHES

STATIONS FOR NAVIGATOR, W/T.OP, AND ENGINEER

1ST PILOT

STATION FOR BOMB AIMER

Artist's impression of the projected 100-ton Bomber of November 1942.

shape, and comparable designs, some tailless, were put forward by other firms, but all were rejected by the Air Staff in favour of increased production of Lancasters, and it seemed that no further interest would be taken in the project.

Then, just before Christmas 1942, the M.A.P., at the request of Lord Beaverbrook (who had become Lord Privy Seal after resigning as Minister of Aircraft Production), called a meeting of chief designers to discuss the practicability of developing a civil transport of similar range and performance, as a post-war challenge to the monopoly already attained by American manufacturers. Once again the Bristol Company was not invited, but Frise immediately protested against exclusion, sought B.O.A.C. opinions on large aircraft on 7 January 1943, and went to the meeting in London on 14 January armed with the Company's proposal for a 5,000-miles transport derived from the '100-ton bomber'. The Cabinet had set up an Inter-Departmental Committee, under the chairmanship of Lord Brabazon of Tara, to enquire into the types of civil aircraft needed in the immediate post-war period, and this committee reported to the Cabinet on 9 February with a recommendation for five types of aircraft, ranging from a London–New York non-stop express airliner to a small feeder transport for internal services. The first project, known as Brabazon Type I, was to have priority in design and prototype construction, although production models could not go into service for at least five years; such a project could only be undertaken by a firm with long experience of the structural problems involved, and it was assumed that a firm already building large bombers would receive the contract. However, all such firms were already engaged in bomber production, with no spare capacity for a large new project, and on 11 March it was announced in the House of Lords by Viscount Cranborne and in the House of Commons by Sir Archibald Sinclair that the Bristol Company was to be invited to design the Brabazon Type I airliner on condition that other work was not affected.

In April Sir Wilfred Freeman sent the formal invitation to the Company and asked for the firm's views on allocation of the sub-contracts necessary to get so large an aircraft built. The Company submitted a memorandum, and on 29 May the Ministry intimated that two prototypes would be ordered with a maximum of ten more production aircraft in view, although materials were to be ordered only for the prototypes.

A cruising speed of 300 m.p.h. had been chosen for the 100-ton bomber to minimise vulnerability, and duration was a secondary consideration, but passengers needed a much larger body than bombs and there was no consensus of opinion on how many passengers should be carried. B.O.A.C. stated that passengers would not tolerate a non-stop flight longer than 18 hours and recommended 200 cu. ft. per passenger for ordinary comfort and as much as 270 cu. ft. for luxury travel; it was generally agreed that a high standard of comfort should be provided for as many passengers as possible, and that the air-conditioning system should ensure an equivalent cabin altitude no greater than 8,000 ft. when flying at 35,000 ft. The first layout in April showed a body of 25 ft. diameter divided by a level floor into two decks, with sleeping berths for 80 passengers, together with a dining-room, promenade and bar; alternatively there were day seats for 150 passengers. The sleeper version was preferred as a paying proposition because a supplementary fare for sleeping berths was acceptable; passengers needed less food and entertainment while sleeping, and the weight penalty of air-conditioning, sanitation, food and water for 70 additional day passengers was substantial. It soon became clear that the drag of a 25 ft. body was too high and a single-deck layout of 20 ft. diameter was next examined, providing a bar and promenade, but no dining-room, for 52 sleeping passengers or 96 day passengers. Both M.A.P. and the Second Brabazon Committee (including industry and B.O.A.C. members) favoured a medium-sized body associated with a fairly high speed, and on 5 August the Committee recommended adoption of the Company's proposal for a 50-passenger aircraft of 250,000 lb. all-up weight, to be defined by Specification 2/44, and B.O.A.C. promised support for this layout, although they preferred a smaller one for only 25 passengers.

A small civil project team at Ivor House, Clifton, undertook extensive preliminary layout work to determine the best arrangement of power plant and landing gear as well as interior accommodation, and by November 1944 the main features of the design, Type 167, were crystallised, with four pairs of coupled Centaurus engines mounted forward of the front spar driving co-axial tractor airscrews, a conventional tail unit, a fuselage maximum diameter of 16 ft. 9 in., a nose-wheel landing gear with multiple wheels and flexible fuel tanks in the outer portions of the wing; the designation Type 168 was reserved for a possible military variant, but no design work on this was ever done. The overall design was orthodox, extreme care being taken to reduce and control weight at all stages, and the aluminium-clad light-alloy plates and sheet material were rolled to specially close tolerances and checked for uniformity of gauge in the middle of the sheet as well as at the edge; rivets were graded to fit their holes accurately and their tail lengths were controlled to save weight; in so large a structure it was possible to defeat the 'square-cube law' by determining the exact sections needed to carry the stresses, and the wing weight was kept down by sharing the span-wise loads between many evenly spaced extruded stringers which replaced the concentrated booms of a conventional two-spar wing. Similar use was made of continuous stringers in the fuselage, heavy longerons being reduced to a minimum. Mock-up construction began, methods of manufacture were examined by a co-ordinating committee and the first manufacturing drawings were issued in April 1945. At first it was proposed to build the prototypes at Weston-super-Mare, but the subsoil was unsuitable for a runway of the strength required, so reluctantly the Company had to extend the Filton runway, although this involved closing a new dual-carriageway bypass road and demolition of part of Charlton village; naturally this raised local protests and the proposals were not finally agreed by all the parties concerned until March 1946, after the whole project had been referred to the Cabinet in June

1945. This was only one of the many legal, political and technical problems which arose after construction of the first prototype began in October 1945 and delayed the first flight until 4 September 1949. In the intervening period, quite apart from the aeroplane itself, a prodigious supporting programme was undertaken, including static structural testing of a complete half-scale wing at the R.A.E., pressure testing of a front-fuselage specimen, endurance and type tests of the coupled power-plant on a wing-mounted test-rig and exhaustive functioning tests of all the hydraulic flying control units and landing gear mechanisms, the complex electrical installation and the air-conditioning system, to say nothing of the construction of a specially strong runway and 8-acre three-bay assembly hall. The cold weather of early 1947 delayed completion of the latter, and only the east bay was ready to receive the fuselage shell with its integral 100 ft. span inner wing and 55 ft. span tail plane when this assembly was taken out of its building jig and towed half a mile to its final erection site on 4 October 1947, an operation more like the launching of a ship than usual with a land aeroplane. Indeed the method of constructing the Brabazon, in a light-weight skeleton cradle mounted on removable vertical stanchions, owed more to shipbuilding methods than to aircraft practice. During the 23 months which elapsed between this event and the first take-off flight tests on a Lancaster (*RE131*) proved the hydraulic surface control units, and a Buckmaster (*RP164*) flight-tested the combustion heaters for wing and tail de-icing; the outer wings, fin and rudder were assembled; landing gear, hydraulic, electrical and fuel systems were installed and in December 1948 the complete aircraft (No. 12759) was rolled out for initial engine runs, fuel loading and ground resonance tests having been cleared some weeks earlier.

It had been agreed in 1946 to fly the first prototype as an unfurnished test-bed with a comprehensive array of data-recording equipment, although the possibility of furnishing it later for commercial use was not excluded. The second prototype (No. 12870) was to be fully furnished and equipped to carry 100 passengers, and powered by four double-Proteus turbine engines, which were also adopted for the Saunders-Roe Princess flying boat of similar size to the Brabazon. The requirements for Brabazon I Mark II were set out in Specification 2/46, to which a tender design was formally submitted in June 1947, the date by which it had originally been hoped to fly the first prototype. The economy of the Proteus engine in civil operation relied on a minimum cruising speed of 330 m.p.h. at 35,000 ft.; this could only be permitted if a satisfactory gust alleviation device were installed to protect the wing from the direct effects of the severe gust design cases on which the airworthiness authorities insisted; this comprised a gust-detector in the nose, 80 ft. ahead of the wing, which moved the ailerons symmetrically in the sense needed to cancel the effect of the gust, and an aileron reponse rate of not less than 60 degrees per second was required. Without such a device there would be either an unacceptable limitation of cruising speed or an equally unacceptable increase in wing structure weight. The second prototype had an improved

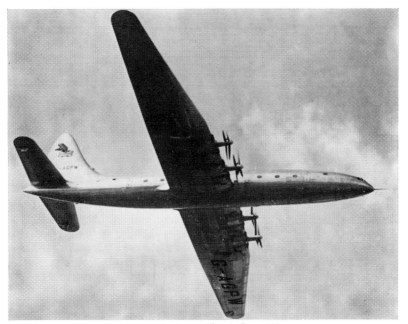

Brabazon flying over Filton in June 1950.

wing structure incorporating integral fuel tanks, with top-hat section stringers instead of Z-section, but flexible fuel-bags were re-introduced later because of the fire risk with integral tanks in a heavy landing; the dihedral angle of the outer wings was increased from 2 to 4 degrees to reduced trapped fuel and increase wing-tip clearance. A change was made from fully duplicated power controls to aerodynamic servo-tab controls with modified power assistance and partial manual reversion, and the full-span servo-tabs required straight trailing edges for the rudder and elevators. A further design change, subject to trial on the first prototype, was a four-wheeled bogie main undercarriage unit, to reduce the runway loading at existing airports. Although most of the difficulties associated with the second prototype were solved, the gust alleviation problem proved intractable and was a compelling technical reason for the abandonment of the Brabazon I Mark II when half-built, although the decision was mainly a political and financial one. The size of the project seems to have overawed the authorities, who tended to demand 'both belt and braces', as, for instance, by insisting on the addition of mass-balances to control surfaces designed from the start to be irreversible and therefore flutter-free, whose actuators had been proved by endurance tests to be reliable.

On 4 September 1949 the Company's newly appointed Chief Test Pilot, A. J. Pegg, found no difficulty in handling the Brabazon I (*G-AGPW*) on its first flight; subsequent flights went as planned, and even when a hydraulic

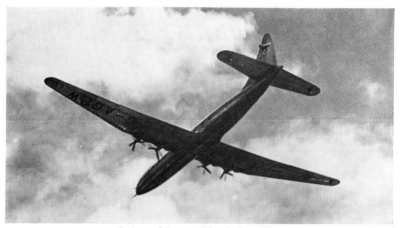

Brabazon flying over Filton in June 1950.

pipe failure (which occurred on 16 January 1950 during W. F. Gibb's first flight as pilot in charge) necessitated landing with flaps up, the Filton runway and reversing airscrews proved adequate. On its demonstration flights at London Airport on 15 June 1950, and at Farnborough in September the same year, the Brabazon was acclaimed for its smooth and easy manœuvrability on the ground, short take-off run and even shorter landing run. Partial furnishing of the rear fuselage with a bar and 30 B.O.A.C. reclinable seats for demonstration to official passengers confirmed how silence, comfort and freedom from claustrophobia and fatigue could be achieved in a really large aeroplane as in no smaller type. It is true that recurrent fatigue cracks in the airscrew mounting structure prevented the issue of an unrestricted Certificate of Airworthiness in connection with its proposed hire as a peak-load carrier by B.E.A., furnished for 180 passengers for the London to Nice service, and that it would have had an overall airframe fatigue life of only 5,000 hr. in the light of later experience, but ten years after the event it still seems regrettable that its total flying time had amounted to less than 400 hours when it was broken up in October 1953. A spare nose wheel and oleo-leg assembly was the only relic saved from the wreckers for exhibition in the Science Museum, London, but so satisfactorily compact a component can give future generations little idea of the majestic flight and serene progress of the Brabazon, whose size and beautiful lines deceived the eye into seriously underestimating its actual speed.

Like Brunel's *Great Eastern* steamship, the Brabazon was a pioneer on the grand scale born a generation too soon for its environment. Soon after its demise, wiseacres confidently predicted that no civil aeroplane so large would ever again be built, but within ten years fleets of 300,000 lb. airliners were the order of the day, and by the late 1980s weights had risen to over 850,000 lb.

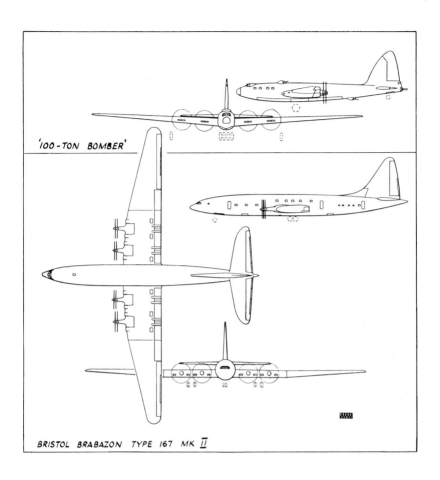

'100-TON BOMBER'

BRISTOL BRABAZON TYPE 167 MK II

Both Brabazons at Filton before being scrapped in 1953.

329

Type:	167, Brabazon I
Manufacturers:	The Bristol Aeroplane Co. Ltd., Filton, Bristol
Power Plants:	(Mk 1) Eight 2,500 hp Bristol Centaurus XX
	(Mk 2) Four 7,000 hp Bristol Coupled-Proteus 710
Span:	230 ft
Length:	(Mk 1) 177 ft; (Mk 2) 178 ft 10 in
Height:	50 ft
Wing Area:	(Mk 1) 5,317 sq ft (Mk 2) 5,422 sq ft
Empty Weight:	(Mk 1) 145,100 lb (Mk 2) 160,000 lb
All-up Weight:	(Mk 1) 290,000 lb (Mk 2) 330,000 lb
Max. Speed:	(Mk 1) 300 mph (Mk 2) 360 mph
Cruising Speed:	(Mk 1) 250 mph (Mk 2) 330 mph
Cruising Altitude:	(Mk 1) 25,000 ft (Mk 2) 35,000 ft
Range:	5,500 miles
Accommodation:	(Crew) 12 (Passengers) 100
Production:	(Mk 1) 1 (Mk 2) 1 (not completed)
Sequence Nos.:	(Mk 1) 12759 (Mk 2) 12870

First prototype 170 before first flight at Filton in December 1945.

The Bristol Freighter and Wayfarer, Type 170

Although the Bristol Aeroplane Company's part in the post-war national civil aviation plan was to build the Brabazon I, a 'bread-and-butter' project was also needed during the first years of peace, and a design suitable for quick production (both at home and in Australia) was sought. After considering a possible passenger and freight-carrying derivative of the Buckingham, using standard inner wings, power plants, landing gear and tail unit combined with a large capacity high-wing body and extended outer wings, attention was turned to something simpler to build and cheaper to operate, developed from the Bombay, which had achieved a very high utilisation in North Africa with exceptional economy.

The new design evolved in 1944, Type 170, was a short-range general-duty transport embodying the structural design experience gained during the war years, with a 98 ft. span wing of the same section and taper ratio as the Bombay, but with swept-back leading edge and straight trailing edge and simplified two-spar construction. A single fin and rudder with trim-tabs replaced the Bombay's complex empennage; the Bombay had been designed with neutral longitudinal stability, because of the limited power of its early auto-pilot, and this had made it more difficult to fly than it might have been, but the 170 was designed to use a modern Sperry auto-pilot and could be trimmed to fly 'hands-off'. The body was flat-sided, with a trap-door in the nose accepting bulkier packages than the Bombay's side door. The engines proposed were a new version of the Perseus, using nine Centaurus cylinders and developing 1,150 h.p. for take-off.

On being shown this entirely private venture design, the Air Staff recognised its potential as a military freighter of a type urgently recommended by General Orde Wingate for carrying vehicles and supplies to jungle airstrips in the Burma campaign, and agreed to order two prototypes if the fuselage were enlarged to carry a standard 3-ton army truck or equivalent load, Specifications 22/44 and C.9/45 being successively drafted to define this version. The resulting fuselage provided unobstructed entry through side-hinged nose doors to a freight hold 32 ft. long and 8 ft. wide, with a minimum height under the wing of 6 ft. 8 in. Extra space was available in a smaller compartment aft, with its own side door, and the total cargo capacity was 2,360 c. ft. When it was plain that the war would end before the Bristol 170 could reach Burma, cost calculations for typical civil operations showed that, in terms of ton-miles per gallon of fuel, it would be advantageous to increase the weight and use more powerful but readily available Hercules engines, so the gross weight was raised from 30,000 lb. to 35,000 lb., to give an estimated disposable load including fuel of 13,000 lb. In the final design, the engines were Hercules 630 (i.e. civil 130) with single-speed M ratio blowers giving 1,670 h.p. for take-off, and the maximum range was 1,100 miles at an economical cruising speed of 150 m.p.h. At such a short range and low speed the fuel weight saved by making the landing gear retractable was less than the structure weight saved by keeping the gear fixed, amounting to some 400 lb.; the fixed gear was cheaper to make and maintain and immune from most causes of mechanical failure and no hydraulic system was needed, because the wheel-brakes and split-type wing flaps could be operated pneumatically.

A comprehensive survey of world markets indicated some scope for a utility passenger and freight transport in underdeveloped areas, so it was decided to produce Type 170 in two versions, the Freighter with nose-doors and a strong floor, and the Wayfarer with a fixed nose and furnishings for up to 36 passengers, both types having windows, escape hatches and cabin heating equipment. To meet the intense competition of American war-surplus transports, available at low prices and backed by almost inexhaustible stocks of spares, the M.O.S. was prepared to assist makers of British civil aircraft to export them and agreed to purchase two prototypes of Type 170 and to pay most of the cost of the production jigs; two more prototypes were built as demonstrators by the Company and a first production batch of 25 was laid down.

The first prototype, No. 12730 (*G-AGPV*), was flown at Filton by C. F. Uwins on 2 December 1945; he found it satisfactory in most respects, but required the tail plane to be lowered and increased in span to achieve 'hands-off' trim over the desired wide range of centre of gravity positions. At first, *G-AGPV*'s nose doors were fixed, and it had round cabin windows instead of the rectangular ones standardised for production aircraft; the small mud-guards originally fitted were discarded and only mud-scrapers were retained on the main wheels. After maker's trials at Filton, the first prototype was repainted in R.A.F. markings, as *VR380*, and delivered to Boscombe Down on 24 September 1946.

Meanwhile, the second prototype, No. 12731 (*G-AGVB*), furnished as a 32-seater Wayfarer, flew on 30 April 1946, and on 8 May A. J. Pegg made a proving flight to Jersey and back; on 7 June it received the first unrestricted C. of A. granted to a new post-war aircraft, and two days later was chartered to Channel Islands Airways in charge of E. A. Swiss as chief pilot; by 25 October it had carried 10,000 passengers between Croydon and Jersey via Southampton in 358 flights totalling 460 hours. The third prototype, No. 12732 (*G-AGVC*), was fully equipped as a Freighter and flew on 23 June 1946; on 3 August it left Filton, piloted by Tim Sims, on a demonstration tour of North and South America, crossing the Atlantic via Prestwick, Keflavik, Bluie West and Goose Bay to Toronto. Thereafter it covered 31,000 miles in 215 hours before arriving at Rio de Janeiro on 15 December 1946 by way of Vancouver, Los Angeles, Mexico City, Havana, Trinidad, Bogota, Quito, Lima, La Paz, Santiago, Buenos Aires, Montevideo and Sao Paulo. After a major inspection at Sao Paulo it was flown back to Toronto via Natal, Georgetown, Nassau, Daytona Beach and Jacksonville, thus completing 41,000 miles in 331 flying hours. In February 1947 it was chartered to Canadian Pacific Air Lines for urgent mail delivery to Baie Comeau and to lift 250 tons of mining equipment to a new coalfield in Labrador, where the only airstrip was rolled snow on the frozen surface of Knob Lake; there on 19 March a main undercarriage leg was damaged and replaced in time for Sims to take-off, just as the ice began to break due to an early thaw.

From the Arctic Circle, *G-AGVC* was next chartered to Linea Aeropostal Venezolana to carry fresh meat from abbatoirs on ranches at Barranquilla to Caracas, during July and August 1947, after which it returned to Toronto for 400 hours inspection, flew back to Filton in March 1948 and was chartered to Silver City Airways to inaugurate the Lympne to Le Touquet car ferry on 13 July 1948. In October 1948 it was transferred to the Berlin Air Lift until February 1949, when it returned to Filton, having unfailingly demonstrated its ability to handle loads of unprecedented size and variety in every extreme of climate and emergency.

The fourth prototype, No. 12733 (*G-AGUT*), was fully furnished as a 32-seater Wayfarer and flew for the first time on 15 September 1946, but followed a much less adventurous career than its fellows, for only nine days later it was repainted in R.A.F. markings as *VR382* and delivered to the Telecommunications Research Establishment at Defford, where it was joined early in 1949 by *VR380*, which had been converted to a Wayfarer after completing handling tests in July 1947 with extended wings of 108 ft. span, fitted with racks for under-wing stores. Both *VR380* and *VR382*, fitted as flying laboratories, were to be seen carrying nose radomes of various shapes and sizes until November 1958.

G-AGPV returned to civil register in 1958, showing typical R.R.E. radome test installation.

Immediately after *G-AGPV*'s early flights had confirmed the performance predictions, work began on the production batch of 25 aircraft, Nos. 12734 to 12758. Enquiries and provisional orders came in quickly and had reached more than 30 by the end of the annual S.B.A.C. Show at Radlett in September. Inevitably customers insisted on individual requirements being met and, where substantial orders were at stake, sub-variants of the Freighter and Wayfarer became necessary. A system of Mark Numbers was then introduced as follows:

Mark I: Freighter, nose doors, heavy floor, crew toilet.
,, IA: as Mk. I for mixed traffic; 16 passenger seats and one passenger toilet aft of rear spar.
,, IB: as Mk. I, to B.E.A. special requirements.
,, IC: as Mk. IA, to B.E.A. special requirements.
,, ID: as Mk. IA, to B.S.A.A. special requirements.
,, II: Wayfarer, fixed nose, no seats, crew toilet.
,, IIA: Wayfarer, 32 seats, pantry, one passenger toilet.
,, IIB: as Mk. IIA, to B.E.A. standard, two passenger toilets.
,, IIC: Wayfarer, 20 seats forward of rear spar, luggage hold and single toilet aft, for I.N.A.

The second prototype corresponded to Mk. IIB, the third to Mk. I, the fourth to Mk. IIA, and while still unfurnished, the first represented Mk. II. Since the fixed nose was quicker to manufacture than the doors, all but the fourth in the first dozen production aircraft were Wayfarers; the first two were retained by the Company as demonstrators, *G-AHJB* being allocated to South America and *G-AHJC* to Europe and North Africa. On 28 June *G-AHJB* left Filton with three additional long-range tanks installed in the cabin, en route for Buenos Aires via Lisbon, Rabat, Bathurst, Natal and Rio de Janeiro.

G-AHJB, the first production Wayfarer IIA, with 900-gallon tanks in cabin, at Filton on 29 June 1946 before taking off for South America.

Unfortunately, it missed the radio beacon at Natal and continued southwards for 400 miles before having to be ditched 100 miles off-shore when fuel ran out; existing orders for two Wayfarers from Brazil and 15 Mk. IA Freighters from Argentina were not affected, and *G-AHJC* created an excellent impression at the Radlett show. Meanwhile *G-AHJD* went into service with Airwork on leave charters for the Sudan government between Gatwick and Khartum, while *G-AHJF* and *'JG*, the only production Mk. II Wayfarers, were bought by British-American Air Services to carry flowers and fruit from Mediterranean growers to markets in Paris and London. These were followed off the production line by two Mark IIA Wayfarers for R.E.A.L. of Sao Paulo, three of the same for Dalmia Jain Airways of Delhi, one of each for Bharat Airways and Skytravel and two Mk. IIC Wayfarers (the only examples built) for Indian National Airways; deliveries of Mk. IA Freighters to the Argentine government began with *G-AHJE* on 25 October, the first of eight allocated from the first production batch; a second batch of 25, Nos. 12760 to 12784, was authorised and soon afterwards a batch of 50, Nos. 12785 to 12834, was laid down after consultation with M.O.S. Of the first batch, Nos. 12756 (*G-AICM*) and 12757 (*G-AICN*) were reserved as the first of 13 Mk. IIB and nine Mk. IB, respectively, for British European Airways, but this option, like that of B.S.A.A. for three Mk. ID, was not taken up and *G-AICM* and *G-AICN* remained unsold for a time; in the summer of 1947 the former was completed as a Mk. I Freighter for M.O.S. and chartered to Hunting Air Surveys for a photographic survey of the Persian oilfields, for which purpose it was fitted with optically flat camera windows in the nose doors. This opera-

VT-CGW, one of the only two Wayfarers IIC for I.N.A., at Filton in September 1946.

334

tion followed a tour of Spain and the Middle East by *G-AHJF*, which had been converted to Mk. IA in March 1947; once it was flown by the Shah of Persia, and many times it showed how bulky loads could be accommodated in its capacious hold. In July, *G-AHJD* was similarly converted to Mk. I by Airwork Ltd. and later equipped with a level-loading horse-box for Air Contractors Ltd. to fly racehorses from France to Ireland. About the same time, *G-AHJG* was furnished as a Mk. IIA and flown as *ZS-BOM* by Suidair International Airways between Croydon and Johannesburg, but returned to Filton after a heavy landing at Croydon, and in December 1947 was chartered to Silver City Airways for transporting refugees following the partition of India and Pakistan; for this operation all seats were removed and 117 refugees were carried on one flight across the border. One Wayfarer (*F-BCJA*) was sold in December to Cie. des Transports Aériens Intercontinentaux of Paris, who also bought two Freighters (*F-BCJM* and '*JN*) a few months later for

G-AICR, a Freighter IA with extra-low pressure tyres and removable door for oil-field operations in Ecuador, 1947.

service between France, North Africa and Syria. Two Mark I Freighters, Nos. 12761 and 12762 (*G-AICR* and '*CS*) were fitted for supply dropping and had extra low-pressure tyres for landing on unprepared airstrips at Shell Mera, the Shell Oil Company's high-altitude oilfield in Ecuador, where they operated under extreme climatic conditions from April 1947 until 1949, when the project was ended by an earthquake.

On 20 March 1947 a demonstration Mk. IA No. 12793 (*G-AIMC*), *Merchant Venturer*, left Filton on a sales tour of Australia and New Zealand, during which many forms of cargo, including vehicles, horses and other animals, and stores of all kinds were successfully handled; it was chartered to QANTAS for work in the New Guinea goldfield, but came to grief when, after landing up-hill on the sloping airstrip at Wau, the parking-brake cable broke and the aircraft ran away backwards down the strip and was damaged beyond repair.

At the 1947 S.B.A.C. Show at Radlett, two Freighters were on view; No. 12812 (*G-AIMW*), a standard Mk. I, and No. 12766 (*G-AIFF*), the first

Mk. XI, featuring the 108 ft. span round-tipped wing tested earlier on *VR380*, which allowed the all-up weight to rise by 2,000 lb. to 39,000 lb., larger fuel tanks being installed to increase the range as an alternative to carrying extra payload. The Freighter's potential with this wing could not be fully exploited until more powerful Hercules 672 engines became available in December, and with these it became Mk. 21 and the gross weight rose to 40,000 lb. Only two aircraft were delivered to the interim standard: No. 12792 (*SE-BNG*), a Mk. XI with wing de-icing and special cargo-hold heating for the Swedish firm A/B.T.Flyg, and No. 12795 (*ZS-BVI*), a Mk. XIA mixed-traffic transport for Suidair. Both flew away in August 1947, but *SE-BNG* crashed into a mountain near Amalfi while returning from Ethiopia on 18 November, and *ZS-BVI*, transferred to the British Register as *G-AIME* in October, was modified to Mk. 21 standard.

Two versions of the 'New Freighter' were offered, the unfurnished Mk. 21 and the convertible Mk. 21E; the latter had cabin heating, sound insulation and 16 pairs of quickly removable seats, together with a movable bulkhead, combining the roles of the Mks. I, IA and IIA. A fixed-nose Wayfarer (Mk. 22A) was also offered but never built. In June 1948 *G-AIFF* toured Portugal, Spain, the Near East and India; meanwhile aircraft on the production line were quickly completed to the new standard and deliveries began in May to Aviacion y Comercio of Bilbao and Cie. Air Transport of Paris; two more Mk. 21E, Nos. 12779 and 12775, went to Central African Airways as *VP-YHW* and *VP-YHZ*, respectively, but were later transferred to West African Airways. Many owners of earlier Freighters had them brought up to the new standard at major overhaul; eight were converted to Mk. 21 and seven to Mk. 21E, in addition to nine new Mk. 21 and 20 new Mk. 21E. One of each version was supplied for evaluation to the Pakistan Air Force in August 1948 and led to a contract for 30 of a specially equipped Mk. 21P variant, and conversion of two existing Wayfarers to the same standard; these all had windows in the nose doors like *G-AICM*.

Another Mk. 21, No. 12755 (*G-AICL*), chartered to Australian National Airways in November 1948 for the 'Air-Beef' operation in Northern

G-AICL leaving Filton in November 1948 to inaugurate the 'Air-Beef' service in Australia; as *VH-INJ* this Freighter 21 flew 26,000 hours in A.N.A. service.

336

Freighter 21P *G798* of the Pakistan Air Force flying over Himalayan foot-hills near Ghilgit in 1952.

Territories, was so successful that after a year it was retained as *VH-INJ* and joined by two rebuilt Freighters, *VH-INK* and *VH-INL*, formerly *G-AHJC* and *G-AICR*, respectively.

The third prototype, *G-AGVC*, had inaugurated the Lympne–Le Touquet car ferry service from 13 July to 5 October 1948 when it was transferred to the Berlin Air Lift to carry bulk cargo from Hamburg to Gatow in company with *G-AHJC* (which had been on the job since July) and *G-AGVB* and *G-AHJD* which had previously been converted to Mk. 21. It was withdrawn from Berlin in February 1949 for a charter flight to Egypt, but engine damage caused it to be returned for repair to Filton, where it was converted to a military freighter, with Hercules 238 engines, double oil-coolers in the centreplane leading edge, larger airscrews, extra tankage and a strong floor to R.A.F. Transport Command requirements, which permitted a take-off weight of 42,000 lb., although it could not obtain a civil C. of A. at this weight unless its performance was shown to meet revised regulations, so a programme was begun on *G-AIFF* to demonstrate compliance. On 6 May 1949, while being flown by R. J. Northway, accompanied by several senior engineers, for the purpose of measuring rate of climb and engine temperatures on one engine and also strain-gauging the rear fuselage during yawed cruising flight, it fell into the sea off Portland Bill with the loss of all on board; salvage was impossible and the only eye-witnesses were the crew of a submarine several miles away, so the cause of the accident could not be determined. Certification of the Mk. 21 was not affected and deliveries continued with two for West African Airways fitted with 54 special lightweight seats, three Mk. 21E for the Royal Australian Air Force and five for Saudi Arabian Airlines, including a Mk. 21E demonstrator, No. 12790 (*G-AILZ*), *African Enterprise*, which left Filton on 4 January 1949 on a month's intensive tour of Africa.

The military prototype, ex-*G-AGVC*, was shown at the 1949 S.B.A.C. Show with experimental marking *G-18-2*, and a ready market awaited it as soon as C. of A. could be obtained. Meanwhile *G-AHJJ*, sold in 1946 as a Mk. IIA to Dalmia Jain and by them in 1947 to Indian National Airways,

337

had been brought back and converted to a Mk. 21 for Silver City Airways; on 21 March 1950 it crashed near Cowbridge, Glamorganshire, and the cause was found to be structural failure of the fin during single-engined climb, in circumstances so similar to the loss of *G-AIFF* that there could be no reasonable doubt that both accidents were due to the same cause. After confirmatory tests, a dorsal fin was approved to prevent rudder-locking in the extreme yaw condition, and thus modified *G-AGVC* received a new C. of A. as Mark 31, at an all-up weight of 44,000 lb. when fitted with Hercules 734 engines. The first production Mk. 31, No. 12826 (*G-AINK*), was temporarily allotted military serial *WH575* for winter trials in Canada, but was damaged at Filton when both engines cut during a take-off with simulated single-engine failure. It was replaced in the flight development programme by the second production Mk. 31, No. 12827 (*WJ320*), which underwent full trials at Boscombe Down, Winnipeg and Singapore and was eventually

Freighter 31 *ZK-AYG* of Straits Air Freight Express, with blanked-off windows

delivered to Aer Lingus as *EI-AFP* in June 1951. Meanwhile *G-AINK* was rebuilt to the civil Mk. 31 standard and sold to Straits Air Freight Express, New Zealand, as *ZK-AYG*, together with No. 12828 (*G-AINM, ZK-AYH*). Three with military equipment went to the R.N.Z.A.F., two similarly equipped to the R.C.A.F. and one to Associated Airways of Edmonton as *CF-GBT*. The R.N.Z.A.F.'s fourth Freighter, No. 12927, a standard Mk. 31, was the 101st production Bristol 170; thereafter new batches of ten aircraft were authorised as dictated by the order book; Nos. 12928 to 12936 were the last nine Mk. 21P for Pakistan and No. 12937 was the first Mk. 31E (*EI-AFQ*) for Aer Lingus, who also took delivery of a second Mk. 31 and two more Mk. 31E. Several of both versions were purchased at home by Silver City and Aviation Traders, and abroad by Aviacion y Comercio and Iberia in Spain; Wardair, Central Northern Airways and Pacific Western Airlines in Canada and Air Vietnam and Aigle Azur in south-east Asia; they were supplied also to the air forces of Iraq and Burma and repeat orders were received from the R.C.A.F., R.N.Z.A.F. and S.A.F.E.

The largest single contract for Freighters was for a special military variant, Mk. 31M, developed from the R.N.Z.A.F. and R.C.A.F. military versions specifically for the Pakistan Air Force, to whom 38 were delivered between December 1953 and June 1955; two of these, Nos. 13159 and 13160 (*S4406*

338

and *S4407*), were equipped as V.I.P. transports, the remainder being used for general duties mainly in mountainous terrain. All were equipped for supply-dropping, and in 1961 five were fitted with spray-booms for anti-locust operations in Sind Province; five others were resold, two in 1955 to Trans-Australia Airlines for use in New Guinea and three in 1961, two to S.A.F.E. and one to British United Airways. Two final Mk. 31M, Nos. 13219 and 13249 (*9699* and *9700*), were delivered to the R.C.A.F. in July 1955, followed by Mk. 31, No. 13253 (*9850*), in April 1957. The last Freighters delivered new were both Mk. 31, No. 13255 going to S.A.F.E. as *ZK-BVM* on 20 February 1958 and No. 13250 to Dan-Air Services at Blackbushe as *G-APLH* on 25 March 1958.

The latest and best known variant of the Bristol 170 was the Mark 32, which was developed at the request of Silver City Airways to provide greater volumetric capacity for car-ferry operations. In this variant the fuselage nose was lengthened by 5 ft. and the fin and tailplane were increased in area; the Superfreighter, as it was called by Silver City, could accommodate three medium or two large motor cars together with 23 passengers in a comfortable cabin aft of the hold. The first, No. 13073 (*G-AMWA*), was delivered on 31

The first Freighter 32 on test at Filton in 1952.

March 1953, five followed between April and June, three more were added to the fleet in 1954 and a final five in 1956. Air Charter also acquired two Mk. 32 in April 1955, two in December 1956, one in April 1957 and one in June 1957; still needing more capacity in 1958, Air Charter converted two of their existing Mk. 31, *G-AMLP* and *G-AMSA*, to Mk. 32; Silver City also converted *G-AMWA* into a so-called 'Super-Wayfarer' by installing seats for 60 passengers, for their London–Paris air-coach service in June 1958. By December 1961 the Bristol Freighters on the car ferries between Britain and the mainland of Europe had carried about 600,000 cars and well over one and a half million passengers; in October 1962 the Freighters of Air Charter and Silver City Airways were integrated into a single fleet as British United Air Ferries, comprising five Mk. 21, one Mk. 31 and 18 Mk. 32; traffic was still increasing, and although larger four-engined aircraft were introduced in 1962, forty-one civil Freighters were in service in 1970. By the end of 1963 *G-AMWB* had made 26,000 landings and *G-AMWD* 24,000, matched in New Zealand by *ZK-BEO* with 25,000 landings in 13,000 flying hours. Although the wing spar lower booms were subject to replacement after 25,000 landings, this repair could be done twice or even three times if neces-

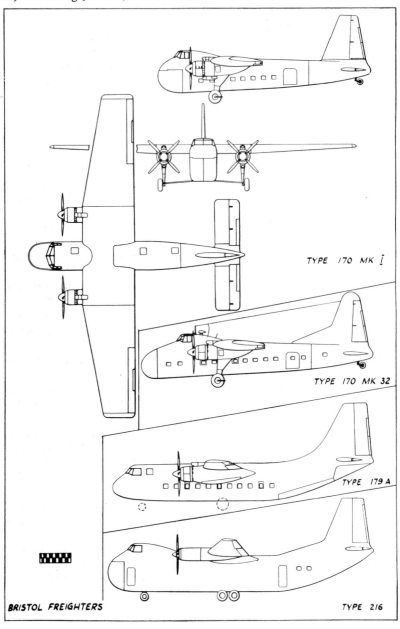

TYPE 170 MK I

TYPE 170 MK 32

TYPE 179 A

BRISTOL FREIGHTERS

TYPE 216

sary, giving a potential overall life for short-haul operations of 60,000 landings, equivalent to over 25 years of average ferry service.

Individually the highest number of flying hours was 26,000, achieved by the veteran *VH-INJ* of A.N.A.; after ten years on the 'Air-Beef' service it was transferred to the Tasmania–Melbourne ferry, on which it was employed until 1962. Only one Freighter never flew away from Filton at all; this was No. 12789 (*G-AILY*), a Mk. II reserved for experimental work, which, after only a few hours flying in 1948 with the class 'B' mark *R-37*, was grounded for static tests and trial installations, such as the paratroop doors for the P.A.F. aircraft. A temporary experimental variant was No. 12763, originally a Mk. IIA (*G-AICT*) chartered to Airwork in March 1948 and converted to Mk. 21E a year later. In 1951 it was fitted with 0·7 scale Britannia tail-plane, elevators and rudder, with a representative dorsal fin, to provide handling data on the aerodynamic servo-tab controls and artificial feel system adopted for the Britannia. Flown for some months with the experimental mark *G-18-40*, it was restored to Mk. 21E and delivered to West African Airways as *VR-NAL* in April 1952, returning to the British Register as *G-AICT* when purchased by East Anglian Flying Services.

As a type the Bristol 170 has had a very lengthy service life, with a handful of the 214 aircraft built still in use in 1988 when the third edition of this book was being prepared. Manufacture of the Bristol 170 extended from December 1945 to March 1958. By the end of 1963 112 were still in service, after amassing over a million flying hours in operations all over the world and in all extremes of climate. During 1963 variants earlier than the Mk. 31 were withdrawn from service as they reached their next major inspection, but some 40 civil survivors were still earning their 'bread-and-butter' in 1970.

One of the major operators of the type was Safe Air, based at Blenheim Airport in New Zealand. This airline was formed in 1951 as Straits Air Freight Express and began operations with two Bristol 170s. At one stage it had eleven of these aircraft on its books and the type was in service with the operator for 35 years.

Safe Air built up extensive experience with the aircraft and its Bristol Hercules engines. When they were withdrawn from service one of its Bristol 170s (*ZK-CWF*) had flown 31,977 hours. On the engine side, the time between overhauls (*TBO*) of the Hercules reached 3,000 hours in 1978, the highest engine *TBO* in the world. And by March 1985 one Safe Air's Hercules engine had achieved a total running time since new of 20,987 hours, when it was believed to be the longest running piston engine in the world.

Safe Air finally ended operations with the Bristol 170 on 30 September 1986 when its last two aircraft in service (*ZK-CLT* and *ZK-CLU*) had completed 19,022 flying hours during 18,720 flights and 21,314 hours in 25,978 flights respectively. The airline donated *ZK-CLT* to the R.N.Z.A.F. and *ZK-CLU* went to The Founders Park Inc, Nelson,

New Zealand. It had four other Bristol 170s in service in 1983, but these were progressively withdrawn from operations. Three of these aircraft, *ZK-CRM*, *ZK-CWF* and *ZK-CRK*, were scrapped and *ZK-CPT* went to the Marlborough Aero Club at Blenheim.

Subsequently two Bristol 170s which had been operated by Hercules Airlines (*ZK-EPD* and *ZK-EPF*) were flown across the Pacific via Pago Pago and Honolulu in September and October 1987 on delivery flights to Trans Provincial Airlines of Prince Rupert, Canada. One Bristol 170 was known to be in flying condition in England by early 1988—an ex-R.N.Z.A.F. aircraft then being offered for sale by Instone Air Line—and Rolls-Royce and British Aerospace believed there were still a few others in Australia and New Zealand.

The Instone aircraft, *G-BISU*, was delivered from New Zealand in 1981. Based at Stansted, it was used by the airline up to the end of 1987 for freight operations and bloodstock services, flying racehorses between Britain, Ireland, France, Germany and Italy.

When put on sale by Instone this Bristol 170 had completed 15,867 flying hours and a considerable amount of its airframe structure life remained unused.

SPECIFICATIONS AND DATA

Type:	170, Freighter and Wayfarer
Manufacturers:	The Bristol Aeroplane Co. Ltd., Filton, Bristol
	Western Airways Ltd., Weston-super-Mare, Somerset
Power Plants:	(Mks I, IA, II, IIA, IIB, IIC, XI, XIA) Two 1,675 hp Bristol Hercules 632
	(Mks 21, 21E, 21P) Two 1,690 hp Bristol Hercules 672
	(Mks 31, 31C, 31E, 31M, 32) Two 1,980 hp Bristol Hercules 734
Span:	(Mks I & II) 98 ft; (Mks XI, 21, 31, & 32) 108 ft
Length:	(Mks I, II, XI, 21, 31) 68 ft 4 in; (Mk 32) 73 ft 4 in
Height:	(Mks I, II, XI, 21, 31) 21 ft 8 in; (Mk 32) 25 ft
Wing Area:	(Mks I & II) 1,405 sq ft; (Mks XI, 21, 31 & 32) 1,487 sq ft
Empty Weight:	(I & II) 23,500 lb; (IA) 24,000 lb; (IIA & IIC) 25,500 lb; (XI) 24,500 lb; (XIA) 25,000 lb; (21) 26,500 lb; (21E) 28,000 lb; (31) 27,000 lb; (31E) 28,500 lb; (32) 29,550 lb
All-up Weight:	(I & II) 36,500 lb; (IA, IIA & IIC) 37,000 lb; (XI & XIA) 39,000 lb; (21 & 21E) 40,000 lb; (31, 31E & 32) 44,000 lb
Max. Speed:	(I, IA, II, IIA & IIC) 240 mph; (XI & XIA) 195 mph; (21, 21E, 31, 31E & 32) 225 mph
Cruising Speed:	(All Mks) 163 mph
Ceiling:	(I, IA, II, IIA & IIC) 22,000 ft; (XI & XIA) 19,000 ft; (21 & 21E) 21,000 ft; (31, 31E & 32) 24,500 ft
Range:	(I, IA, II, IIA, IIC) 600 miles; (XI, XIA, 21, 21E) 900 miles; (31, 31E, 32) 820 miles

Accommodation: (I, II & XI) 3; (IA & XIA) 3 plus 16; (IIA, 21E & 31E) 3 plus
32; (IIC) 3 plus 20; (21 & 31) 3, or 2 plus 15 plus 2 cars,
or 3 plus 52; (32) 2 plus 23 plus 3 cars, or 3 plus 60
Production: (All Mks) 214; for details see Appendix B
Sequence Nos.: See Appendix B

The first prototype Britannia at Filton in July 1952.

The Bristol Britannia, Type 175

In the light of later experience, it is easy to criticise the recommendations
of the first Brabazon Committee, but the conclusions reached in 1943 were
remarkably shrewd, considering the state of the art at that date. Only one of
the categories specified, the 100,000 lb. Brabazon Type III, failed to mature,
but was closely paralleled by the Lockheed Constellation in America, recognised by 1946 as one of the world's most efficient, economic and versatile airliners. So when, in December 1946, B.O.A.C. required a Medium
Range Empire (M.R.E.) transport, the Company pointed out that a slightly
strengthened Constellation 749 with Centaurus 660 engines would fill the bill
and proposed to convert several available airframes, thereafter building
Constellations under licence at Filton, but the Treasury refused to consider
so large a dollar transaction at that time.

B.O.A.C.'s recommendations were embodied in Specification 2/47 issued
early in 1947, to which the Company and four other firms tendered a total
of eight designs. None of these matched the requirement exactly, but the
Bristol Type 175 project was the most promising, and in October a joint
working party met at Filton to decide on the optimum size of the aircraft. As
first tendered, the design was a low-wing monoplane with a span of 120 ft., a
gross wing area of 1,620 sq. ft., an all-up weight of 94,000 lb., four Centaurus 662 engines and accommodation for either 32 first class or 36 tourist
passengers. Since the Centaurus was larger than necessary for the specified

343

payload, some improvement in profitability was to be gained by an increase in wing span and area to permit the gross weight to rise to 107,000 lb., corresponding to accommodation for 40 or 44 passengers at the same standard of comfort as before. This proposal, submitted in August, was considered by the October working party, which finally agreed on a span of 130 ft., a wing area of 1,775 sq. ft. and a gross weight of 103,300 lb. representing 42 or 48 passengers plus their baggage and 3,370 lb. of freight; this payload was to be carried at 310 m.p.h. over the Johannesburg to Nairobi stage of the African trunk route against the maximum headwind for that stage. Bristol Proteus turbines and Napier Nomad compound engines were also considered, and the Company was prepared to guarantee the performance with Centaurus engines, though not at that stage with Proteus.

On 2 February 1948 the Ministry of Supply agreed to order several prototypes, provided B.O.A.C. would order at least 25 production aircraft; since the new fleet was intended to enter service by 1954, it was not possible for B.O.A.C. to delay a production order until after the first flight of the prototype. The technical risk thus imposed was difficult for B.O.A.C. to accept, and on 5 July 1948 the M.O.S. decided to order three prototypes without waiting for B.O.A.C.'s order; all were to be Centaurus-powered, but the second and third were to be suitable for conversion to Proteus and the third was to be fully equipped for operation in the B.O.A.C. fleet. The all-up weight specified for the 42 seat first-class version was 104,650 lb. Still the production contract was delayed, but in October 1948, having ordered 22 Canadair Argonauts as an interim fleet for the African and Far East routes, B.O.A.C. decided to take an interest in the Proteus version, and the working party was recalled to Filton to ascertain the best parameters for a larger and more versatile aircraft suitable for either Centaurus or Proteus power. A compromise was reached with a span of 140 ft., wing area of 2055 sq. ft., all-up weight of 118,000 lb. with Centaurus or 119,000 lb. with Proteus, and interior layouts for 42, 50 or 64 day passengers, or 38 sleeping berths. In November B.O.A.C. agreed to order 25 aircraft of this size designed for Proteus engines but operating initially with Centaurus, but the formal contract was not signed until 28 July 1949.

During this waiting period, the Company investigated the application of the 175 to the Atlantic route, at a gross weight of 130,000 lb. with fuel tankage increased to 5,790 Imperial gallons, which was feasible because runway and terrain clearance restrictions imposed by the secondary airports on the Empire routes did not apply to Atlantic terminals. At this weight the Proteus gave an excellent take-off performance, and the payload of 23,500 lb. allowed up to 83 passengers to be carried; apart from a complete revision of the interior layout, the only major modification required was a four-wheeled bogie instead of twin wheels for each main undercarriage unit; unfortunately this could only be retracted backwards because of the Proteus tail-pipe position, and the former advantage of free fall in emergency was lost. Both Centaurus and Proteus engines were still provided for, but during 1950 such excellent progress was made with Proteus 3 bench-running that in December B.O.A.C. asked for all their 25 aircraft to be delivered with this engine. Deletion of the Centaurus allowed the nacelles to be reduced in frontal area and one prototype to be cancelled, components already made for the Centaurus prototype being used for a functional mock-up, on which to conduct a wide range of ground tests which would otherwise have been necessary on a flying prototype. The original Fowler wing flaps were changed to a more efficient double-slotted design, and the fuselage main floor was redesigned to incorporate longitudinal seat attachment rails.

The structural design of Type 175 embodied lessons learned from the Brabazon project, which had provided the Company with an unequalled store of basic design data. The wing, comprising a box-spar uniformly tapered from centre-line to tip in plan and thickness, was very stiff in bending and torsion; a nearly ideal skin-stringer combination was evolved which enabled the number of the internal ribs to be greatly reduced, and at first it was intended to carry all the fuel within the box-spar in integral tanks, but because of fire risk in a crash flexible fuel bags were substituted, although in the final development integral tanks were added in the outer portion of the wing. The fuselage, of constant 12 ft. diameter for 50 ft. of its length, was similarly designed without structural bulkheads within the pressurised portion, which permitted the utmost versatility in furnishing layouts for different operators and routes. The flying controls were operated entirely by aerodynamic servo-tabs without power assistance, artificial feel proportional to airspeed being superimposed on the very small natural stick-forces; the control circuits employed torque shafts and were developed from the system designed for the second Brabazon.

During 1951 a full-scale wing, with 40 ft. of fuselage attached, was proof-loaded and then tested to failure, which occurred at 98% of the designed ultimate loading; a minor modification at the site of primary failure then raised the ultimate strength to 104% of the designed value. As a result of these tests it was possible to raise the all-up weight once more, to 140,000 lb., the fuel capacity being correspondingly increased to 6,750 Imp. gal.; B.O.A.C. agreed to accept all their aircraft at the new weight, and the second prototype was modified to conform to this standard. A further reappraisal of space utilisation by B.O.A.C. in 1952 established 90 passenger seats as the basic tourist layout with six abreast seating, and it was found possible to tap air from the engine compressors for cabin pressurisation and ventilation, which saved the weight of the mechanically driven cabin blowers which, in the first prototype, had been found unduly noisy compared with the quiet running of the Proteus. By this time the type name Britannia had been formally approved by both B.O.A.C. and M.O.S.

The first prototype, No. 12873 (*G-ALBO*), made its first flight at Filton on 16 August 1952, piloted by A. J. Pegg and powered initially with Proteus 625 engines having only three-quarters of the output of the developed Proteus 705. The flight revealed oversensitivity of the elevator control and temporary reluctance of the main undercarriage to lock down, both of which were corrected by simple modifications before the next flight and subsequent first appearance at the S.B.A.C. Display of 1952. Thereafter the only substantial modifications necessary were to improve the nacelle shape and extend the engine tail pipes aft, to increase lateral stability by fitting up-turned wing tips of slightly greater span and to improve handling during the approach by introducing aileron and elevator anti-float springs and interconnecting the inboard aileron servo-tabs with the rudder control. Proteus 705 engines were installed in August 1953, in time for *G-ALBO*'s second appearance at the S.B.A.C. Display.

On 23 December 1953 the second prototype, No. 12874 (*G-ALRX*), was flown at the higher all-up weight of 140,000 lb., but on 4 February 1954, after only 51 hours' flying, a reduction gear failure allowed the compressor turbine of the starboard inner engine to overspeed and disintegrate, causing an oil fire of such severity that Pegg decided on an immediate forced landing on the mud of the Severn estuary to safeguard the passengers, including senior Company executives and two representatives of K.L.M. The landing was made with only the two port engines running, but at one point even these had been cut by a short circuit induced by the fire and were only restarted by an exemplary display of pelmanism and prestidigitation by Ken Fitzgerald and Gareth Jones, two of the technical specialists on board. Although mud effectively doused the fire and so preserved the evidence of its origin the aircraft was caught by the rising tide and when retrieved next day was damaged by salt water beyond repair; components salvaged from it were utilised subsequently in the Company's Service School for crew training purposes. To maintain the urgent flight development programme *G-ALBO* was modified to the 140,000 lb. standard, without the extra tankage, and recommenced flying in March 1954, only to be grounded in May for wing repairs after a flap torque-tube failure during stalling tests had caused the aircraft to half-roll before pilot, W. F. Gibb, could regain control, imposing an overload of 3 g. It was then decided to use the first production Britannia, No. 12902 (*G-ANBA*) for general flight development, after its first flight on 5 September 1954, and to allocate the next three aircraft to a 2,000 hours' programme of C. of A. testing and route proving, in which B.O.A.C. crews participated to help out the Company's personnel. No. 12903 (*G-ANBB*) and No. 12904 (*G-ANBC*) made their first flights on 18 January and 29 June, respectively, and meanwhile *G-ALBO* returned to service in time for preliminary tropical performance trials at Idris in October 1954. Full tropical trials were completed by *G-ANBA* at Johannesburg and Khartum in March 1955, confirming a take-off weight of 150,000 lb. for production aircraft, and early in 1956 this was raised to 155,000 lb., associated with a landing weight of 123,000 lb., following undercarriage modifications. After flying totals of 652 hours and 277 hours, respectively, on this intensive development programme, *G-ANBA* and *G-ANBB* were flown to Short Brothers and Harland Ltd. at Belfast for completion and furnishing to B.O.A.C. fleet standard; *G-ANBC* was already

G-ANBC on route-proving trials in August 1955.

finished to this standard for a programme of 250 hours' route-proving flights under normal traffic conditions to Nairobi, Entebbe, Johannesburg, Karachi, Lod, Cairo, Idris and Rome; to the last two places, full complements of 98 crew and passengers (the latter being employees of the Company and B.O.A.C.) were carried to act as 'guinea-pigs'; these flights lasted from 9 September to 19 November, representing an annual utilisation of 2,150 hours. The fourth production Britannia, No. 12905 (*G-ANBD*), was furnished with first-class seating and a lounge-bar and did not fly until November 1955, so it was too late for the main development programme but, together with *G-ANBC*, was formally handed over to B.O.A.C. at London Airport on 30 December 1955, immediately after the full Certificate of Airworthiness had been granted; both aircraft were then based at Hurn, where B.O.A.C. crews were mustered for training by senior pilots who had themselves completed some 600 hours' conversion flying on *G-ALBO* at Filton under Company supervision. Six more Britannias were delivered to B.O.A C. during 1956, but in March that year the first case occurred of engine 'flame-out' while flying in icing cloud formations in the intertropical front over Uganda. This was a most troublesome problem, for its cause was obscure, and successive modifications to cure it were only partly successful, but by the end of the year the complex 'slush-icing' phenomenon was fully understood and had been remedied by a combination of hot air jets to remove ice precipitation in the air intake and platinum glow plugs in four of the eight combustion chambers to ensure automatic relighting immediately a flame-out occurred. During flight tests to prove the various power plant de-icing modifications, *G-ALBO* was fitted with a water-spray rig ahead of the starboard inner nacelle, which at one stage mounted a power plant designed by the R.A.E. with separate N.A.C.A. ramp-type flush inlets; this was reasonably ice-free, but exacted too high a performance penalty. B.O.A.C.'s Britannias entered public service on the Johannesburg route on 1 February 1957 and successively took over the services to Australia, Tokyo, Colombo, Singapore and Hong Kong from Argonauts and Constellations by October 1957, delivery of the first 15 aircraft, Nos. 12902 to 12916 (*G-ANBA* to *G-ANBO*), being completed in August, when *G-ANBA* re-emerged fully furnished from Belfast. By December the

347

annual utilisation of this fleet reached an average of 3,000 hours per aircraft, and in August 1958 the unprecedented figure, for this type of trunk route, of 3,750 hours per aircraft had been recorded. By this time also, the Proteus 705 engines had been approved to run 1,600 hours between overhauls, and trials were in progress to obtain clearance at 1,900 hours; by 1962 their life had been extended to 2,400 hours.

The remaining ten aircraft of the original contract were not built because of discussions which began in August 1952 on a possible freighter version of the Britannia. Apart from an increase in volumetric capacity for this role, it was essential to lengthen the fuselage in front of the wing to obtain clearance between the proposed large cargo door and the port inboard airscrew; the fuselage was therefore lengthened by 82 in. forward of the wing and 41 in. aft, to maintain the best centre of gravity position for the payload, and this was found to improve all-round performance and handling. B.O.A.C. took an option on five of the freighter version, but I.A.T.A. support could not be obtained for B.O.A.C. all-cargo operations on profitable routes, and B.O.A.C. then examined the economics of the long-bodied Britannia with either an all-passenger layout or one having a strong floor forward of the wing for mixed traffic. To distinguish between these variants, the original Britannia was designated Series 100, the all-cargo version Series 200, the mixed-traffic version Series 250 and the long-bodied passenger version Series 300, the all-up weight for all three long variants being 155,000 lb.

B.O.A.C. examined the Britannia 300 in relation to the Atlantic route, since it seemed likely to be more suitable than the Comet 2 for this duty, but the increased volumetric payload was alternative to fuel load, which left the 300 slightly worse off than the 100; however, B.O.A.C. agreed to take ten Series 300 in place of the last ten of the original order, in addition to the option on five Series 200 which had not been cancelled. A design study by the Company then showed that the required extra fuel could be carried in the outer wing without exceeding existing wing strength limits, and the basic design for Series 300LR, using integral transfer tanks outboard of the normal fuel bags, was completed in May 1955. At the same time the landing gear and fuselage skin were strengthened and up-rated Proteus 755 engines gave a performance to match the fuel and payload increase, the maximum take-off weight being raised to 175,000 lb.; two of these power plants were installed in the outboard nacelles of *G-ALBO* for endurance testing. Three months previously manufacture had begun of the first Britannia 300 at Filton, and seven more at the second-source production line set up by Short Brothers and Harland at Belfast. B.O.A.C. asked for long-range tanks to be incorporated at the earliest possible stage into their Series 300 during manufacture and agreed to order a further ten 300LR aircraft if this could be done, at the same time cancelling two of the short-range Series 300 as well as their option on the Series 200. The new fuel system could be installed in only the last five Belfast machines since the earlier ones were already too far advanced for modification.

As soon as news of the Britannia 300 and 300LR was announced, world-wide interest was shown by long-haul operators, and negotiations began with El Al Israel Airlines and Canadian Pacific Airlines which led to contracts in 1955 to supply three and four Series 300LR to these respective operators for the Atlantic route. As each customer required a different interior layout, to say nothing of different instruments and equipment, the designation 300LR was changed to 310 and sub-variants were numbered 311 for the prototype, 312 for B.O.A.C., 313 for El Al and 314 for Canadian Pacific. The Series 300 converted to long range at Belfast still retained their original thinner fuselage skin and lighter landing gear, which limited their take-off weight to 165,000 lb. and these were designated 305. By this time B.O.A.C. would have preferred not to take delivery of these interim aircraft, and when M.O.S. agreed to purchase the Filton-built first machine as a prototype (301) and the Company, having flown the tenth Britannia 102, No. 12911 (*G-ANBJ*), on a demonstration tour across Canada and back via San Diego and Mexico in August 1957,

G-ANBJ landing at San Diego, California, in August 1957.

received firm enquiries from Capital Airlines for five of the others, a new contract was negotiated which released B.O.A.C. from their obligation to take any Series 305 in return for a firm order for 18 312s, bringing the total B.O.A.C. Britannia fleet up to 33. Although the Capital Airlines' sale was frustrated by financial difficulties, American civil airworthiness approval for the Britannia 305 was eventually obtained and Northeast Airlines made a bid for them, but again required long-term credit facilities which could not be arranged. The two short-range Britannia 302s were bought by Aeronaves de Mexico following earlier enquiries by Aerovias Guest; numbered 12918 and 12919 and initially registered *G-ANCB* and *G-ANCC* for B.O.A.C. service, they flew on 26 June and 24 July 1957 and were delivered on 1 November and

Britannia 302 *XA-MEC* of Aeronaves de Mexico refuelling at Prestwick *en route* to Gander in November 1957.

16 December with the Mexican marks *XA-MEC* and *XA-MED*. The Britannia 301, No. 12917 (*G-ANCA*), first flew on 31 July 1956 and was reserved for C. of A. tests and engine development at Filton; it had been previously painted in Capital Airlines' livery for demonstration purposes, and the same colour scheme with modified outlines was retained.

The first Britannia Series 310, with fuel tankage of 8,580 Imp. gallons, No. 13207 (*G-AOVA*), made its first flight on 31 December 1956 and was reserved for C. of A. tests to supplement *G-ANCA*'s programme; designated Britannia 311, it later undertook a long series of Proteus 765 development tests which culminated in flights to Singapore in December 1957 under monsoon conditions, during which the engines remained unaffected by the severe icing encountered. The first Britannia 312, No. 13230 (*G-AOVB*), furnished for 99 passengers, flew on 5 July 1957 and was delivered to B.O.A.C. on 10 September for proving flights on the Atlantic route, but suffered damage to two engines in storm-clouds near Jacksonville on 30 September, which necessitated a landing at Miami; this incident received maximum publicity in the American press, and the cause was traced to a change in stator material which led to rubbing and seizure of the compressor blading when suddenly 'doused' by heavy concentrations of slush-ice; this was a further icing complication added to those already encountered on the Proteus 705, but the final modifications, already referred to, provided a complete cure

G-ANCA temporarily painted in Capital Air Lines livery before first flight.

Britannia 311 *G-AOVA* on test in August 1957.

First Britannia 312 *G-AOVB* for B.O.A.C. taking off on first flight at Filton on 5 July 1957.

and the first London to New York Britannia 312 service was flown on 19 December 1957.

Meanwhile El Al, having taken delivery of their three Britannia 313s, Nos. 13232–4 (*4X-AGA*, *'B* and *'C*), on 12 September, 20 October and 28 November, respectively, made a spectacular non-stop proving flight from New York to Tel Aviv, 6,100 miles at an average speed of 401 m.p.h., on 19 December 1957, which ranked as a distance record for civil aircraft; El Al's scheduled Atlantic operations commenced on 22 December with one flight per week, the frequency increasing to five flights per week within six months;

El Al's first Britannia 313 *4X-AGA* at Idlewild before flying 6,100 miles non-stop to Lod in December 1957.

since the round trip from Tel Aviv to New York and return totalled 12,000 miles, this small fleet of three aircraft was averaging over 3,000 hours per annum by June 1958, and a fourth Britannia 313 was ordered on 18 July. On 8 January 1958, taking advantage of favourable winds, *4X-AGB* flew the 3,444 miles from New York to London in 7 hours 44 min., at a block speed of 445 m.p.h.; this was 18 min. less and 11 m.p.h. faster than a flight by *G-AOVC* over the same stage two days previously in similar weather conditions.

Canadian Pacific Air Lines took delivery of their four Belfast-built Britannia 314s, Nos. 13393–13396 (*CF-CZA*, *'B*, *'C* and *'D*), on 9 April, 30 April, 31 May and 29 June 1958, respectively, and began the first scheduled flight on the polar route from Vancouver to Amsterdam on 1 June, continuing with ten round flights per month averaging 30 hours for each return trip; on 16 July the west-bound flight of 4,800 miles was completed in just under 14 hours at an average speed of 346 m.p.h. Having taken delivery of two further Britannias, No. 13428 (*CF-CZX*) from Filton on 3 July, and No. 13453 (*CF-CZW*) from Belfast on 6 August, C.P.A. began using Britannias on their Vancouver to Tokyo service on 24 August 1958, and on 20 September set up a new record for this 4,700 miles route with a flight of 11 hours 44 min., at an average speed of 400 m.p.h. Aeronaves de Mexico, with only their first Britannia 302 available for traffic, began an arduous schedule over the 2,093 miles Mexico City–New York route on 18 December 1957, and maintained this service daily for six days a week, with only one day off each week for maintenance, for a whole month until the second Britannia was available. Deliveries of Britannia 312s to B.O.A.C. did not end with No. 13430 (*G-AOVS*) on 22 September 1958, for some months earlier B.O.A.C. decided not to accept *G-AOVA* as part of the fleet because of the wear and tear sustained during its development flying and ordered a new aircraft to take its place; this machine, No. 13427 (*G-AOVT*), delivered on 2 January 1959, was a timely replacement for *G-AOVD* which crashed near Hurn on 24 December 1958 during a check flight, apparently through a misreading of the altimeter while descending through cloud. This was only the second fatal Britannia accident, the first having occurred on 6 November 1957 when *G-ANCA* dived into a wood at Downend, Bristol, from a low altitude, killing all the 15 crew and technicians on board; the cause was never definitely determined, but was almost certainly a runaway autopilot, due to an electrical fault, and an immediate modification was introduced to prevent its recurrence. Britannias were to fly half a million more hours before suffering their third fatal accident, the first to involve fare-paying passengers, which occurred at night on 22 July 1962 when *CF-CZB* crashed at Honolulu, killing 27 of the 40 persons on board; this exceptional safety record compared with an established average of 300,000 hours between fatal accidents for large piston-engined airliners.

It had been intended to use *G-ANCA* for the development of the high-powered Bristol Orion turbine engine, with which B.O.A.C. had planned to re-engine their Britannia 312 fleet at a later date, and one was installed in the port outer nacelle of *G-ALBO* in August 1956, with promising results. A

G-ALBO with Orion installed at port outer position, at Filton in 1957.

whole range of developed Britannias (Series 400) with this engine was proposed, and an eventual Britannia replacement, the Bristol 187, with a two-deck body, thinner wing and slender nacelles, was the subject of a joint design study discussed between the Company and Convair of San Diego, but essential government support was limited, by Treasury insistence, to only one new turboprop project and, when the choice had to be made, the Rolls-Royce Tyne was favoured at the expense of the Orion, so development of the latter ceased in 1958.

In February 1955 the Company received an order from M.O.S. for three mixed-traffic Britannias, which at first it was hoped to lease to charter operators. These were built at Belfast, and Short Brothers and Harland undertook the detail design of the large cargo door and strong floor. These three, designated Britannia 252, Nos. 13450–'2, were at first registered as *G-APPE, 'F* and *'G*, but were later assimilated to a fleet of 20 fully developed Britannias ordered for R.A.F. Transport Command, designated Britannia 253 by the Company but renamed Britannia C. Mark I by the Air Ministry. The first flight of this variant was made at Belfast on 29 December 1958, with improved Proteus 255 engines of higher output and a full-length metal floor designed at Belfast, together with fittings for aft-facing seats, stretchers or cargo and R.A.F. instruments and radio facilities. The second and third

First Britannia C Mk 1 delivered by Short Bros. & Harland to R.A.F. Transport Command in June 1959.

Britannia 252s were delivered to Transport Command for crew training on 19 March and 8 April 1959, as Britannias C. Mk.2, in R.A.F. markings as *XN398* and *XN404*, respectively; the other, *G-APPE*, required retrospective modifications and was delivered on 28 October 1959 as *XN392*. Deliveries of the 20 Britannias C.Mk.1 to Nos. 99 and 511 Squadrons began with *XL636* from Belfast on 4 June and *XM498* from Filton on 17 October 1959; five were built at Filton, Nos. 13510–'4 (*XM498, XM517–520*), and 15 at Belfast, Nos. 13397–13400 (*XL635–638*), Nos. 13454–'7 (*XL657–660*) and Nos. 13508–'9 (*XM496* and *497*); the last-named two were also the last to be delivered, on 17 September and 2 December 1960, respectively.

They were not, however, the last Britannias to be sold, for the five Belfast-built Series 305, left in the market when the Northeast negotiations failed in June 1958, proved attractive to independent operators tendering for Air Ministry trooping charters. The first 305, No. 12920 (*G-ANCD*), painted temporarily in the livery of Compania Cubana de Aviacion, was flown 27,400 miles on a marathon 23-day sales tour of Spain, Portugal, Cuba and Latin America, returning to Filton on 30 June 1958 and being then leased to El Al after refurnishing as a Britannia 306 (*4X-AGE*) to fill the gap until delivery of El Al's fourth Britannia 313, No. 13431 (*4X-AGD*), on 7 March 1959. Reverting to its British registration, *G-ANCD* was then sold to Air Charter Ltd. for trooping, with the new designation Britannia 307, joining *G-ANCE* of the

Britannia 307 *G-ANCE* on delivery to Air Charter Limited in September 1958.

same standard, which had been purchased by Air Charter on 30 September 1958. Another charter operator, Hunting-Clan Air Transport Ltd., ordered two 124-passenger variants, Britannia 317, for trooping; these were Nos. 13425–'6 (*G-APNA* and '*B*) and were delivered on 31 October and 11 December 1958; like all later Britannias, these had round-tipped duralumin airscrew blades which were more efficient and less vulnerable to stones thrown up in reverse pitch than the square-tipped hollow-steel blades originally preferred by B.O.A.C. Meanwhile Cubana, after *G-ANCD*'s demonstration at Havana in June, ordered two of yet another version, Britannia 318, with an option on two more, and the Company decided to risk building two aircraft to the latest modification standard, Britannia 320, for stock. Cubana's first 318, No. 13432 (*CU-T668*), was delivered on 6 December 1958 and the second, No. 13433 (*CU-T669*), on 6 February 1959. The

Cubana's first Britannia 318 *CU-P668* on test at Filton in December 1958.

option to take the third was then exercised, and this machine, No. 13437 (*CU-T670*), was delivered on 15 May, but the political situation in Cuba made it uncertain for a time whether the fourth Britannia would be required; however, this option also was taken up and No. 13515 (*CU-T671*) was delivered on 25 August 1959. After this the market for Britannias became quiet, because, in spite of its reliability and economy, it was beginning to meet competition from the Lockheed Electra and jet transports such as the Comet 4 and Boeing 707. It was therefore decided not to continue Britannia production unless a really substantial number of one variant was ordered.

The two 320s, Nos. 13516 and 13517, the last to be laid down, were furnished to Canadian Pacific Air Lines requirements and leased to them for 18 months under the designation Britannia 324, being delivered as *CF-CPD* on 17 October and *CF-CPE* on 14 November 1959. When the hiring period expired they were returned to Filton and purchased by Cunard Eagle Airways in March 1961, being registered *G-ARKA* and *G-ARKB*. Two more Britannias, Nos. 12922 and 12923 (*G-ANCF* and *'G*), were purchased by the Argentine operator Transcontinental for service between Buenos Aires, Sao Paulo, Rio de Janeiro, Caracas and New York; equipped to carry 104 passengers, they were designated Britannia 308 and delivered as *LV-GJB* and *LV-GJC* on 16 and 17 December 1959. By the end of that year Britannias all over the world had flown a quarter of a million hours and carried three-quarters of a million passengers, without a single fatal accident on scheduled service. Only Cubana, bedevilled by politics, failed to obtain high utilisation

Britannia 308 *LV-GJB* of Transcontinental S.A. in ferry marking *LV-PPJ* before delivery to Argentina in December 1959.

from its Britannias, and in March 1960 had leased its first 318 (*CU-T668*) to Eagle Airways as *G-APYY*, but on completion of this lease late in 1961 it was transferred by Cubana to Czechoslovakia as *OK-MBA*, becoming the first Britannia to operate behind the Iron Curtain. Apart from those for R.A.F. Transport Command, only three more Britannia deliveries were to be made in 1960, one from Belfast and two from Filton. The first was No. 12924 (*G-ANCH*), which became a Britannia 309 for Ghana Airways and was delivered as *9G-AAG* on 17 July; the second was the veteran *G-AOVA*, rebuilt to a similar 319 standard and delivered to Ghana Airways as *9G-AAH* on 8 November; finally, the first of all the 85 Britannias, *G-ALBO*, still with Proteus 705 engines inboard, a Proteus 755 at starboard outer and an Orion at port outer, became the last to leave Filton, on 30 November 1960, when it was ferried to R.A.F. St. Athan to become an instructional airframe, being at last scrapped in June 1968, having flown nearly 1,800 hours. Britannias originally owned by national flag-carriers began to change hands at the end of 1961 and were readily acquired by charter operators; in this way British United Airways hired *G-AOVE* and *G-AOVI* from B.O.A.C. and purchased *G-ARWZ* (formerly *4X-AGB*) and *G-ARXA* (formerly *4X-AGC*) from El Al, to join the two 307s and two 317s already in their fleet. In November 1962 B.O.A.C. withdrew all their 14 Britannia 102s from service, and in 1963 sold five 312s to British Eagle International Airways (formerly Cunard-Eagle) to supplement the two 324s already Eagle-owned; the remainder of the B.O.A.C. 312 fleet were withdrawn progressively in 1964, as the Vickers VC10 entered service.

First Canadair CL-28 Argus Mk 1 for the R.C.A.F. in 1957.

Although Britannia production in Britain ceased earlier than had once been hoped, its progeny continued to multiply in Canada, thanks to a licence granted to Canadair Limited in March 1954 for the manufacture of both a maritime reconnaissance derivative and a transport version of the Britannia for the Royal Canadian Air Force. The first, designated CL-28 and named Argus, had a redesigned unpressurised fuselage with two large weapons bays and was powered by Wright Turbo-compound piston engines, whose fuel economy at low altitude gave the aircraft a maximum duration of 24 hours on patrol; the first of these was delivered on 30 September 1957 and the thirty-third and last in July 1960. The second type, designated CL-44, was a further

Canadair CL-44 Yukon of the R.C.A.F. which flew Mr. Lester Pearson to London Airport on 8 May 1963. (*Photo E. A. Shackleton.*)

lengthened variant of the Britannia 253, originally intended to have Orions but revised for Rolls-Royce Tyne turboprops, the first model, named Yukon, of which 12 were built for No. 437 Squadron, R.C.A.F., having large cargo doors on the port side fore and aft of the wing; these were followed by 28 of a second model, CL-44 D, having a swing-tail rear entry for endways loading of ready-palleted or bulky freight; this made its first flight on 16 November 1960, and in July 1961 the first of seven entered service with Seaboard World Airlines, followed by twelve for the Flying Tiger Line and four for Slick Airways, production continuing into 1964. One CL-44 D, *N228SW*, was leased to B.O.A.C. in whose livery it was to be seen at London Airport alongside its Britannia cousins, an image of what might have continued at Filton, if Orion development had not been stopped. As a final variant, four CL-44s, fully furnished for 160 passengers and with the swing-tail feature deleted, were sold in 1965 to the Icelandic airline Loftleidir, for transatlantic tourist traffic, later to be extended by 15 ft. and furnished for 189 passengers as CL-44 Js.

Canadair CL-44 D swing-tail freighter prototype *CF-MKP-X* on its maiden flight from Cartierville on 16 November 1960. (*Canadair photo.*)

Two unbuilt projects derived from the Britannia were examined in the early months of 1955; the first was Type 189, corresponding in role and layout to the Canadair CL-28, but to the requirements of R.A.F. Coastal Command as a Shackleton replacement; the second was a high-wing tail-loading heavy cargo-carrier, Type 195, having the Britannia wing in common with the

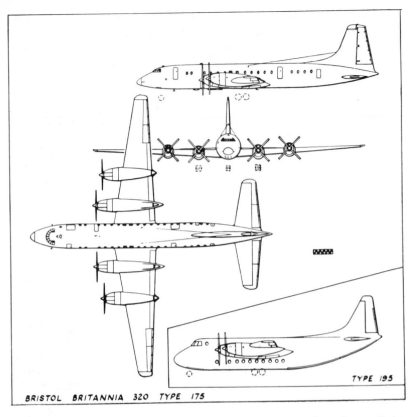

BRISTOL BRITANNIA 320 TYPE 175

TYPE 195

first layout of the Short S.C.5, of which the final enlarged version, called at first the Short Britannic, later went into limited production at Queen's Island as the Belfast, whose wings were designed and manufactured at Filton under sub-contract to Short Brothers and Harland Ltd.

In its first six years of airline service, the Britannia proved itself to be one of the safest and most reliable transport aeroplanes ever produced; its structural integrity and efficiency established Dr. A. E. Russell as one of the world's leading airframe designers, who made the last of the propeller-airliners also the best; had all the smallest of the thousands of its proprietary items attained the same reliability as the airframe—probably an unrealisable ideal—the Britannia could have reached a standard of engineering perfection never before achieved in any aeroplane. During the period February 1957 to November 1962 the 79 Britannias in service flew over 222 million miles in 717,000 flying hours, carrying some three million passengers and making more than 20,000 landings. On their widely diverse routes, B.O.A.C. achieved an annual utilisation of 3,800 hours per aircraft, while El Al on their exclusively long-haul transatlantic routes, in 1960 averaged $11\frac{1}{2}$ hours per aircraft per day, or 4,200 hours annually.

358

Although no longer competitive in airline fleet service after 1964, the Britannia remained pre-eminent as a charter aircraft plying at high load factors. Forty-six were still in civil use in 1970, in addition to 22 of R.A.F. Air Support Command, having logged over $1\frac{3}{4}$ million flying hours (600 million miles) with some 30 different operators. B.O.A.C. pilots, initially suspicious of an aeroplane in which 'the pilot isn't connected to the controls and the propellers aren't connected to the engines and everything else is done by electricity', had expressed genuine regret at parting with their Britannias, which they summed up as the most 'kindly' aircraft they had ever flown.

Between 1970 and 1988 when the third edition of this book was prepared Britannias continued in service with a wide range of operators, but on a diminishing scale. By March 1988 only four aircraft were still operating, according to information from Rolls-Royce, which has provided continuing support for the Britannia's Proteus engines. Three of these Britannias were with Aero Caribbean of Havana, which operates charter passenger and cargo services, and one with Katale Air Transport/Zaïre Aero Service.

Thus 31 years after the type entered service four of the 82 Britannias produced were still in use. Between 1970 and March 1988 Britannias were in service with 32 different operators including the Royal Air Force, which disposed of its fleet in 1975–76. Total engine hours during this period were 1,697,000, equivalent to over 420,000 aircraft flying hours. These operators, according to product-support records, were Aer Turas; Aero Caribbean; Aéreostransportes Entre Rios; Afrek (Athens); African Cargo Airline; African Safari Airways; Air Faisel; Airline Engineering; Angkasa Civil Transport, Indonesia; A.M.A. Zaïre; Air Spain; British Air Services; Britannia Airways; Caledonian Airways; Centre Air Afrique; Cubana; Donaldson International Airways; Euro World; Gaylan Air Cargo; Gemini Air Transport; Guinness Peat; Intercontinental Cattle Meats Ltd; International Aviation Services; Invicta Airways; Katale Air Transport/Zaïre Aero Service; Lloyd International; Monarch Airlines; North East Airlines; Redcoat Air Cargo; the Royal Air Force; Royal Aircraft Establishment, Boscombe Down; and Young Cargo.

By March 1986, when only five of the original 82 Britannias were still in service, total flying hours on the type were 1,965,913, giving an average of nearly 24,000 flying hours per aircraft. The aircraft with the longest flying life was a Britannia 312 (*G-AUVF*) which had accumulated 44,116 hours before going out of service in September 1982. Three others had exceeded 42,500 hours before they ended their operating lives.

SPECIFICATIONS AND DATA

Type:	175, Britannia (and derivatives)
Manufacturers:	The Bristol Aeroplane Co. Ltd. ⎫ Filton,
	Bristol Aircraft Ltd. ⎭ Bristol
	Short Bros. & Harland, Ltd., Queen's Island, Belfast, N.I.
	Canadair Limited, Cartierville, Montreal, Canada

(101) Four 2,800 ehp Bristol Proteus 625
Four 3,780 ehp Bristol Proteus 705

⎧ One 4,120 ehp Bristol Proteus 755
⎨ Two 3,900 ehp Bristol Proteus 705
⎩ One 5,500 ehp Bristol Orion

(102) Four 3,900 ehp Bristol Proteus 705

(252, 301, 302, 307–309, 311–319, 324) Four 4,120/4,450 ehp
Bristol Proteus 755, 756, 757, 761 or 765

(253) Four 4,400 ehp Bristol Proteus 255

(CL-28) Four 3,700 hp Wright Turbo-Cyclone R-3350-EA-1

(CL-44) Four 5,730 ehp Rolls-Royce Tyne Mk. 515/10

Variant	101, 102	252	253	301, 302	306–309	311–319
Span	142 ft 3 in	142 ft 3 in	142 ft 3 in	142 ft 3 in	142 ft 3 in	142 ft 3 in
Length	114 ft	124 ft 3 in	124 ft 3 in	124 ft 3 in	124 ft 3 in	124 ft 3 in
Height	36 ft 8 in	37 ft 6 in	37 ft 6 in	37 ft 6 in	37 ft 6 in	37 ft 6 in
Wing Area	2,075 sq ft	2,075 sq ft	2,075 sq ft	2,075 sq ft	2,075 sq ft	2,075 sq ft
Empty Weight	88,000 lb	90,500 lb	90,600 lb	92,500 lb	90,000 lb	82,537 lb
All-up Weight	155,000 lb	185,000 lb	185,000 lb	185,000 lb	185,000 lb	185,000 lb
Max. Payload	25,000 lb	33,100 lb	37,400 lb	29,500 lb	33,100 lb	34,900 lb
Range with						
max. payload	3,450 miles	4,268 miles	4,268 miles	3,496 miles	4,268 miles	4,268 miles
Cruise Speed	362 mph	355 mph	360 mph	357 mph	357 mph	357 mph
Max. Range	4,580 miles	5,334 miles	5,334 miles	4,440 miles	5,334 miles	5,310 miles
Crew	7	4–6	4–6	4–7	4–7	4–7
Passengers:						
1st class	61	—	—	73	82	82
Coach (max.)	90	139	139	139	139	139
Cargo Space	665 cu ft	5,850 cu ft	6,120 cu ft	900 cu ft	845 cu ft*	900 cu ft
Production	17	3	20	3	5	35
Sequence Nos.			See Appendices B and D			

* In 1964 the two 308s were resold to British Eagle, who converted them to 252 standard with forward cargo doors and 5,850 cu. ft. cargo space; they were redesignated 308F. Two 307s and five 312s were similarly modified later.

Variant	324	CL-28 Mk 1	CL-28 Mk 2	CL-44-6	CL-44 D
Span	142 ft 3 in	142 ft 2 in	142 ft 3 in	142 ft 3 in	142 ft 3 in
Length	124 ft 3 in	122 ft 1 in	128 ft 3 in	136 ft 7 in	*136 ft 7 in
Height	37 ft 6 in	36 ft 8 in	36 ft 9 in	36 ft 8 in	37 ft 6 in
Wing Area	2,075 sq ft	2,075 sq ft	2,075 sq ft	2,075 sq ft	2,075 sq ft
Empty Weight	86,400 lb	81,000 lb	81,000 lb	88,850 lb	88,872 lb
All-up Weight	185,000 lb	148,000 lb	148,000 lb	205,000 lb	210,000 lb
Max. Payload	34,900 lb	—	—	60,480 lb	66,128 lb
Range with					
max. Payload	4,268 mls	—	—	2,360 mls	3,320 mls
Cruise Speed	357 mph	290 mph	290 mph	380 mph	375 mph
Max. Range	5,340 mls	4,000 mls	4,000 mls	4,490 mls	4,950 mls
Crew	4–7	15	15	4–6	3–7
Passengers:					
1st class	82	—	—	—	—
Coach (max.)	139	—	—	134	*160
Cargo Space	900 cu ft	—	—	6,900 cu ft	7,250 cu ft
Production	2	13	20	12	27
Sequence Nos.	See Appendices B and D	nil	nil	nil	nil
			* CL-44 J: 151 ft 9 in; 189 coach passengers.		

The Bristol Helicopters

The helicopter, familiar as a toy in medieval Europe and invented much earlier in Asia, attracted the attention of engineers and philosophers from Leonardo da Vinci onwards, but little success with a full-sized vehicle was achieved until 1923 when Juan de la Cierva showed that his Autogiro, with hinged blade-roots, had a cruise performance comparable with a fixed-wing aeroplane, with the added ability to climb and descend very steeply. The true helicopter then became feasible, and consistent success was reached when Igor Sikorsky in America developed the anti-torque tail-rotor as a means of stabilising and steering a machine with a single main rotor, counter-rotating coaxial rotors having suffered from mechanical complexity. Sikorsky's success was due to sound development and financial support, and was emulated in Europe by both sides in the Second World War, experimental work in England being concentrated at the Airborne Forces Experimental Establishment at Ringway, Sherburn-in-Elmet and Beaulieu, where a rotorcraft design team was directed by Raoul Hafner, who after experimenting with helicopters in Austria had come to England in 1933 and later produced the A.R.III Gyroplane, resembling the Autogiro but having a sensitive cyclic-pitch control instead of Cierva's cruder tilting rotor hub.

After the Allied invasion of Europe began in June 1944, Horsa and Hamil-car gliders proving adequate for delivering troops and weapons to the battle-front, Hafner's development of rotor-craft for the same purpose was relegated to a low priority. So, a few months later, when the Bristol Aeroplane Company formed a Helicopter Department of its Aircraft Division and looked for men with talent and experience in this field, Hafner and some of his colleagues were released from A.F.E.E. to form the nucleus of the Company's helicopter design team. The Company acquired all the assets, patents and manufacturing rights of the pre-war A.R.III Construction Partnership and Hafner was charged with the design and development of a single-engined four-seater helicopter, suitable for military and commercial operation with high reliability and economy.

In June 1944, study began of a layout based on a 500 h.p. Bristol Aquila engine, but as the tools and jigs for its manufacture had been disposed of early in the war, it was impracticable to revive this engine. Other engines were considered, including the Armstrong Siddeley Cheetah, the Fedden Flat Six and the Alvis Leonides, but the Cheetah was underpowered, the Fedden only a prototype and the Leonides not yet cleared for series production, so the well-tried Pratt and Whitney Wasp Junior of 450 h.p. was chosen for the first two prototypes of the new Bristol helicopter, which was designated Type 171 and defined by Specification E.20/45.

The design of the 171 occupied two years, during which period exhaustive tests and endurance runs were made on all the mechanical components. The airframe comprised a tubular steel framed engine and rotor gearbox mounting attached to a light alloy front fuselage and stressed skin tail boom structure. Satisfactory wooden monocoque rotor blades and suspension were designed and complete rotors spun on a test tower (the first of its kind) tall enough to simulate conditions above the ground cushion. While the rotor was being endurance tested on the tower for 70 hours, the engine and transmission underwent 30 hours' endurance running in the airframe with a brake fan substituted for the rotor. After stripping and thorough inspection of all parts, the rotor was assembled to the aircraft, and ground running of the complete machine began on 9 May 1947. Low-speed running showed the need for tabs to correct the effects of blade manufacturing inaccuracies, but the first full speed run on 20 June elicited blade flutter which built up rapidly; this was investigated by further rotor running on the tower and cured by fitting weights in the blade tips to bring the C.G. forward and so raise the critical flutter speed outside the operational speed range.

On 27 July the first test flight was made by H. A. Marsh, who made a number of short trips, some with passengers, totalling half an hour. By February 1948 the second prototype, No. 12836 (*VL963*), had begun flying, and the first prototype, No. 12835 (*VL958*), had flown 40 hours. After about 10 hours' local flying *VL963*, piloted by E. A. Swiss, made its first cross-country flight from Filton to Lee-on-Solent in turbulent conditions. Eric Swiss also flew *VL958* from the City of London to Biggin Hill in under 10 min. on 30 September in the 'Hare and Tortoise' demonstration of rapid transit between city centres. On 20 January 1949 *VL963* was demonstrated at Brize Norton to the Navy, Army and Air Force medical services and proposals for a casualty evacuation version were discussed. Meanwhile civil airworthiness requirements for helicopters had been defined, and after completing the necessary tests *VL963* was registered *G-ALOU* and on 25 April 1949 received the first C. of A. ever issued to a British helicopter, to permit it to fly to the Paris Salon, where it was exhibited during May. Subsequently it reverted to its service marks and was delivered to the R.A.E., where it remained in regular use for four years.

The prototype 171 Mk. 2 (No. 12869) with Alvis Leonides engine was completed in the summer of 1948 and shown statically at the S.B.A.C. Show, after which prolonged testing of its vertically mounted engine and trans-

Type 171 Mk 3 demonstrator *G-ALSX* hovering in 1951.

mission assembly delayed its first flight until 3 September 1949 when, after a brief initial flight, the rotor disintegrated at the second attempt at take-off, through a combination of engine torque surging with an unsuspected weakness in the trailing edge of the new rotor blade design. Fortunately nobody was injured by the debris, and with a strengthened rotor the machine was flown successfully first at Filton and later at Boscombe Down and Farnborough, but its civil mark *G-AJGU* was not used, all flying being done as *VW905*. Like the two Mk. 1 prototypes, the Mk. 2 had two doors and two passengers on the rear seat.

As a result of experience with the prototypes, changes were made in the 171 Mk. 3; the nose was shortened to improve downward view and width increased by 8 in. for three passengers on the rear bench seat; the accessory drive was transferred from the engine to the rotor gearbox, which was driven through a free-wheel clutch, so that essential services were not lost during an autorotative descent after engine failure; as in the prototypes, the rotor was designed to store sufficient kinetic energy to ensure safe transition from hovering to autorotation, and low-level power-off landings could be demonstrated with confidence and became an essential feature of flying training.

Twenty-five sets of Mk. 3 components were made in 1949 and a production batch of 15 (Nos. 12886 to 12900) was assembled. Although all 15 were allotted civil registrations, only two retained them, the remainder being reserved by M.O.S. for development and experimental work at Filton,

Sycamore H.R.12 *WV783* with modified door and winch for air/sea rescue role, 1953.

363

Sycamore H.R.14 *XG509* demonstrating use of winch.

Farnborough and Boscombe Down. No. 12886, *G-ALSR*, after completion of type testing, was loaned to British European Airways in 1953 and 1954 and subsequently delivered to the R.A.E. as *XH682*. No. 12892, *G-ALSX*, retained as Company demonstrator, received a C. of A. on 3 May 1951 and after a long and active life was sold to Williamson Diamonds Ltd., being delivered in Bristol Freighter *G-AILW* to Uganda in January 1958; however, when Dr. Williamson died suddenly soon after its arrival, it came back to Filton and was retained for Company communications. Nos. 12887, '8, '9 became *WA576, 577* and *578*, the last being modified into the prototype of an R.A.F. ambulance version, Sycamore H.C.10, and went to Malaya for operational trials in 1949 and was formally accepted on 14 August 1951; aerodynamic trials with dummy side fairings for this role were done earlier on *VL963*. Next came the Army communications variant, Sycamore H.C.11, of which the first, No. 12890 (*WT923*), flew on 13 August 1950 and was accepted on 29 May 1951, followed by three more, *WT924, 925* and *926*, between October 1951 and May 1952. Three further Mk. 3 machines were *WT933, WT939* and *WV695*, the last being sold to the R.A.A.F. as *A91-1* for duties at the Woomera rocket range; *WT933* went to Khartum for tropical trials and *WT939* to Canada for winterisation trials, being later used for naval trials on H.M.A.C. *Perseus*. The last three of the first 15 were completed as Sycamore H.R.12s for R.A.F. Coastal Command, *WV781, 782* and *783*; the first two of these were similar to the H.C.11, but *WV783* had a Westland hydraulic winch for air-sea rescue work. Both the Mk. 3 and H.C.11 had two

364

The first two Sycamore 52 helicopters for the German Federal Government in 1955.

sliding doors, but the H.C.10 had hinged front doors and two extra doorways into which plastic blisters could be fitted to enclose two stretchers carried transversely. The third H.R.12 had a forward sliding door on the port side, but the starboard doorway was located aft under the winch and was closed by a roll-up canvas door with zip-fasteners at each side. Various modifications were designed for incorporation in later production Sycamores. For shipboard operation the undercarriage was increased in height to reduce danger from a coning-down rotor; for civil use the body was extended to increase baggage space aft of the engine bay, which incidentally reduced drag and improved cruising performance, this version being Mk. 3A.

The remaining sets of components were used in the second production batch of ten, including four H.R.12 of which the first, *WV784* for Coastal Command, was redesigned to carry sonar with a crew of two, and the last three were similar to *WV783* but equipped with the tall landing gear for the Royal Australian Navy and renamed H.R.50. Two winch-equipped Sycamore H.R.13 (*XD196* and *XD197*) with the tall landing gear were built for air-sea rescue evaluation by R.A.F. Fighter Command, and two civil machines, *G-AMWG* and *G-AMWH*, were built as Mk. 3A for B.E.A. The last two in this batch were *G-AMWI*, the Company's demonstrator, finally completed to full Mk. 4 standard with enlarged baggage locker and tall undercarriage, and the first Sycamore H.R.14, *XD653*. In the Mk. 4 and H.R.14 the pilot's position was changed from left to right hand to conform to American standard practice, and the opportunity was taken to incorporate as many as possible of the good features of all earlier Marks, including the four-door arrangement of the H.C.10, into one universal design.

With the adoption of the H.R.14 by the R.A.F. for all roles, production went ahead, and in April 1953 the Sycamore went into service with No. 275 Squadron at Linton-on-Ouse; No. 194 Squadron was formed soon afterwards in Malaya and No. 284 in Cyprus in May 1955. An immense amount of operational development was also done by the Joint Experimental Helicopter Unit formed at Middle Wallop in April 1955 by the R.A.F. and Army.

Type 171 Mk 4 *G-AMWI* as dual-control trainer for German pilots at Old Mixon, 1957.

Export orders were accepted from Belgium, who bought three, and from the German Federal Government, who eventually took delivery of 50, designated Mk. 52, two of them being equipped as V.I.P. transports, and the remainder allocated to various service duties; one Mk. 4 was also supplied to the R.A.A.F. at Woomera as *A91-2*. To centralise production and development, all the Company's helicopter work was transferred to the Old Mixon factory at Weston-super-Mare, beginning in March 1955 with the Sycamore production line; the 95th and subsequent Type 171 machines were built at Weston, and production continued until 178 had been delivered, the last two being Sycamore H.C.51, of which seven in all were supplied to the Royal Australian Navy. Apart from *G-AMWI* only two other civil Mk. 4s were delivered as such; these were No. 13270 (*G-AOBM*), demonstrated in Canada and Mexico in 1955 as *CF-HVX*, and No. 13493 (*G-AODL*), which was sold to Australian National Airways in 1956 as *VH-INO*. *G-AMWI* in five years' flying was demonstrated in France, Germany, Spain, Switzerland and Austria, then employed as dual-control trainer for the German pilots between June 1957 and January 1958, and finally sold in Australia in 1961.

Type 173/1 *G-ALBN* hovering at Filton in August 1952.

The next Bristol helicopter, Type 173, combined two sets of Sycamore power plants and rotors in a 13-passenger tandem layout. The rotor gearboxes were interconnected by a shaft and each engine drove through a free-wheel clutch so that if one engine failed the other continued to drive both

366

rotors. The first prototype, No. 12871 (*G-ALBN*), using well-tried components, made its first hovering flight on 3 January 1952, piloted by C. T. D. Hosegood, who found difficulty in moving in any direction but backwards. The following day ground resonance developed on alighting after the second flight, and it was July before this problem was overcome by modifications to the rotor-hub drag dampers and landing gear. The major control problem was pitch-up in forward flight, but on 24 August 1952 the 173 Mark 1 made its first circuit away from the Filton runway, in time to appear as scheduled at the S.B.A.C. Show. During 1953, as *XF785*, the 173 Mk. 1 was evaluated by the R.A.F. and underwent three days' trials at sea on board H.M.S. *Eagle*.

XF785 (ex *G-ALBN*) at sea on H.M.A.C. *Eagle* in 1953.

Subsequently it received a set of four-bladed rotors designed to avoid primary resonance of the fuselage and appeared in this form at the 1957 S.B.A.C. Show; by then the original upswept tailplane, which increased the tendency to roll when yawed, had been replaced by a low-set flat tailplane with fins at each end; but this arrangement was not entirely successful, and a solution was only found with the compound anhedral tailplane evolved for Type 192.

The second prototype, Type 173 Mk. 2, had a revised undercarriage with castoring front wheels and fixed rear wheels and small stub wings fore-and-aft, with fins on the aft wing tips. This arrangement was designed to offload the rotors during forward flight and so improve cruise speed. The 173 Mk. 2, No. 12872 (*G-AMJI*), made only a few flights with the stub wings fitted; then they were removed because the Admiralty became interested in developing the type for carrier work, for which optimum hovering performance was essential, so an upswept tailplane was added and the machine was used for

Type 173/2 *G-AMJI* with original stub wings at Filton in 1953.

367

naval trials as *XH379*; as a result of these the Company was promised a substantial order for a revised twin-rotor helicopter for Naval duties. In August 1956 *XH379* was loaned to B.E.A. for operational trials by their Helicopter Unit, and meanwhile three 173 Mk. 3 prototypes, Nos. 13204–'6, were built; these resembled the Mk. 2 but had 850 h.p. Leonides Major engines driving four-bladed rotors and a taller aft rotor pylon to increase forward tilt of the aft rotor, thereby improving stability in pitch and reducing interference from the forward rotor. Although provisionally registered *G-AMYF–'H*, they were built to a M.O.S. experimental contract as *XE286, 287* and *288*; they were scheduled for Leonides Major development trials for the design of operational tandem helicopters for the R.A.F. and Royal Navy, for which specifications were issued in 1953. A Naval requirement, HR.146, covered a ship-based general-purpose machine for attacking surface and submarine vessels as well as normal rescue and communications roles, at first with Leonides Majors, to be replaced in later production by Napier Gazelles; HR.149 was similar for the Royal Canadian Navy; the R.A.F. requirement, H.150, was for a general-purpose land-based helicopter for personnel and paratroop transport, casualty evacuation and to lift bulky loads by means of an external strop. The Company tendered three designs: Type 191 to meet HR.146, Type 192 to meet H.150 and Type 193, a variant of Type 191 for production in Canada, to meet HR.149. In April 1956 contracts were awarded for three 191 prototypes with Leonides Major and 65 production 191s with Gazelles 22 192s, with either Leonides Majors or Gazelles, and four 193s, a total of 94 aircraft, Nos. 13274 to 13367.

Type 173/3 *XE286* hovering at Old Mixon in November 1956.

The third 173, *XE286*, began hovering trials on 9 November 1956 which were discontinued because of trouble experienced with engine overheating and transmission failures in ground rig running. Although transmission difficulties were no more severe than normal at this stage of development, and were quickly cured, they were used as political ammunition to justify cancellation of the 191 contract by the Admiralty in favour of a Westland-built version of the Sikorsky S.58. This attack on the Company's reputation for sound mechanical development was entirely unwarranted, as later proved by the success of the Belvedere's transmission, but Type 193 was cancelled soon afterwards in a Canadian economy drive, so the Company was allowed to abandon the Leonides Major and concentrate solely on the Gazelle for the 192,

368

two of the first three Alvis-engined 191 airframes already built being fitted out as Gazelle ground test rigs and the third as a controls fatigue rig; at the same time the R.A.F. order for the 192 was increased to 26, all with Gazelles. In

Type 191 after conversion to Gazelle test-rig, at Old Mixon in 1957.

Type 173/5 *XE288* on test gantry at Old Mixon in 1956, in B.E.A. livery.

1958 developed Gazelles of 1,650 h.p. each became available and the old problem of single-engined flight performance and safety vanished, because only 800 h.p. was normally required from each engine and the short-term maximum power of a single turbine was thus equal to the normal power of two engines.

After Admiralty support was withdrawn, the fifth 173, *XE288*, received the civil registration *G-AORB*, but neither it nor *XE287* got beyond the ground-running stage. *XE288* had been intended for carrier trials at sea and had a shortened fuselage and long-stroke 'four-poster' landing gear of the type proposed for Type 191. Much thought had been given to the design of a landing gear to eliminate ground resonance even on a moving deck; the first six examples of the 191 would have had long-stroke oleo-legs on outriggers linked to longitudinal torsion bars below the fuselage centre-line so as to permit free rolling without vertical or lateral displacement of the fuselage; the front landing gear had castoring wheels and was higher than the rear, for loading of a ventral weapon bay; in the later production 191 and the 192 a similar result was obtained by a simpler geometry.

Prototype Type 192 *XG447* and Type 173/1 *XF785*, both with end-plate fins, hovering at Old Mixon in July 1958.

The prototype 192, No. 13342 (*XG447*), made its first flight at Weston-super-Mare on 5 July 1958 and thereafter embarked on a comprehensive development programme, followed by nine pre-production aircraft, *XG448* to *XG456*, of which *XG449* and *XG455* were initially reserved as non-flying control rigs; all these were brought to full production standard before delivery to the R.A.F., but at first had wooden rotor blades and anhedral tailplanes with end-plate fins. Type clearance trials began at Boscombe Down in April 1960 with *XG452*, which in June established a record by flying from Gatwick to Idris, Tripoli, for tropical trials at an average speed of 130 m.p.h. via Rome and Malta; in August it underwent high-altitude trials at Chambèry, and in September it was shown statically at the S.B.A.C.

Pre-production Belvedere *XG451* using external strop to lift Bristol-Ferranti Bloodhound guided missile.

370

Display, *XG451* being flown on that occasion. In October 1960, *XG453, 454* and *456* were handed over to the R.A.F. Trials Unit at Odiham. The eleventh and subsequent aircraft, named Belvedere H.C.1, were completed to full production standard with metal rotor blades, powered flying controls and compound anhedral tailplanes approximating to the ideal parabola, a shape evolved by stages and found to be a very satisfactory compromise, rendering autostabilisation unnecessary for I.F.R. clearance. Further improvements in production Belvederes include sliding instead of upward hinged doors, improved air-intakes and larger low-pressure wheels.

The first production Belvedere, *XG457*, was delivered to Odiham in August 1961; 24 were built and the type continued in service with the Royal Air Force until March 1969. By the time that deliveries of production Belvederes began this helicopter had ceased to a Company product, because in February 1960 the former Bristol Helicopter Department had become the Bristol Helicopter Division of Westland Aircraft Ltd. At this time the Company was actively designing a civil variant, the 192C, and a large-bodied military version, the 192D. A still larger civil design, Type 194, was also investigated, having a fixed

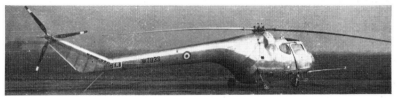

Type 171 Mk 3 *WT933* modified in 1958 with extra fin area to represent Type 203.

wing amidships to offload the rotors during cruising flight and powered by four D.H. Gnome turbines in pairs driving two six-bladed rotors designed to reduce vibration at high forward speeds. However, none of these projects met with sufficient response from potential operators to warrant manufacture.

Other Bristol unbuilt helicopter projects included Type 181, with twin Proteus engines, a large 80-passenger twin-rotor 'Bealine Bus' in anticipation of B.E.A.'s specification for a transport helicopter in 1952; Type 190, an ultra-light two-seat Army scout with rotor-tip ramjets, tendered in April 1954 to Specification HR.144T and nicknamed *Little Henry*; Type 199, Hafner's proposal for a large Convertiplane with tilting-wing-mounted power plants driving rotors with a variable thrust line for both vertical take-off and forward flight; Type 203, an eleven-seater single-rotor Sycamore replacement with either a D.H. Gnome or an Armstrong Siddeley P.181 free-turbine engine, using many proved Sycamore assemblies, proposed in October 1957 and partly manufactured; and Type 214, a similar but larger 18-seater utility helicopter using a single 192 rotor powered by two D.H. Gnomes, laid out in March 1959.

Among helicopter projects which did not receive type numbers were the first tandem rotor design, a small two-seater powered by a Cirrus Minor, designed in January 1946 to the same requirements as the Cierva W.14 (Skeeter), and a large 10-ton crane helicopter with an asymmetric layout and a four-bladed rotor of 80 ft. diameter with twin tip turbines on each blade, proposed in 1959.

SPECIFICATIONS AND DATA

Types: 171, 173, 181, 190, 191, 192, 193, 194, 199, 203 and 214; Bristol Helicopters

Manufacturers: The Bristol Aeroplane Co. Ltd. ⎫ Filton,
Bristol Aircraft Ltd. ⎭ Bristol
Westland Aircraft Ltd. (Bristol Helicopter Division), Old Mixon, Weston-super-Mare, Somerset

(a) *Types Built:*—

Type	171 Mk 1	171 Mk 2	171 Mk 3 & 3A	171 Mk 4	173/1
Power Plant	One 450 hp P & W Wasp Jr	One 550 hp Alvis Leonides			Two 550 hp Alvis Leonides
No. of Rotors & Blades	1 × 3	1 × 3	1 × 3	1 × 3	2 × 3 (later 2 × 4)
Rotor Diameter	47 ft 5 in	48 ft 7 in	48 ft 7 in	48 ft 7 in	48 ft 7 in (later 48 ft 9 in)
Fuselage Length	41 ft 4 in	41 ft 6 in	42 ft	42 ft	55 ft 2 in
Height	13 ft 10 in	13 ft 10 in	13 ft 10 in	14 ft 7 in	15 ft
Empty Weight	3,800 lb	3,770 lb	3,450 lb	3,810 lb	7,820 lb
All-up Weight	4,850 lb	5,200 lb	5,600 lb	5,600 lb	10,600 lb
Max. Cruise Speed	132 mph	132 mph	132 mph	132 mph	115 mph
Cruise Range	230 miles	300 miles	330 miles	330 miles	185 miles
Accommodation	4	4	5	5	2 + 13
Production	2	1	23	154	1
Sequence Nos.	12835 12836	12869	inc. Sycamore Mks 10 11 12 13 14 51 52 50		12871
			See Appendix B		

Type	173/2	173/3 & 4	173/5	191/1	192
Power Plant	Two 550 hp Alvis Leonides	Two 850 hp Alvis Leonides Major			Two 1,465 hp Napier Gazelles
No. of Rotors & Blades	2 × 3	2 × 4	2 × 4	2 × 4	2 × 4
Rotor Diameter	48 ft 7 in	48 ft 9 in	48 ft 9 in	48 ft 9 in	48 ft 11 in
Fuselage Length	55 ft 2 in	54 ft 2 in	50 ft 3 in	50 ft 3 in	54 ft 4 in
Height	15 ft	17 ft	17 ft	16 ft 9 in	17 ft
Empty Weight	7,820 lb	9,840 lb	9,840 lb	11,400 lb	11,085 lb
All-up Weight	11,000 lb	13,500 lb	13,500 lb	17,000 lb	19,000 lb
Max. Cruise Speed	115 mph	115 mph	115 mph	115 mph	138 mph
Cruise Range	185 miles	300 miles	300 miles	500 miles	460 miles
Accommodation	2 + 13	2 + 14	2 + 14	2 + 16	3 + 18
Production	1	2	1	3	26
Sequence Nos.	12872	13204 13205	13206	13274– 13276	13342– 13367

(b) *Types Projected (but not built):—*

Type	181	190	191/2	192C	192D
Power Plant	Two 3,940 shp Bristol Proteus	Two 83 thp Bristol Ramjets	Two 1,465 shp Napier Gazelles	Two 1,465 shp Napier Gazelles	Two 1,465 shp Napier Gazelles
No. of Rotors & Blades	2 × 5	1 × 2	2 × 4	2 × 4	2 × 4
Rotor Diameter	72 ft	26 ft	48 ft 11 in	48 ft 11 in	48 ft 11 in
Fuselage Length	100 ft	16 ft 5 in	50 ft 3 in	54 ft 4 in	56 ft 2 in
Height	28 ft 6 in	7 ft 9 in	16 ft 9 in	18 ft 4 in	18 ft 2 in
Empty Weight	30,000 lb	400 lb	10,400 lb	12,400 lb	11,700 lb
All-up Weight	48,000 lb	1,200 lb	18,000 lb	20,000 lb	19,000 lb
Design Cruise Speed	226 mph	80 mph	138 mph	138 mph	138 mph
Design Cruise Range	300 miles	40 miles	500 miles	500 miles	460 miles
Accommodation	2 + 80	2	2 + 16	3 + 23	3 + 30

Type	193	194	199	203	214
Power Plant	Two 1,500 shp Lycoming T 55	Four 1,175 shp D H Gnomes	Four 4,000 shp Rolls-Royce Tynes	One 1,025 shp D H Gnome	Two 1,175 shp D H Gnomes
No. of Rotors & Blades	2 × 4	2 × 6	2 × 4	1 × 3	1 × 4
Rotor Diameter	48 ft 11 in	55 ft	48 ft	48 ft 7 in	48 ft 11 in
Fuselage Length	50 ft 3 in	77 ft	66 ft	42 ft 9 in	41 ft 8 in
Height	16 ft 9 in	24 ft	26 ft	16 ft 2 in	17 ft 6 in
Empty Weight	10,400 lb	19,700 lb	35,300 lb	4,000 lb	6,130 lb
All-up Weight	18,000 lb	33,800 lb	60,000 lb	6,600 lb	11,300 lb
Design Cruise Speed	138 mph	230 mph	400 mph	126 mph	138 mph
Design Cruise Range	500 miles	530 miles	800 miles	320 miles	350 miles
Accommodation	2 + 16	3 + 48	3 + 50	2 + 9	2 + 16

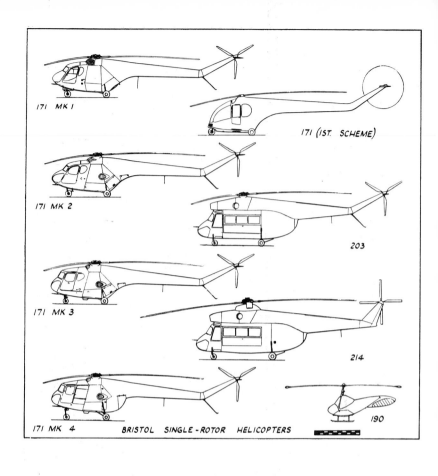

171 MK 1

171 (1ST. SCHEME)

171 MK 2

203

171 MK 3

214

171 MK 4

190

BRISTOL SINGLE-ROTOR HELICOPTERS

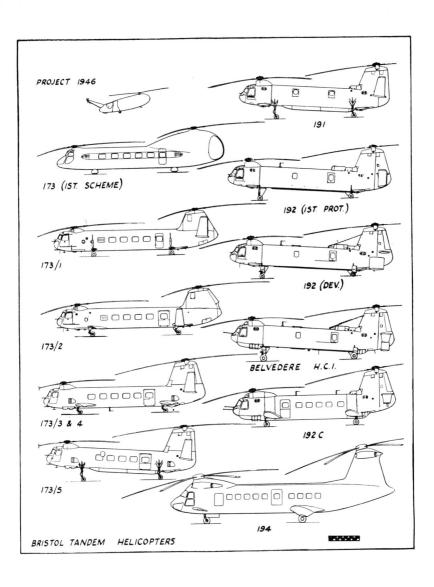

PROJECT 1946

191

173 (1ST. SCHEME)

192 (1ST. PROT.)

173/1

192 (DEV.)

173/2

BELVEDERE H.C.I.

173/3 & 4

192 C

173/5

194

BRISTOL TANDEM HELICOPTERS

Type 188 *XF923* flying in May 1962.

Bristol Turbojet Aircraft

The first Bristol turbojet aeroplane to be built and flown, Type 188, was almost the last true Bristol type to fly, when the British Aircraft Corporation had been in existence for nearly two years. Bristol's apparent lateness in the turbojet field was not due to reluctance to enter it, for in October 1946 the Company had tendered a design for a four-jet high-speed long-range bomber, Type 172, a high-wing monoplane of 110 ft. span and 45 degrees sweepback. This design study was well received by the Air Staff and an experimental programme planned, including a half-scale flying model to investigate stability, control and manœuvrability in advance of the bomber prototype, which might take five years to complete. The model, Type 174, a single-seater with a single Rolls-Royce Nene engine, was expected to fly a year after commencement and was defined by Specification E.8/47. Geometrically similar, the 174 was intended to attain the same speed and altitude as the 172, its engine being located centrally with bifurcated inlets and tail pipes reproducing the external flow conditions of the full-size bomber. Provision was made for boundary layer control by suction at a later stage in the flight trials, and the pilot's cockpit was pressurised to 9 lb. per square inch as proposed for the bomber.

Investigation of high subsonic flow round the wing-body junction showed that the original shape was unsuitable and that the leading edge near the body would have to be more swept than the outer wing rather than unswept as at first proposed. Consequently work on Type 174 was stopped in November 1947 and Specification E.8/47 was revised to define a smaller monoplane powered by an Avon with a 45 degree swept shoulder wing of 33 ft. span, a conventional swept tail unit, a single nose intake and tail jet-pipe, and a tandem landing gear comprising two twin-wheeled units retracting into the body, with lateral support from light outriggers under the wings. This design, Type 176, was begun in February 1948 and proceeded further than the 174, but soon after the mock-up conference in October the Company found itself unable to support both this project and the rapidly developing Type 175 and chose to continue with the latter and to give up the former. Thereafter a small project design team prepared tenders to various specifications issued up till 1953, but none got beyond the brochure stage except Type 182.

This project was tendered in the spring of 1951, to meet Specification UB.109, which called for a mass-produced catapult-launched radio-guided expendable bomber carrying a 5,000 lb. warhead to a target up to 400 miles away at a cruising speed of 600 m.p.h. The relative merits of moulded Durestos and welded steel were compared and the former material was found to be both lighter in weight and cheaper. An expendable steel Bristol turbojet was intended for production aircraft, but as a first step it was decided to build two unmanned but retrievable prototypes (Type 182R) powered by the Armstrong Siddeley Viper; these were built of light alloy material, and the first was completed and the second well advanced early in 1953 when official policy on the project changed, and both airframes were promptly cut up for scrap before either power plant or auto-pilot had been installed. The wing of the Bristol 182 was identical in shape (but not in structure) with that of the Folland Gnat, and a two-thirds scale Durestos moulded wing test specimen was exhibited at the S.B.A.C. Show in September 1953; the expendable BE.17 engine was so promising a design that it was developed in long-life form into the highly successful Orpheus. Although the retrievable prototypes had tricycle landing gear and variable wing incidence, the operational bomber version would have had a fixed wing and no undercarriage.

Type 182R, retrievable prototype of 'Red Rapier', nearly complete at Filton in July 1953.

In February 1953 the Company was invited to tender to Specification ER.134 for an experimental aeroplane capable of reaching and sustaining twice the speed of sound for long enough to enable steady-state kinetic heating effects on the structure to be experienced and recorded. Stainless steel was chosen as the primary structural material, and by 1955 a layout had been established comprising a minimum size fuselage with twin turbojet engines in nacelles mounted half-way along the span of a swept thin wing; this was designated Type 188. Very great difficulty arose in the supply of stainless steel sheet and slabs of the required combination of strength and uniformity and all means of attachment, including rivets, screws and bolts, had to be specially made in compatible materials, since the standard articles were unacceptable at such high loadings and temperatures; even so, the ultimate success of the design depended almost entirely on the satisfactory development by the Company of a new argon arc-welding technique known as 'puddle-welding'. Major assistance was rendered by Armstrong Whitworth Aircraft, who had themselves conducted research on similar lines and to whom manufacture of several major components of Type 188 was subcontracted. As a result of both wind-tunnel tests and rocket-propelled model-flights at high speed and altitude, the aerodynamic shape was modified to give a basically rectangular wing plan between the nacelles, with small swept-back outer wings having horn-balanced ailerons. The all-moving tail-plane was raised to the top of the fin and the chord of the latter extended to cater for single-engine failure at take-off. Originally Rolls-Royce Avon RA.24R engines were proposed, but later D.H. Gyron Junior DGJ.10 engines became available and were substituted; they were mounted forward of the main structural nacelle barrels, which were machined from stainless steel forgings with internal integral ring frames corresponding with the multiple inner and outer wing attachment lugs. The body, although of considerable length, was of oval section no greater in area than that required to accommodate the pilot in a conventional ejector seat; the main undercarriage units retracted inboard, and the single main wheels were arranged to lie vertically within the body aft of the main spar; the twin-wheel nose undercarriage retracted forward into a cell immediately aft of the cockpit. All the flying controls were hydraulically operated, as were the landing gear and the four-part air-brakes in the rear fuselage. Much of the fuselage was occupied by the fuel tanks, and a large compartment forward of the wing contained both the cockpit refrigerating system and a very comprehensive array of electronic recording and telemetering equipment for continuously measuring changes of temperature and pressure, acceleration, vibration and strain and transmitting much of this data to the ground control, where the aircraft's performance and behaviour was under constant surveillance from an operations room manned by a pilot and engineer who were in fact acting as additional crew members although not airborne; in general, the 'ground pilot' was able to monitor all the data transmitted, but would relay to the airborne pilot only information requiring definite action, so saving him from the distraction

Second Type 188 *XF926* taking off and landing at Filton in July 1963.

of indications and warnings about which he could do nothing.

Originally, six examples of Type 188 were ordered, but three were cancelled as an economy measure, and the final contract covered the construction of three airframes, one of which was for structural test; this was delivered by road to Farnborough in May 1960. The first of the two fully equipped prototypes, No. 13518 (*XF923*), was rolled out for the first time on 26 April 1961 for comprehensive pre-flight tests, including engine runs. The intake design posed several problems, and the aircraft was ready for taxying trials in February 1962; cross-winds and other unfavourable conditions conspired to delay the first flight on many occasions from March onwards, but on 14 April all was well and the Company's Chief Test Pilot, G. L. Auty, took-off on the first flight, which was also a delivery flight to Boscombe Down, lasting 23 min. *XF923* made its first public appearance in flight at the S.B.A.C. Show in September 1962 and returned to Filton on 15 November on completion of the initial test programme; the second prototype, No. 13519 (*XF926*), made its maiden flight at Filton on 29 April 1963. The Bristol 188, though among the world's fastest conventional aeroplanes, fell short of its objective in exploring the effects of prolonged kinetic heating because the fuel consumption of its engines proved to be excessive, thus severely curtailing the flight time available at full speed. Consequently both prototypes had much shorter careers than intended and contributed relatively little to the Anglo-French Concorde supersonic transport project.

The latter was the end result of exploratory design studies which began in 1956 with the formation of the Supersonic Transport Advisory Committee within the Ministry of Aviation. Proposals made to this body included the Bristol 198, which began as a Mach 1·3 'M-wing' design, but was changed first to a slender 'delta' with overwing engines to fly at Mach 1·8 and then with underwing engines at Mach 2·2; the powerplant finally chosen comprised six developed Olympus turbojets. The high all-up weight needed for the London–New York route raised a severe sonic boom problem and in 1960, after a brief look at a possible Mach 3 transport (Type 213), the 198 was abandoned in favour of a smaller four-engined version, Type 223. Concurrently, Sud-Aviation of Toulouse had proposed a medium-range supersonic airliner (Super-Caravelle) so nearly coincident with Type 223 that Anglo-French collaboration was agreed upon in 1962 for both the design and production of a Mach 2·2 project, subsequently named Concorde. In support of this programme, the first Fairey F.D.2 *WG774*, sometime holder of the world speed record and already in use at the R.A.E., was redesigned at Filton in 1960 with a lengthened body and slender (though not cambered) ogee wing, to gain experience of high-speed handling behaviour. In its rebuilt form as the Bristol 221, *WG774* was first flown at Filton by Godfrey Auty on 1 May 1964, and went on to provide much valuable data, complementary to that obtained at lower speeds with the Handley Page 115; the latter had been designed for the R.A.E. to Specification X.197, to which the Bristol 215 was a rival tender; had the 215 been built, it would have been Filton's last wooden aeroplane and was planned as a glider, with provision for a small turbojet later if needed.

In parallel with the early supersonic transport studies, the Filton project office also schemed several subsonic rear-engined turbojet transports, including Type 200 for B.E.A.'s medium range routes, Type 201 for B.O.A.C. and in 1958, a smaller version, Type 205, whose features were later combined with those of the similar Hunting 107 to evolve the BAC One-Eleven. Other tenders included Type 204, a gothic-winged canard approach to the TSR-2 requirement defined by O.R. 339, and a family of V/STOL transports, comprising several variants of Type 208 with both vertical lifting jets and vectored-thrust propulsion engines, and the similar Type 209 with vertical lifting fans; a turboprop alternative, Type 222, was to have been a Tyne-powered version of the Lockheed C–130 Hercules with boundary-layer control by suction, built under licence at Filton. All these centred on a preferred cargo-hold size of 40 ft by 10 ft by 10 ft, but a smaller VTOL assault transport, Type 210, was also studied, together with a supersonic, almost wingless, VTOL single-seat strike-reconnaissance project, Type 217, using a single vectored-thrust B.E.53 turbojet. None of these was adopted, but in 1961 a strong submission was made to NATO with a smaller twin-engined version of Type 208 to meet NBMR-4; this was the Bristol 224, powered by two B.E. 58 vectored-thrust turbojets plus eight optional lift engines in removable wing-mounted pods. The final project to bear a Bristol type number, in 1962, was Type 225, an enlarged STOL development of Type 208, offered with alternative fuselages to meet either O.R. 351 for a tactical freighter, or O.R. 357 for a maritime reconnaissance aircraft; both variants would have had wings, tailplanes, powerplants and landing gear in common. Thereafter the Filton project office dealt with new proposals within the rationalised BAC framework, but none carried type numbers in the original Bristol series.

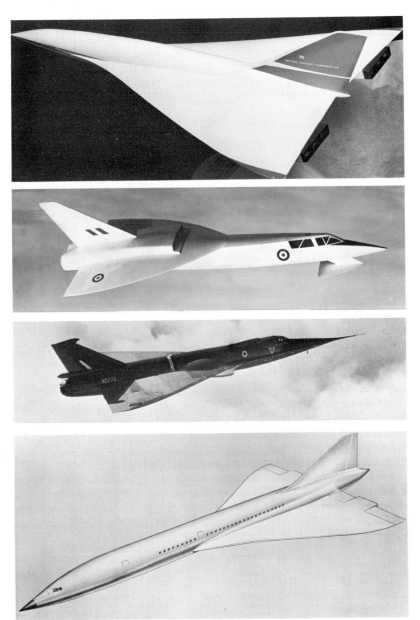

Concorde's Bristol forebears: (*top to bottom*) Type 198, Type 204, Type 221, Type 223.

Bristol V/S.T.O.L. Projects: (*above*) Type 208, (*below*) Type 224.

SPECIFICATIONS AND DATA

Types: 172, 174, 176, 182, 188, 198, 204, 208, 217, 221, 223, 224 & 225
Manufacturers: The Bristol Aeroplane Co. Ltd.   } Filton,
  Bristol Aircraft Ltd.   } Bristol

Type	172	174	176	182	188	198
Power Plant	Four 9000 lb s t Bristol turbojets	One 5000 lb s t Rolls-Royce Nene	One 6500 lb s t Rolls-Royce Avon	One 3000 lb s t Bristol B E 17	Two 14000 lb s t D H Gyron Junior DGJ 10	Six 22,800 lb s t Bristol Olympus 591
Span	110 ft	55 ft	32 ft 6 in	20 ft 10 in	35 ft 1 in	78 ft
Length	100 ft	50 ft	44 ft 10 in	33 ft 10 in	71 ft	180 ft
Height	28 ft	14 ft 9 in	11 ft 9 in	6 ft	13 ft 4 in	40 ft 4 in
Wing Area	2,250 sq ft	562 sq ft	240 sq ft	145 sq ft	396 sq ft	5,270 sq ft
Empty Weight	80,000 lb	—	9,120 lb	7,700 lb	—	160,000 lb
All-up Weight	165,000 lb	26,000 lb	12,200 lb	9,500 lb	—	385,000 lb
Max. Speed	600 mph	600 mph	635 mph	600 mph	1,200 plus mph	1,400 mph
Ceiling	50,000 ft	50,000 ft	49,000 ft	45,000 ft	—	60,000 ft
Max. Range	5,400 mls	—	—	400 mls	—	3,600 mls
Accommodation	4	Pilot only	Pilot only	nil	Pilot only	6 + 122
Production	nil	nil	nil	nil	2	nil
Sequence Nos.	nil	nil	nil	nil	13518 13519	13520 (reserved)

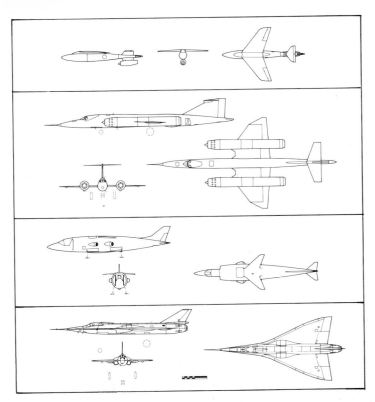

Bristol Turbojets: (*top to bottom*) Type 182, Type 188, Type 217, Type 221.

204	208	217	221	223	224	225
Two 22500 lb s t Bristol Olympus 22SR	Four 18000 lb s t Bristol B E 53/6 + twelve 8000 lb s t B E 59/7	One 18000 lb s t Bristol B E 53	One 14000 lb s t Rolls-Royce Avon RA28R	Four 28000 lb s t B S Olympus 593	Two 18400 lb s t B S Pegasus 5 + eight 8800 lb s t RB 175	Four 12400 lb s t Rolls-Royce Spey RB 168
32 ft 76 ft 6 in 20 ft 9 in 820 sq ft 41000 lb 80000 lb 1400 mph at 50000 ft	135 ft 107 ft 34 ft 5 in 2116 sq ft 80300 lb 176800 lb 440 mph STOL 300 mph VTOL	13 ft 6 in 50 ft 11 ft 8 in 107 sq ft 6700 lb 13900 lb 800 mph	25 ft 57 ft 7 in 13 ft 504 sq ft 14000 lb 18000 lb 1060 mph	70 ft 176 ft 6 in 35 ft 3700 sq ft 104000 lb 251700 lb 1450 mph	79 ft 5 in 77 ft 1 in 20 ft 900 sq ft 41800 lb 77500 lb 400 mph	148 ft 6 in 103 ft 35 ft 8 in 2350 sq ft 86000 lb 217000 lb 450 mph
60000 ft 2000 mls 2	— 4000 mls 5 + 61	— 950 mls Pilot only	50000 ft — Pilot only	60000 ft 3300 mls 6 + 90	— 2350 mls 2 + 62	— 5500 mls 4 (Fr) or 10 (MR)
nil	nil	nil	1 (conversion)	nil	nil	nil
nil	nil	nil	13521 (*ex* F9421)	nil	nil	nil

Appendix A

Bristol Type Number List

From the Company's beginning in 1910 up to the outbreak of war in 1914 the archives contain records of only seven unbuilt projects, all of which have been referred to in this book. They were, in chronological order: the Burney X.1 hydroped biplane; two large naval seaplanes, one (B.C.2) with a 200 h.p. Clerget and the other with a 200 h.p. Canton-Unné; Coanda's canard two-seater monoplane, of which a model was tested in Eiffel's wind-tunnel; Coanda's S.B.5 monoplane, whose unfinished components were the origin of Scout A; the RB two-seater biplane contemporary with S.S.A.; and the 1914 Gordon Bennett racer G.B.1.

All projects from August 1914 onwards, whether built or not, were re-reviewed in 1923 by Capt. Barnwell, who allotted to them retrospective Type Numbers in chronological order. This system of Type Numbers was continued for new projects after that date, commencing with Type 90, being terminated in 1962 after Type 225 had been recorded. Half the 150 unbuilt projects listed were precursors, variants or derivatives of the 117 designs actually built and have already been mentioned in their proper context; much information on the others is contained in the Company's archives, but, since these 'paper aeroplanes' achieved no real existence, it is inappropriate (as well as impossible from considerations of space) to describe them at length. In order to present an overall picture of Bristol design activity the Type Number list is given below.

Type No.	Description or Name	Engine	Date
1	Scout C	80 hp Gnome or le Rhône	1914
2	Scout D	80 hp Gnome	1915
3	Scout D	80 hp le Rhône	1915
4	Scout D	100 hp Mono-Gnome	1916
5	Scout D	110 hp Clerget	1916
6	T.T.A.	2 × 120 hp Beardmore	1916
7	F.3A	250 hp Rolls-Royce	1916
8	S.2A	110 hp Clerget	1916
9	R.2A	120 hp Beardmore	1916
9A	R.2B	150 hp Hispano-Suiza	1916
10	M.1A	110 hp Clerget	1916
11	M.1B	110 hp Clerget	1916
12	F.2A	190 hp Rolls-Royce	1916
13	M.R.1	140 hp Hispano-Suiza	1916
14	F.2B (Bristol Fighter Mk I and II)	Rolls-Royce Falcon	1917
15	F.2B	Sunbeam Arab	1917
16	F.2B	200 hp Hispano-Suiza	1917
17	F.2B	300 hp Hispano-Suiza	1918
17A	F.2B (Frise ailerons)	300 hp Hispano-Suiza	1924
17B	F.2B (Frise ailerons and large tail)	300 hp Hispano-Suiza	1926
18	Scout E	200 hp Ricardo-Halford Cruciform	1917
19	Pusher Scout	200 hp Ricardo-Halford Cruciform	1917
20	M.1C	110 hp Le Rhône	1917

Type No.	Description or Name	Engine	Date
21	Scout F	Sunbeam Arab	1917
21A	Scout F.1	Cosmos Mercury	1918
22	F.2C	200 hp Salmson	1917
22A	F.2C	300 hp Dragonfly	1918
22B	F.2C	230 hp B.R.2	1918
23	Badger I	Dragonfly	1918
23A	Badger II	Jupiter	1919
23X	Badger X	Puma	1919
24	Braemar I	4 Puma	1918
25	Braemar II	4 Liberty	1919
26	Pullman (14 passengers)	4 Liberty	1919
27	F.2B Coupé	Rolls-Royce Falcon	1919
28	Tourer (3-seater Coupé)	Puma	1919
29	Tourer (2-seater open)	Puma	1919
30	Babe Mk I	Gadfly ⎰ Viale ⎱	1919
31	Grampus Mk I	Siddeley Tiger	1919
32	Bullet	Jupiter	1919
33	Pullman (4) central-engineroom, 40 passengers	4 Siddeley Tigers	1919
34	Tourer Seaplane (3-seater open)	Viper	1919
35	Two-seater Ship Fighter to Spec RAF 21	Jupiter	1919
36	Seely	Puma	1919
37	Tramp	4 Pumas	1919
38	A.H.2—Variant of Type 35 for US Navy	Viper	1919
39	A.H.1—Single-seater Ship Fighter for US Navy	Viper	1919
40	F.2B (Bristol Fighter Mk I late production)	Puma	1919
41	Tourer Seaplane (2 seater open)	Beardmore	1919
42	Grampus Mk II	RAF 4a	1919
43	Grampus Mk IV	4 Lucifers	1920
44	Tramp Boat (flying boat version of Type 37)	4 Puma	1920
45	Scandinavian Tourer (wheels or ski) as Type 29	Puma	1920
46	Babe Mk II	Ounce	1919
46A	Babe Mk III	⸰60 hp le Rhône	1920
46B	Babe Monoplane	60 hp le Rhône	1920
47	Tourer (3 seater open)	Puma	1920
48	Seaplane version of Type 47	Puma	1920
49	Colonial—3 seater biplane	Lucifer	1920
50	Mail carrier version of Type 26	4 Liberty	1920
51	Pusher Flying Boat—4 seater	Lucifer	1920
52	MFA—Bullfinch monoplane 1 seater	Jupiter	1920
53	MFB—Bullfinch biplane 2 seater	Jupiter	1920
54	Single-seat high-speed float monoplane	Jupiter	1920
55	D. of R. 4B—long range bomber biplane (Spec. 2/20)	Condor	1920
56	Troop Carrier—biplane (Spec. 5/20)	2 Napier Lion	1920
57	Grampus Mk V (variant of Type 43)	2 Hall-Scott	1920
58	Commercial Biplane—8 seater	Liberty	1920
59	as Type 58 with alternative engine	Jupiter	1920
60	Three-seater Coupé cantilever monoplane	Lucifer	1920
61	Three-seater Amphibian Boat monoplane (pusher)	Jupiter	1920
62	Commercial Biplane—10 seater	Lion	1920
63*	Ultra-light single-seat monoplane	5 hp	1921
64*	Maximum speed monoplane	3000 hp	1921
65*	Man-powered pusher biplane	—	1921
66	Hydrovane Flying Boat—single engine—twin screws	Lion	1921
67	Two-seat Fighter Reconnaissance biplane	Lion	1921
68	Three-seat Fleet Spotter biplane (D. of R. 7A)	Lion	1921
69	Two-seater Reconnaissance Biplane (D. of R. 3)	Lion	1921
70	Two-seater Reconnaissance Monoplane (D. of R. 3A)	Lion	1921
71	Three-seater Coast Defence Torpedo Triplane (D. of R. 9)	Cub	1921
72	Racing Monoplane	Jupiter	1921
73	Taxiplane	Lucifer	1921
74	Commercial Triplane—26 passengers	3 Jupiter	1921
75	Commercial Biplane—10-seater	Jupiter	1921
75A	Express Freighter conversion of Type 75	Jupiter	1924

* Examples for lecture to Cambridge Aeronautical Society

Type No.	Description or Name	Engine	Date
76	Jupiter-Fighter (F. 2B conversion)	Jupiter	1923
76A	Bifuel Jupiter-Fighter (G-EBHH)	Jupiter	1923
76B	Swedish Jupiter-Fighter (G-EBHG)	Jupiter	1923
77	M.1D (conversion of Type 11)	Lucifer	1922
78	Fighter C—two seater biplane	Jupiter	1922
79	Brandon (ambulance version of Type 75)	Jupiter	1923
80	Fighter D—two-seater monoplane	Jupiter	1922
81	Dual-control trainer version of Type 29 with Frise ailerons and oleo landing gear	Puma	1923
81A	Version of Type 81 for Greek Navy with radio fittings and large rudder	Puma	1925
82	Coast Defence Torpedo Biplane	2 Lion	1923
83A	Primary Training Biplane (P.T.M.)	Lucifer	1923
83B	As 83A (with enlarged rudder and elevators)	Lucifer	1925
83C	As 83A (streamlined for competition)	Lucifer	1927
83D	Projected twin-float seaplane variant	Lucifer	1927
83E	Strengthened variant for engine test	Titan	1928
84	Bloodhound (metal wings and tail)	Jupiter	1923
84A	Bloodhound (wooden wings and tail)	Jupiter (VT)	1923
84B	Bloodhound (wooden wings and tail)	Jupiter (S)	1923
85	Seely with R.A.E. Supercharger	Jupiter (S)	1923
86	Tourer—2-seater (includes Falcon conversion of Type 81A by Greek Navy)	Falcon	1923
86A	Tourer—3-seater version of Type 86	Falcon	1923
87	Three-seater Fleet Reconnaissance Biplane	Jupiter	1923
88	Bulgarian Tourer—1st version	Viper	1923
88A	Bulgarian Tourer—2nd version	Viper	1926
89	Advanced Trainer (conversion of Type 81)	Jupiter	1924
89A	As Type 89, plywood-covered fuselage	Jupiter	1926
90	Berkeley	Condor	1923
91	Brownie I	Cherub I	1923
91A	Brownie I	Cherub III	1924
91B	Brownie II	Cherub III	1926
92	Laboratory biplane	Jupiter	1924
93	Boarhound I	Jupiter	1924
93A	Beaver I	Jupiter	1925
93B	Boarhound II (Mexico)	Jupiter	1927
94	Single-seat Fighter Biplane (pusher)	Jupiter	1924
95	Bagshot (Spec. F.4/24)	2 Jupiter	1925
96	Bristol Fighter Mk III (revised F.2B)	Falcon	1925
96A	Bristol Fighter Mk IV (with H.P. slots)	Falcon	1927
97	Commercial Biplane for Imperial Airways	Jupiter	1925
98	Single-seat light racing monoplane (Brownie III)	Cherub	1925
99	Badminton	Jupiter	1925
100	Commercial Biplane for Imperial Airways	2 Jupiter	1925
101	Two-seat Fighter	Jupiter	1926
102A	Single-seat Fighter derived from Badminton	Jupiter	1926
102B	Twin-float seaplane version of Type 102A	Jupiter	1926
103	High-speed single-seat monoplane	Mercury	1926
104	Single-seat light monoplane	Cherub	1926
105	Single-seat Fighter biplane (Spec. F.9/26)	Mercury	1926
105A	Bulldog Mks I, II, IIA, III, IIIA, IV, IVA	Jupiter or Mercury	1927
105D	Bulldog for Denmark	Jupiter	1930
105J	Bulldog built in Japan (J.S.S.F.)	Jupiter	1930
106	Two-seat General Purpose Biplane	Jupiter	1927
107	Bullpup	Mercury	1927
108	Twin-engined Night Bomber (Spec. B.19/27)	2 Jupiter	1927
109	Long-range Biplane	Jupiter	1927
110	Cabin Biplane—3 passengers	Titan	1928
110A	Cabin Biplane—4 passengers	Neptune	1928
111A	High-wing Cabin Monoplane for Imperial Airways	3 Jupiter	1928
111B	High-wing Cabin Monoplane for Mr van Lear Black	3 Titan	1928
112	Single-seat C.O.W. gun fighter (Spec. F.29/27)	Mercury	1928
113	Commercial Biplane for Imperial Airways	3 Jupiter	1928
114	Commercial Biplane (scaled-up Type 110A)	Jupiter	1929
114A	Type 114 with revised wing as Type 118	Jupiter	1929
115	Three-engined Monoplane Troop-carrier (Spec. C.16/28)	3 Jupiter	1929

Type No.	Description or Name	Engine	Date
116	Troop-carrier version of Type 113 (Spec. C.16/28)	3 Jupiter	1929
117	Twin-engined Freight Carrier	2 Jupiter	1929
118	Two-seat General Purpose Biplane	Jupiter	1929
118A	Type 118 with Mercury V for service trials	Mercury	1931
119	Trainer version of Bulldog	Mercury	1930
120	Type 118 with enclosed gunner's cockpit	Pegasus	1931
121	Type 120 with increased wing area (Spec. G.4/31)	Pegasus	1931
122	Type 121 with pilot ahead of wings (Spec. G.4/31)	Pegasus	1931
123	Single-seat biplane fighter (Spec. F.7/30)	Goshawk	1933
124	Bulldog Trainer (Spec. T.12/32)	Jupiter	1932
125	Low-wing monoplane derivative of Type 122	Pegasus	1931
126	High-wing monoplane derivative of Type 122	Pegasus	1931
127	Single-seat monoplane fighter (Spec. F.7/30)	Goshawk	1932
128	Type 127 with alternative engine	Mercury	1932
129	Single-seat pusher monoplane fighter (Spec. F.7/30)	Mercury	1932
130	Twin-engined Monoplane Troop carrier (C.26/31)	2 Pegasus	1932
130A	Bombay Mk I (Production by Short & Harland Ltd)	2 Pegasus	1936
131	Twin-engined Bomber (Spec. B.9/32)	2 Pegasus	1933
132	Two-seat turret fighter monoplane	Hydra	1933
133	Single-seat fighter monoplane (Spec. F.7/30)	Mercury	1933
134	High-speed Mailplane monoplane—single-engine	Pegasus	1933
135	Civil monoplane—twin engines	2 Aquilla	1933
136	Single-engined day bomber (Spec. P.27/32)	Perseus	1933
137	Convertible 14-passenger or cargo civil derivative of Type 130	2 Pegasus	1933
138	High-altitude single-seat monoplane	Pegasus	1933
138A	Revised version of Type 138 to Spec. 2/34	Pegasus	1934
138B	As Type 138A with liquid-cooled engine	Kestrel	1934
139	Single-engined Freighter (last Bristol biplane project)	Pegasus	1934
140	Two-seat pusher fighter with nose turret (Spec. F.5/33)	Perseus	1934
141	Three-seat fighter with nose turret (Spec. F.22/33)	2 Aquila	1934
142	*Britain First*	2 Mercury	1934
142M	Blenheim I and II	2 Mercury	1935
143	Type 135 revised to Type 142 standard	2 Aquila	1934
143F	Military version of Type 143 for Finland	2 Mercury	1934
144	Bomber derived from Type 130 (Spec. B.3/34)	2 Perseus	1934
145A	Long-range monoplane (fuel in body)	2 Phoenix	1935
145B	Long-range monoplane (fuel in wing)	2 Phoenix	1935
146	Single-seat eight-gun fighter (Spec. F.5/34)	Perseus	1935
147	Two-seat turret-fighter (Spec. F.9/35)	Perseus	1935
147A	As Type 147 with higher performance	Hercules	1936
148	Two-seat Army Co-operation Monoplane (Spec. A.39/34)	Perseus	1935
148B	As Type 148 with higher performance	Taurus	1935
148A	Proposed unarmed version for engine test	Hercules	1935
149	Bolingbroke I and Blenheim III & IV	2 Mercury	1936
150	Land-based Torpedo Bomber (Spec. M.15/35)	2 Perseus	1935
151	High-speed single-seat monoplane (Spec. 35/35)	Hercules	1936
152	Beaufort (all Marks)	2 Taurus or 2 Twin Wasp	1936
153	Fighter derived from Type 151 (Spec. F.37/35)	Hercules	1936
153A	Twin-engined alternative to Type 153	2 Aquila	1936
154	Four-engined civil monoplane— 24 passengers (high-wing)	4 Aquila	1938
155	Twin-engined Composite Bomber (Spec. B.18/38)	2 Taurus	1938
156	Beaufighter (all Marks except III & IV) (Spec. F.17/39)	2 Hercules or 2 Merlin	1938
157	Proposed bomber variant of Type 156 (Spec. B.19/38)	2 Hercules	1939
158	Proposed slim-body variant of Type (Beaufighter Mks III & IV)	2 Hercules or 2 Griffon	1939
159	Four-engined Bomber (Spec. B.1/39)	4 Hercules	1939
160	Bisley I & Blenheim V (Spec. B.6/40)	2 Mercury	1940
161 ⎫ 162 ⎭	Beaumont, bomber derivative of Type 156 (Mk I Hercules, Mk II Merlin) (Spec. B.7/40)	2 Hercules or 2 Merlin	1940
163	Buckingham B.1 and C.1	2 Centaurus	1941
164	Brigand (all Marks except Mk II)	2 Centaurus	1942
165	Brigand II, trainer variant of Type 164	2 Centaurus	1943
166	Buckmaster I, trainer conversion of Type 163	2 Centaurus	1943

Type No.	Description or Name	Engine	Date
167	Brabazon I, Mk I	8 Centaurus	1943
	Mk II	4 Coupled Proteus	1945
168	Reserved for possible military variant of Type 167	—	
169	Proposed photo-reconnaissance variant of Type 163	2 Centaurus	1944
170	Freighter and Wayfarer (all Marks)	2 Hercules	1945
171	Four-seat single-rotor Helicopter { Mk I / Other Marks	Wasp Jr / Leonides	1945
172	High-speed long-range bomber	4–6 BE 10 Olympus	1946
173	13-seat twin-rotor Helicopter	2 Leonides or Leo. Major	1946
174	Half-scale Type 172 (Spec. E.8/47)	Nene	1947
175	Britannia—all Series	4 Proteus	1947
176	3/10 scale Type 172 (Spec. E.8/47/2)	Avon	1948
177	Subsonic jet fighter (Spec. F.3/48)	2 Olympus	1948
178	Rocket Fighter (Spec. F.124T)	—	1949
179	Freighter (replacement for Type 170) Twin-boom	2 Hercules	1951
179A	Ditto with upswept rear fuselage	2 Hercules	1953
180	Supersonic variant of Type 177	2 Olympus	1953
181	Large Helicopter for B.E.A.	2 Proteus	1953
182	Expendable Bomber (Spec. UB.109)	B.E.17	1951
182R	Metal prototype of Type 182	Viper	1953
183	Variable sweepback research monoplane (ER.110T)	Nene	1952
184	Delta research monoplane project	Nene	1952
185	Rocket-powered interceptor project	Spectre	1952
186	Low-level bomber project (Spec. B.126T)	—	1952
187	Britannia replacement—('double-bubble')	4 Orion.	1953
188	High-speed research monoplane	2 Gyron Jr	1953
189	Maritime Reconnaissance derivative of Type 175	4 Nomad	1955
190	Scout Helicopter (Spec. HR.144T)	Tip Jets	1954
191	Naval derivative of Type 173 { Series 1 / (Spec. HR.146) { Series 2	2 Leonides Major / 2 Gazelle	1954
192	R.A.F. derivative of Type 173 (Spec. H.150)	2 Gazelle	1954
193	R.C.A.F. version of Type 191 (Spec. HR.149)	2 Lycoming T55	1954
194	Large civil compound tandem helicopter	4 Gnome	1955
195	High-wing rear-loading Freighter for R.A.A.F.	4 Proteus	1955
196	Expendable unmanned bomber variant of Type 188	2 Avon or BE 36	1955
197	Studies for civil transport with boundary layer control	4 Orion	1956
198	Supersonic Transport design studies for S.T.A.C. leading to Mach 2·2 slender delta	6 Olympus 591	1956–60
199	Tilt-wing Convertiplane (VTOL) project	4 Tyne or Proteus	1956
200	Medium-range Jet Transport for B.E.A.	3 Olympus 551	1956
201	Long-range version of Type 200 for B.O.A.C.	3 Olympus 551	1956
202	Medium-range low-altitude bomber	2 Olympus	1957
203	Sycamore replacement—single engine	Gnome	1957
204	Supersonic tactical strike reconnaissance (OR 339)	2 Olympus	1957
205	Short-range version of Type 200	3 Olympus 551	1958
206	Maritime reconnaissance tender for NATO (NBMR2)	2 Tyne	1958
207	Maritime reconnaissance tender for NATO (NBMR2)	2 Mamba + BE 53 Pegasus	1958
208	V/STOL freighter—jet lift (OR351)	BE 53 Pegasus + BE 59	1958
209	V/STOL freighter—fan lift (OR351)	BE 53 Pegasus + BR 59	1958
210	V/STOL assault transport—jet lift	various	1958
211	Type 205 with wing-mounted engines (layout only)	4 BE 47	1958
212	Strategic military transport (preliminary)	—	1959
213	Supersonic transport study (Mach 3·0)	Olympus	1959
214	Twin-engined development of Type 203	2 Gnome	1959
215	Research slender delta glider (Spec. X.197)	none—Viper later	1959
216	Car-ferry freighter design for Silver City	2 Dart	1959
217	Supersonic VTOL strike reconnaissance	Pegasus	1959
218	Executive 4-seater (first layout)	2 Continental IO-470	1959
219	Executive 5-seater (single engine) designs sold	Continental IO-470	1959
220	Executive 5-seater (twin engines) to Beagle	Continental IO-470	1959
221	Fairey F.D.2 with ogee wing (Spec. ER.221D)	Avon 28R	1960
222	Lockheed C-130 with boundary layer control (OR351)	4 Tyne	1960
223	Supersonic transport (Mach 2·2)	4 Olympus 593	1961
224	V/STOL transport for NATO (NBMR4)	2 Pegasus + RB.175	1961
225	{ STOL transport (OR351) } with common / { Maritime recce (OR357) } components	4 RB.168-1 Spey	1962

388

Appendix B

Bristol Sequence Numbers

Sequence numbers, or constructor's numbers of individual Bristol aircraft, ran from 1 to 13521, with gaps corresponding to lost records or cancellations. The sequence numbers of all Bristol aircraft known to have been built in the Company's own factories are listed below, with service or civil registration marks where appropriate. Other aircraft built in the Company's factories but not of Bristol design are listed in Appendix C and aircraft of Bristol design built by other contractors or licensees are listed in Appendix D.

Type	Monoplane, Biplane or Triplane	Sequence Numbers	Identification
Boxkite	B	7–32, '4, '7–44, '7–'9, 55, 60–'3, '5–'7, '9, 79, 93, '9, 119, '24–'9, '33–'9, '79, '80, 203, '4, '7, '22, '6, 347, '94–'9	99 = 24, 139 = 35, 394–'9 = 942–'7
Tractor	B	33	
Tractor	M	35–'6	
Type T	B	45, 51–'4, 78	
Tractor	B	59	
Prier s/s	M	46, 56–'7, 68, 81, 95–'8, 102	
Prier 2s	M	58, 71–'6, 82–91, '4, 107–'9, '30, '55, '6	75 = 256, 91 = 261
Burney	M	92(X.2), 159(X.3)	
G.E.1	B	64	
G.E.2	B	103, '4	W.O. Comp. nos 12, 13
G.E.3	B	112, '3	
Coanda (school)	M	77, 132, '85, '6, '8, '9	
Coanda (side/side)	M	80, 110, '64–'6, '76, '7	
Coanda (comp)	M	105, '6	{ W.O. Comp nos 14, 15 263, 262
Coanda-Daimler	M	111	
Coanda (mil)	M	118, '21–'3, '31, '42–'54	
Coanda Hydro	B	120	
Coanda B.R.7	B	157, '8, '60–'3, '78	
Coanda T.B.8	B	(converted) 118, '21, '43, '4, '7, '8, '9, '51–'3, '96, 218 (new) 197, '8, 225, '7, '8, 331 –'42, 870–'93	196 = 948, 197 = 916, 198 = 153, 225 = 43, 227 = 917, 331–'42 = 1216–'27, 870–'81 = 8442–'53, 882–'93 = 8562–'73
Coanda T.B.8H	B	205 (rebuilt from 121)	15
Coanda S.B.5	M	183 (not completed)	
Coanda P.B.8	B	199	
Coanda S.S.A.	B	219	
Coanda G.B.75	B	223	610
Scout A	B	206	
Scout B	B	229, '30	633, '48
Scout C	B	450, '51–'62, '3–'79, '80–'5, '6–'91, '2–523, '4–'60, 771 –'83, '4–820	1243, '602–'13, '244–'60, 4662–'7, 1261–'6, 4668–'99, 3013–'49, '50–'62, 5291–'327
Scout D	B	1044–'93, '4–'173, '381–'430, '837–'66	5554–'603, 7028–'57, 8951–9000, A 1742–'91, N 5390–'419

Type	Monoplane, Biplane or Triplane	Sequence Numbers	Identification
T.T.A	B	1375, '6	*7750, '1*
F.3A	B	1485, '6 (cancelled)	*A 612, '3*
S.2A	B	1377, '8	*7836, '7*
M.1A/B/C	M	1374, '481–'4, 2719–'843	*A 5138–'42, C 4901–5025*
F.2A	B	1379–'80, '431–'80	*A 3303–'54*
M.R.1	B	2067, '8	*A 5177, '8*
F.2B (RR)	B	2069–'518, '851–3150, 3151–'450, '451–'750, '4–4253, '7–956, 5107–'15, '8–'23, '5–'406	*A 7107–'300, B 1101–'350, C 751–1050, C 4801–'900, C 4601–'800, D 7801–8100, E 2151–'650, F 4271–'970, H 1390–8, '401–'6, 8–'689*
F.2B (Arab)	B	4957-5106, '16, '7, '24	*H 1240–389, '99, '400, '400, '7*
F.2B (Puma)	B	5407–'24 (5425–'656 cancelled), 5659–'714 (from Standard Co.)	*H 1690–'707 (H 1708–'39, J 1231–'430 canc.), E 5253–'308 (Stand.)*
Scout E	B	2844 (cancelled)	
Scout F	B	2845–'50	*B3989–'94*
Braemar	T	3751, '2	*C 4296, '7*
Pullman	T	3753	*C 4298 (G-EASP)*
Badger I	B	4254–'6	*F 3495–'7*
Badger II	B	5657	*J 6492*
Badger X	B	5658	*K 110 (G-EABU)*
Babe	B	5865, '6, '75	*G-EASQ, 'QD, (not reg.)*
Tourer (2s)	B	5867, '8, '81, '92, 6120–'3	*G-EAIZ, 'NR, (USA), 'VU, 'XA, M-AFFA, G-EAWB, (Newfoundland)*
Tourer (3s)	B	5873, '4, '6–'80, '91, 6108–'19	*(2 seaplanes), G-EART, (5 USA), 'XK (AUDF), M-AAAF, AFFF, G-AUDG, EAWR (M-AEAA), (spare), EAWQ (M-AAEA), AUDH(DZ), 'DI, 'CA(DX), 'DJ, 'DK*
Bullet	B	5869	*G-EATS*
Seely	B	5870	*G-EAUE (J 7004)*
Tramp	T	5871, '2	*J 6912, '3*
Grampus	B	5882–'4 (cancelled)	
M.1C (civ.)	M	5885–'7	*G-EASR, (USA), 'VO (M-AFAA)*
M.1B/D	M	5888	*G-EAVP*
F.2B Mk II	B	5893–6107, '62–'221, '721–'804, '56, '7, 6858–'63	*J 6586–'800, 60 for A.M., 7616–'99, 2 RNZAF, I.F.S. Army 17–22*
F.2B (R)	B	6156–'61, '243–'372, '85–'509, '29–'708, '806–'55, '64–'917, '40–'51, '68–'87	6 to Greece, remainder ex RAF stores for conversion to Mk II (139 dual c.)
		7020,–'39, '90–'119, '25–'54 '8–'77	For conversion to Mk III (25 dual)
F.2B Mk III	B	6988,–7017, '40,–89, '120–'2	*J 8429–'58* (dual), *8242–'91*, 3 RNZAF
F.2B Mk IV	B	7236–'64, '301–'10, '2–'21, '419–'38, '556–'9, '68–'81	Converted from Mks II & III (24 dual)
F.2B (Hisp.)	B	6140–'4, '223–'38, '510–'21, 7222–'31	*(Type 17) M-MRAZ, 'Y, 'X, 'I, 'CO (Type 17A) G-EBCN + 15* a/f to SABCA, 12 to Spain (Type 17B) 10 to Mexico
Ten-seater	B	6124, '45–'7	*G-EAWY, 'BEV, J 6997, (spare)*
Bullfinch	M	6125, '6	*J 6901, '2*
Bullfinch	B	6127	*J 6903*
Racer	M	6148	*G-EBDR*
Taxiplane	B	6153–'5	*G-EBEW, 'EY, 'FY*
Bloodhound	B	6222, '709–'11	*G-EBGG, J 7248, '36, '7*
Puma School	B	6239–'42, '712–'7	*G-EBFR, 'S, 'T, 'U, 6 to Greece*
P.T.M.	B	6373–'8, '922–36, '60–'2, 7266	*G-EBFZ, 'GA, 'B, 'C, 'D, 'E, 'NB, 'C,* 12 for Chile, *B-BEPK,* 3 for Hungary, *G-EBYT*
Jupiter-F.2B	B	6379–'81	*G-EBGF, 'HG, 'HH*
Type 89	B	6382, '522–'5, '918, '9, '63, '4	*G-EBIH, 'JA–'C, (spare), 'ML, 'N, 'NZ, 'OA*

Type	★	Sequence Numbers	Identification
Type 89A	B	6965–'7, 7124, '56, '7, '221, '34, '65, '350–'2, '711, '2	G-EBOC, 'D, 'QS, 'T, 'SB, 'H, (spare), 'VR, 'YL, AAGF, 'LO, 'WJ, 'BPL, 'M
Type 88, 88A	B	6383, '4, '937–'9	B-BECA, 'HA, 'BA, 'TO, 'KA
Brownie	M	6526–'8	G-EBJK, 'L, 'M
Berkeley	B	6718–'20	J 7403–'5
Boarhound I	B	6805	G-EBLG
Beaver	B	7123	G-EBQF
Boarhound II	B	7232, '3	2 for Mexico
Laboratory	B	6920	Not registered
Badminton	B	6921	G-EBMK
Bagshot	M	7018	J 7767
Type 101	B	7019	G-EBOW
Bulldog I	B	7155, '267	Not registered
Bullpup I	B	7178	J 9051
Bulldog II	B	7235, '322–'47, '53–'8, '64–'403, '39–'45, '7–'58	J 9480, '567–'75, G-AAHH, J 9576–'84, (Japan), J 9585–'90, 5 to Latvia, 1st USN, K 1079–'101, 2 to Siam, A 12–1 to '8, J 9591, 2nd USN, G-ABAC, Sweden 1201–'3, (Chilean dem.), 7 to Latvia, 12 to Estonia
Bulldog IIA	B	7446, '59–'550, '82–'9, '90–'689, '91–'710, '3–'26, '46 '73, '744 (s-s)	G-ABBB, K 1603–'94, Sweden 5211–'8, K 2135–'234, '476–'95, '859–'72, '946–'63, 3504–'13, 4189 (stainless steel)
Bulldog 105D	B	7564–'7	Denmark J-151–'4
Bulldog IIIA	B	7560, '745	R-5, R-7 (G-ABZW, K 4292)
Bulldog TM	B	7727–'43, '77–'807, '27–'37	K 3170–'86, '923–'53, 4566–'76
Bulldog IVA	B	7808, '10–'26	R-8 (G-ACJN), Finland BU 59–75
Type 109	B	7268	G-EBZK
Type 110A	B	7348, '9	G-AAFG, (2nd not assembled)
Type 118	B	7561	R-3 (G-ABEZ, K 2873)
Type 119	B	7690 (cancelled)	
Type 120	B	7562	R-6 (K 3587)
Type 123	B	7775	No mark
Type 132		7774 (cancelled)	
Type 133		7776	R-10
Type 130		7809	K 3583
Type 138A		7840	K 4879
Type 138B		8136	L 7037
Type 142		7838	R-12 (G-ADCZ, K 7557)
Type 143		7839	R-14 (G-ADEK)
Type 146		7841, '2	K 5119, 2nd (K 8088) cancelled
Type 148		7843, '4, 8167	K 6551, '2, 3rd cancelled
Blenheim I		7986–8135, '7–'66, '380–'849, '918–'49, 9222–'39	K 7033–'182, Finland BL 104–'21, Turkey 2501–'12 (2 + G-AFFP–'Z), L 1097–'530, G-AFCE, 'F, L 1531–'46, 4817–'34, '903–'34, G-AFLA–'S (Turkey 397–408, '85–'90)
Bolingbroke		8168–'301 (cancelled)	
Blenheim IV		8850–'917, 9240–'471, '862–'73	L 4835–'902, N 6140–'74, '176–'220, '3–'42, P 4825–'64, '98–'927, 6885–'934, '50–'61, G-AFXD–'O (Greece)
Beaufort I		8302–'79, '950–9221, '472–'556, 10972–'1331, '6–'554	L 4441–'518, 9790–'838, '51–'97, '932–'72, N 1000–'47, '74–'118, '45–'86, W 6467–'506, '18–'43, X 8916–'39, AW 187–221, '34–'43, DD 945–'59, '74–'99, DE 108–'26, DW 802–'36, '51–'98, 913–'62, '77–'99, DX 114–'57, EK 969–'99, EL 123–'41, JM 431–'70, '96–517, '45–'93, LR 885–908, '20–'63, '76–'99, LS 113–'28

★ Monoplane or Biplane to Type 123, thereafter all Monoplanes.

Type	Sequence Numbers	Identification
Beaufort II	9557–'61, '894–10043, '962–'71, 11555	*AW 244–'53, '71–315, '35–'84, DD 870–911, '27–'44, LS 129*
Beaufort (T)	11556–'683, '784–'904	*LS 130–'49, ML 430–'76, '89–524, '40–'86, '99–635, '49–'92, 705–'22*
Blenheim V	9874, '5	*AD 657, '61*
Beaufighter I	9562–'7, '9–70, '3–711, 10194–'271, '419–'543	*R 2052–'7, '9, '60, '3–'101, '20–'59, '80–'209, '40–'69, T 3228–'50, '70–'2, '90–'333, '48–'55, V 8219–'33, '46–'89, '307–'56, '70–'85*
Beaufighter II	9568, '71, '2, '712–'861, 10044–'193, '272–'418	*R 2058, '61, '2, '270–'84, '300–'49, '70–'404, '30–'79, T 3009–'55, '70–'107, '37–'83, '210–'27, '356–'89, '410–'47, V 8131–'70, '84–'218*
Beaufighter VIF	10544–'961, '1684–'783, '2305–'454	*V 8386–'419, '33–'72, '89–'528, '45–'94, '608–'57, '71–'720, '33–'78, '99–'848, '62–'901, BT 286–303, MM 838–'87, '99–948, ND 139–'86, '98–243, '55–'99, 312–'22*
Buckingham	11332–'5, '905–'2023	*DX 249, '55, '9, '66, KV 301–'46, '58–'72, 402–'50, '71–'9*
Buckmaster	12024–'135	*TJ 714, '7, RP 122–'56, '70–215, '28–'46, VA 359–'68*
Brigand I	12455–'7, '629–'709, '26–'9, '837–'68, '76, '901	*MX 988, '91, '4, TX 374, RH 742–'77, '92–832, '50–'2, VS 828–'39, '54–'77, WA 560, WB 236*
Brigand Met. 3	12710–'25	*VS 812–'27*
Brigand T.4	12877–'85	*WA 561–'9*
Brabazon I	12759 (Mk 1), 12870 (Mk 2)	*G-AGPW (VX 206), VX 343*
Type 170: Mk I	12732, '56, '61, '2, '88, '812	*G-AGVC, 'ICM, 'R, 'S, 'LX, 'MW*
Mk IA	12737, '49–'54, '8, '60, '4, '5, '8, '9, '70, '1, '87, '93	*G-AHJE (LV-XII), LV-XIJ, 'L-'X, G-AILW, 'MC*
Mk II	12730, '8, '9, '89	*G-AGPV, 'HJF, 'G, R 37 ('ILY)*
Mk IIA	12733–'6, '40–'3, '6, '7, '63, '81, '802	*G-AGUT, 'HJB-'D, 'H–'K, 'N, 'O, 'ICT, 'FV, F-BCJA*
Mk IIB	12731	*G-AGVB*
Mk IIC	12744, '5	*VT-CGV, 'W (G-AHJL, 'M)*
Mk XI	12766, '92	*G-AIFF, SE-BNG*
Mk XIA	12795	*ZS-BVI (G-AIME)*
Mk 21	12755, '7, '73, '4, '6, '82, '4, '5, '91, '7, '8	*G-AICL (VH-INJ), EC-ADI, F-BEND, 'C, EC-ADH, F-BECR, G-AIFY, G 776, G-AIMA, EC-AEG, F-BECT*
Mk 21E	12748, '67, '72, '5, '7–'9, '80, '3, '6, '90, '4, '9, '801, '5, '7, '9	*F-BENH, SA-AAD, 'C, G-AIFO (VP-YHZ), EC-ADK, 'L, VP-YHW, G 775, SA-AAB, EC-AEH, SA-AAA, 'E, WB 482, F-BENX, WB 483, '4, F-BENV*
Mk 21P	12796, '800, '3, '4, '6, '8, '10, '1, '3–'9, '20–5, '928–'36	*G 789, '90, '80, '2, '77, '91, '83–'8, '92–'809*
Mk 31	12826–'31, '927, '3058–'61, '72, '80, '1, '124, '34–'43, '62, '5, '210, '14–'6, '8, '50, '3, '5	*WH 575, WJ 320, ZK-AYH, G-AINN–'O, CF-GBT, NZ 5904–'8, G-AMLJ, NZ 5909, Iraq 330, '1, NZ 5910, '1, CF-FZU, 'TFX-'Z, F-VNAR, 'S, G-AMSA, Burma UB 721, F-OAOT, 'U, Burma UB 722, Iraq 368, '9, G-ANMF, NZ 5912, G-APLH, RCAF 9850, ZK-BVM*
Mk 31C	13079, '217	*RCAF 9698, XJ 470*
Mk 31E	12937, '3074–'8, 125, '6, '9, '30	*EI-AFQ, G-AMLL, EC-WHN, EI-AFT, EC-WHO, G-AMLP, EC-AHH–'K*
Mk 31M	13154–'61, '3, '4, '6–'93, '219, '49	*PAF S 4401–'38, RCAF 9699–'700*
Mk 31M (NZ)	12832–'4	*NZ 5901–'3*
Mk 32	13073, '127, '8, '31–'3, '211–'3, '251, '2, '4, '6–'9, '60–'3	*G-AMWA–'F, 'NWG–'I, 'VR, 'S, 'WJ, 'PAU, 'OUU, 'V, 'NWK–'N, 'PAV*

Type	Sequence Numbers	Identification
Conversions since first delivery:—		
to I	12736, '8	*G-AHJD, 'F*
to IIA	12730, '39 '44	*G-AGPV, 'HJG, 'JL*
to 21	12731, '8, '9, '41, '2, '66, '81	*G-AGVB, 'HJF, 'G, 'I, 'J, 'IFF, 'V*
to 21E	12735, '46, '61, '3, '76, '95, '812	*G-AHJC, 'N, 'ICR, 'T, 'FR, 'ME, 'W*
to 21P	12745, '7	*G 779, '81*
to 31	12732, '3176, '87	*G-AGVC, VH-TBA, 'B*
to 31C	12829, '30	*RCAF 9697, '6*
to 31E	13154, '5, '216	*ZK-CAL, 'M, G-ANMF*
to 32	13078, '142	*G-AMLP, 'SA*
Type 171 (Sycamore):		
Mk 1	12835, '6	*VL 958, '63 (G-ALOU)*
Mk 2	12869	*VW 905 (G-AJGU)*
Mk 3	12886–'8, '91, '2, '4, '6	*G-ALSR, WA 576, '7, WT 933, G-ALSX, A 91–1, WT 939*
Mk 3A	13068, '9	*G-AMWG, 'H*
Mk 4	13070, '1, '194, '9, '200–'3, '70, '403, '506, '7	*G-AMWI–'K, OT-ZKA–'C, A 91–2, G-AMWU, 'OBM (CF-HVX), 'DL (VH-INO), 2 spare a/f*
HC 10	12889	*WA 578 (G-ALSU)*
HC 11	12890, '˄, '5, '7	*WT 923–'6*
HR 12	12898– ˅00, '3062	*WV 781–'4*
HR 13	13066, '7	*XD 196, '7*
HR 14	13144, '5, '9–'53, '95–'8, '220–'9, '39–'48, '64–'9, '71–'3, '368–'92, '402, '4–'6, '8–'10, '2–'5, '7, '38, '41, '4, '7, '60, '8, '71, '4	*XE 306–'22, XF 265–'9, XJ 362–'4, '80, '1, XG 500–'6, '8–'23, '38–'49, XJ 383–'5, XG 507, XJ 895–'8, 915–'9, XL 821, '3, '4, '7–'9, '20, '2, '5, '6*
Mk 50	13063–'5	*XA 219–'21*
Mk 51	13146–'8, '401, '7, '504, '5	*XD 654–'6, XK 902, XL, 507, XN 448, 635 (became XR 592)*
Mk 52	13411, '6, '39, '40, '2, '3, '5, '6, '58, '9, '61–'7, '9–'70, '2, '3, '5–'503	*AS 321–'30, BA 176–'8, BB 176–'8, BD 176–'8, CA 327, '8, CB 011–'9, CC 061–'9, DA 391, '2, DB 391, '2, GA 119, '247, GB 117, SC 201–'4*
Type 173	12871, '2, '3204–'6	*G-ALBN (XF 785), 'MJI (XH 379), XE 286–'8*
Type 175 (Britannia):		
101	12873–'5	*G-ALBO, 'RX,* F/Mock-up
102	12902–'16	*G-ANBA–'O* (BOAC)
301	12917	*G-ANCA*
302	12918, '9 ⎱	*XA-MEC, 'D* (Aeronaves de Mexico
307	12920, '1 ⎰ built at Belfast	*G-ANCD, 'E* (BUA)
308	12922, '3	*LV-GJB, 'C* (Transcontinental)
309	12924	*9G-AAG* (Ghana)
311/319	13207	*G-AOVA (9G-AAH)* (Ghana)
312	13230, '1, '5, '8, '2925, '6, '3418–'24, '9, '30, '27	*G-AOVB–'T* (BOAC)
313	13232–'4, '431	*4X-AGA–'D* (El Al)
314	13393–'6, '453 (Belfast); '28 (Filton)	*CF-CZA–'D, 'W; 'X* (CPAL)
317	13425, '6	*G-APNA, 'B* (BUA)
318	13432, '3, '7, '515	*CU-T668–'71* (Cubana)
324	13516, '7	*CF-CPD, 'E (G-ARKA, 'B), (CPAL, BUA)*
252 (C. Mk 2)	13450–'2 (built at Belfast)	*G-APPE–'G (XN 392, '8, 404)*
253 (C. Mk 1)	13397–'400, '34–'6, '448, '9, '54 ⎱ Belfast '7, '508, '9 ⎰	*XL 635–'8, XM 489–'91, XL 639, '40, '57–'60, XM 496, '7*
	13510–'4 (built at Filton)	*XM 498, 517–'20*
Type 191	13274–'6	Completed as Test-Rigs Nos. *1, 2, 3* (were *XG 354–'6*)
Type 192 (Belvedere)	13342–'67 (to Westland)	*XG 447–'68, 73–'6*
Type 188	13518, '9	*XF 923, '6*
Type 198	13520	Not built, to Concorde 002
Type 221	13521 (ex. F.9421—F.D.2)	*WG 774*

393

Appendix C

Aircraft built at Filton but not of Bristol design or origin

Type	Biplane or Monoplane	Sequence Numbers	Identification
Zodiac	B	1. (2–6 cancelled)	
B.E.2a	B	114–'7, 140, '1, 168–'74, '90–'5	222, '5–'42
B.E.2b	B	212–'7	including 396, '7, 487
B.E.8	B	201, '2, '8–'11	including 636, '56
B.E.10	B	343–'6 (not completed)	1648–'51
B.E.2c	B	348–'93, 400–'49, 621–770	1652–'747, 4070–'219
B.E.2c (s/s)	B	561–'70	4700–'9
B.E.2d/e	B	894–1043, '174–'373	5730–'879, 7058–'257
B.E.2e	B	1487–'836, 2519–'718	A 2733–'982, 8626–'725, B 4401–'600
Panther	B	5715–'864, '89–'90, 6128–'39, '49 –'52	N 7400–'549, 2 USN, 16 spare a/f
Siskin IIIA	B	7179–'220, '69–'73, '74–'300, '59 –'63, '404–'18	J 8822–'63, 5 recond., J 9304–'30, 5 recond., J 9897–'911
Audax	B	7845–'985	K 5201–'56, 7469–'553
Tempest II	M	12176–'225 ('6–'304, '458–'628 cancelled)	MW 375–'423, '435
*Concorde 002	M	13520	G-BSST
*Concorde 01	M	13522	G-AXDN
*Concorde (202)	M	13523	G-BBDG
*Concorde (204)	M	13524†	G-BOAC (G-N81AC from 7.1.79 to 7.8.80)
*Concorde (206)	M	13525†	G-BOAA (G-N94AA from 7.1.79 to 30.7.80)
* Concorde (208)	M	13526†	G-BOAB (G-N94AB from 7.1.79 to 15.9.80)
*Concorde (210)	M	13527†	G-BOAD (G-N94AD from 7.1.79 to 20.6.80)
*Concorde (212)	M	13528†	G-BOAE (G-N94AE from 7.1.79 to 26.6.80)
*Concorde (214)	M	13529†	G-BFKW (until 28.1.81 then G-BOAG)
*Concorde (216)	M	13530†	G-BOAF

* Design and construction shared by BAC and S.N.I.A.S. (formerly Sud-Aviation), with final assembly and first flight at Filton.

† In 1973 it was decided to cease using Sequence or Constructor's Numbers and to use thereafter Airframe Serial Numbers instead. Thus, the relevant aircraft were duly assigned the following:

Type	Airframe Serial No.	Type	Airframe Serial No.
Concorde (204)	100/004	Concorde (212)	100/012
Concorde (206)	100/006	Concorde (214)	100/014
Concorde (208)	100/008	Concorde (216)	100/016
Concorde (210)	100/010		

Concorde 002 G-BSST taking off from Filton on 9 April 1969—its maiden flight from Filton to Fairford, where it was based for initial handling and performance tests.

Appendix D

Aircraft of Bristol design built by licensees or other contractors

Type	Manufacturer	Quantity	Identification
Coanda Mil. M.	Caproni & Faccanoni, Vizzola Ticino, Italy	2	One became s/n 196 at Filton
„ „ „	Deutsche Bristol-Werke, Halberstadt, Germany	not known	
Coanda-Daimler Biplane	„ „	„	
Coanda T.B.8 ⎫ Coanda S.S.A ⎭	S.A. des Ateliers d'Aviation Louis Breguet, Vélizy & Douai, France	„ „	
F.2B (Arab)	Gloucestershire Aircraft Co. Ltd., Cheltenham	300	C 9836–'985, E 9507–'656
„ „	Marshall & Sons Ltd., Gainsborough, Lincs.	150	D2626–'775
„ „	Sir W. G. Armstrong Whitworth & Co. Ltd., Gosforth & Elswick, Newcastle-on-Tyne	250	E 1901–2150
„ „	Angus Sanderson & Co. Ltd., Newcastle-on-Tyne	250	E 2651–'900
„ „	Standard Motor Car Co. Ltd., Coventry	74	E 5179–'428 (E 5253–'308 to Filton, E 5309–'428 cancelled)
„ „	Harris & Sheldon Ltd., Birmingham	100	F 5074–'173
F.2B (Hispano 200 hp)	Cunard Steamship Co. Ltd., National Aircraft Factory No. 3, Aintree, Lancs.	126	D 2126–'625 (D 2252–'625 cancelled)
F.2B (Puma)	Gloucestershire Aircraft Co. Ltd., Cheltenham	135	H 926–1060
„ „	Austin Motors Ltd., Longbridge, Birmingham	2	H 6055, '8
F.2B (Liberty) (USA O-1)	Curtiss Aeroplane & Motor Corporation, Buffalo, N.Y.	27	(1973 cancelled)
F.2B (Hispano 300 hp)	U.S. Army Engineering Div., McCook Field, Dayton, Ohio	nil	(2000 cancelled)
XB-1A (Wright H 300 hp)	„ „	1	P 90
„ „	Dayton-Wright Airplane Co., Dayton, Ohio	40	incl. P 151, P 180, P 205
Bulldog (JSSF)	Nakajima Aircraft Works, Tokyo, Japan	2	Navy 701
Bombay I	Short & Harland Ltd., Queen's Island, Belfast	50	L 5808–'57
Blenheim I	A. V. Roe & Co. Ltd., Chadderton, Lancs.	250	L 6594–'843 (L 6764–'73 to Finland) (L 6696–'708 to Rumania) (L 6813, '4, '7–'34 to Yugoslavia)
„	Rootes Securities Ltd., Speke, Liverpool, Lancs.	380	L 8362–'407, '33–'82, '500–'49, '97–'632, '52–'701, '14–'61, '76–'800, '27–'76, 9020–'44
„	Ikarus A.D., Zemun, Yugoslavia	16	(+ 24 destroyed before completion)
„	Valtion Lentokonetehdas, Tampere, Finland	45	BL 146–'90

Type	Manufacturer	Quantity	Identification
Bolingbroke I	Fairchild Aircraft Ltd., Longueuil, P.Q., Canada	18	RCAF 702–'19 (705 conv. to Mk II) (717 conv. to Mk III)
,, IV	,, ,,	185	RCAF 9001–'4, '6–'9, '24–'73, '75–'201
,, IV-W	,, ,,	15	RCAF 9005, '10–'23
,, IV-C	,, ,,	1	RCAF 9074
,, IV-T	,, ,,	457	RCAF 9851–10256 (+ 51 spare airframes)
Blenheim IV	A. V. Roe & Co. Ltd., Chadderton, Lancs.	750	N 3522–'45, '51–'75, '78–'604, '8–'31, R 2770–'99, Z 5721–'70, '94–'818, '60–'909, '47–'91, 6021–'50, '70–'104', '44–'93, '239–'83, '333–'82, '416–'55, 9533–'52, '72–'621, '47–'81, '706–'55, '92–'836
,,	Rootes Securities Ltd., Speke, Liverpool, Lancs. and Blythe Bridge, Staffs.	2100	L 9170–'218, '37–'73, '94–'342, '75–'422, '46–'82, R 3590–'639, '60–'709, '30–'79, '800–'49, '70–'919, T 1793–'832, '48–'97, '921–'60, '85–2004, '31–'80, '112–'41, '61–'90, '216–'55, '73–'92, '318–'57, '81–'400, '25–'44, V 5370–'99 '420–'69, '90–'539, '60–'99, '620–'59, '80–'99,' 720–'69, '90–'829, '50–'99, '920–'69, '90–6039, '60–'99, '120–'49, '70–'99, '220–'69, '90–'339, '60–'99, '420–'69, '90–'529, Z 7271–'320, '40–'74, '406–'55, '83–'522, '77–'96, '610–'54', '78–'712, '54–'803, '41–'60, '79–'928, '58–'92
,,	Valtion Lentokonetehdas, Tampere, Finland	10	BL 196–205 (+5 not completed)
Blenheim V	Rootes Securities Ltd., Blythe Bridge, Staffs.	942	AZ 861–905, '22–'71, '84–'99, BA 100–'18, '33–'72, '91–215, '28–'62, '87–336, '65–409, '24–'58, '71–505, '22–'46, '75–624, '47–'91, 708–'57, '80–829, '44–'88, 907–'51, '78–'99, BB 100–'2, '35–'84, DJ 702, '7, EH 310–'55, '71–420, '38–'74, '91–517
Beaufort V	Beaufort Division, Dept. of Aircraft Production, Mascot & Fishermen's Bend, Australia	50	T 9540–'69, '83–'602 (became A 9–1 to A 9–50)
,, VA	,, ,,	30	A 9–151 to A 9–180
,, VI	,, ,,	40	A 9–51 to A 9–90 (ex T 9603–'18, '24–'47,
,, VII	,, ,,	60	A 9–91 to A 9–150
,, VIII	,, ,,	520	A 9–181 to A 9–700
,, IX	(converted from VIII)	46	A 9–701 to A 9–746
Beaufighter IF	Fairey Aviation Co. Ltd., Stockport, Cheshire	25	T 4623–'47
,, ,,	M.A.P., Old Mixon Shadow Factory, Weston-super-Mare, Somerset	240	X 7540–'89, '610–'49, '70–'719, '40–'849, '70–'9
,, IC	Fairey Aviation Co. Ltd., Stockport, Cheshire	300	T 4648–'70 , '700–'34, '51–'800, '23–'46, '62–'99, '915–'9, A 19-1 to A 19-12, T 4932–'42, A 19-13 to A 19-26, T 4979–'90, A 19-27 to A 19-40, T 5005–'7, '27–'46, A 19-41 to A 19-54, T 5075–'99
,, VIF	M.A.P., Old Mixon Shadow Factory, Weston-super-Mare, Somerset	260	X 7880–'99, '920–'4, '6–'36, '40–'69, 8000–'29, '100–'9, '30–'69, '90–'229, '50–'69, EL 145–'92, 213–'8
,, ,,	Rootes Securities Ltd., Blythe Bridge, Staffs.	150	KV 896–944, '60–'81, KW 101–'33, '47–'71, '83–203

Type	Manufacturer	Quantity	Identification
Beaufighter VIC	Fairey Aviation Co. Ltd., Stockport, Cheshire	175	*T 5100–'14, '30–'75, '95–'200, '50–'99, '315–'52*
,, ,,	M.A.P., Old Mixon Shadow Factory, Weston-super-Mare, Somerset	518	*X 7925, '37–'9, 8030–'9, '60–'99, EL 219–'46, '59–305, '21–'70, '85–418, '31–'79, '97–534, JL 421–'54, 502–'49, '65–'82, '84–'92, 619–'28, '39–'48, '59, 704–'12, '23–'35, '56–'79, 812–'26, '36–'55, '69–'75*
,, VI(ITF)	,, ,,	60	*JL 583, '93, 610–'8, '29–'38, '49–'58, 713–'22, 827–'35, '49–'57, JM 104*
,, XIC	,, ,,	163	*JL 876–915, '37–'48, JM 105–'36, '58–'85, 206–'50, '62–'7*
,, T.F.X	,, ,,	2095	*JM 268–'91, 315–'56, '79–417, LX 779–827, '45–'86, '98–914, '26–'59, '72–'99, LZ 113–'58, '72–201, '15–'47, '60–'97, 314–'46, '59–'84, '97–419, '32–'65, '79–'95, 515–'44, NE 193–232, '45–'60, '82–326, '39–'86, '98–446, '59–502, '15–'59, '72–615, '27–'69, '82–724, '38–'79, '92–832, NT 888–929, '42–'71, '83–'99, NV 113–'58, '71–218, '33–'76, '89–333, '47–'90, 413–'57, '70–513, '26–'72, '85–632, RD 130–'76, '89–225, '39–'85, '98–335, '48–'96, 420–'68, '83–525, '38–'80, 685–728, '42–'89, 801–'36, '49–'67, SR 910–'9*
,, ,,	Rootes Securities Ltd., Blythe Bridge, Staffs.	110	*KW 277–'98, 315–'55, '70–416*
,, T.F.21	Beaufort Division, Dept. of Aircraft Production, Australia	364	*A 8-1* to *A 8-364*
Britannia 252	Short Bros. & Harland, Ltd., Queen's Island, Belfast	3	see Appendix B
,, 253	,, ,,	15	,,
,, 300	,, ,,	2	Completed Filton as 302
,, 305	,, ,,	5	,, ,, 307–309
,, 314	,, ,,	5	*CF-CZA–'D, 'W* (see Appendix B)
Britannia derivatives	designed and built by:–		
CL-28 Argus Mk 1	Canadair Ltd., Cartierville,	13	RCAF *20710–'22*
CL-28 Argus Mk 2	Montreal, Canada	20	RCAF *20723–'42*
CL-44-6 Yukon	,, ,,	12	RCAF *15501* (later *15555) 15922* (later *16666), 15923–'32*
CL-44 D 4	,, ,,	24	*CF-MKP-X* (later CL-44 J *TF-LLH* for Loftleidir) *N123SW* to *N127SW, N228SW N229SW* for Seaboard World Airlines *N446T* to *N455T, N1001T, N1002T* for The Flying Tiger Line *N602SA* to *N605SA* for Slick Airways
CL-44 J ('Rolls-Royce 400')	,, ,,	3	*TF-LLF, 'G, 'I* for Loftleidir
CL-44-O (Conroy Airlifter)	converted by Conroy Aircraft Corp., Santa Barbara, Calif., U.S.A.	(1)	*N447T* for Conroy Airlift

Bibliography

Apart from unpublished private papers and Company archives, the following published sources have been consulted by the author, and are recommended to the reader in amplification and support of this history:

General

DORMAN, G.: *Fifty Years' Fly Past* (Forbes Robertson, London 1950)

GIBBS-SMITH, C. H.: *The Aeroplane: An Historical Summary* (H.M.S.O., London 1960)

TAYLOR, J. W. R.: *C.F.S.: The Birthplace of Air Power* (Putnam, London 1958)

THETFORD, O. G.: *Aircraft of the Royal Air Force since 1918* (Putnam, London 1960)

THETFORD, O. G.: *British Naval Aircraft since 1912* (Putnam, London 1960)

1910–1914

DALLAS-BRETT, R.: *History of British Aviation, 1908–1914* (Hamilton, London 1933)

FARMAN, DICK & HENRY: *The Aviator's Companion* (Mills & Boon, London 1910)

GAMBLE, C. F. S.: *The Air Weapon, Vol. I* (Oxford U.P., London 1931)

GARDNER, C. (ed.): *Fifty Years of Brooklands (Pt. II)* (Heinemann, London 1956)

LEWIS, P. M. H.: *British Aeroplanes, 1809–1914* (Putnam, London 1962)

SAHEL, J.: *Henry Farman et l'Aviation* (Bernard Grasset, Paris 1936)

TURNER, C. C.: *The Old Flying Days* (Sampson Low, London 1927)

1914–1918

BRUCE, J. M.: *British Aeroplanes, 1914–1918* (Putnam, London 1957)

GAMBLE, C. F. S.: *The Story of a North Sea Air Station* (Oxford U.P., London 1928)

HALLAM, T. D. (PIX): *The Spider Web* (Blackwood, Edinburgh 1919)

JONES, H. A.: *The War in the Air, Vols. II–VI* (Clarendon, Oxford 1928)

RALEIGH, Sir W.: *The War in the Air, Vol. I* (Clarendon, Oxford 1922)

SAUNDERS, H. St. G.: *Per Ardua* (Oxford U.P., London 1944)

SUTHERLAND, L. W.: *Aces and Kings* (Hamilton, London, n.d.)

1919–1939

BOUGHTON, T.: *The Story of the British Light Aeroplane* (Murray, London 1963)

BURGE, C. G. (ed.): *Air Annual of the British Empire, Vols. I–IV* (Gale & Polden, London 1929–32); *Vols. V–X* (Pitman, London 1933–39)

GREY, C. G.: *History of the Air Ministry* (Allen & Unwin, London 1940)

HIGHAM, R.: *British Imperial Air Routes, 1918–1939* (Foulis, London 1960)

JACKSON, A. J. *British Civil Aircraft, 1919–1959, Vol. I* (Putnam, London 1959)

LONDONDERRY, MARQUESS OF: *Wings of Destiny* (Macmillan, London 1943)

ROTHERMERE, VISCOUNT: *My Fight to Rearm Britain* (Eyre & Spottiswoode, London 1939)

TEMPLEWOOD, VISCOUNT: *Empire of the Air* (Collins, London 1957)

1939–1945

BALCHIN, N.: *The Aircraft Builders* (H.M.S.O., London 1947)

BARKER, R.: *The Ship Busters* (Chatto & Windus, London 1957)

BRYANT, A.: *The Turn of the Tide* (Collins, London 1957)

C.O.I.: *Wings of the Phoenix* (H.M.S.O., London 1949)

CHISHOLM, R.: *Cover of Darkness* (Chatto & Windus, London 1953)

FARRER, D.: *The Sky's the Limit* (Hutchinson, London 1942)

GIBBS, R. P. M.: *Not Peace but a Sword* (Cassell, London 1943)

'GORDON, T. D.': *Coastal Command at War* (Jarrolds, London, n.d.)

HARRIS, Sir A. T.: *Bomber Offensive* (Collins, London 1947)

HUSKINSON, P.: *Vision Ahead* (Werner Laurie, London 1949)

JOHNSON, F.: *R.A.A.F. Over Europe* (Eyre & Spottiswoode, London 1946)

MACMILLAN, N.: *The Royal Air Force in the World War, Vol. I* (Harrap, London 1942)

MITCHELL, A. W.: *New Zealanders in the Air War* (Harrap, London 1945)

POSTAN, M. M.: *British War Production* (H.M.S.O. & Longmans, London 1952)

RAWNSLEY, C. F. & WRIGHT, R.: *Night Fighter* (Collins, London 1957)

RICHARDS, D. & SAUNDERS, H. ST. G.: *Royal Air Force, 1939–1945 (3 Vols.)* (H.M.S.O., London 1953–54)

ROWE, A. P.: *One Story of Radar* (Cambridge U.P., Cambridge 1948)

STEWART, O.: *Air Power and the Expanding Community* (Newnes, London 1944)

WISDOM, T. H.: *Wings over Olympus* (Allen & Unwin, London 1942)

WYKEHAM, P.: *Fighter Command* (Putnam, London 1960)

Company Histories

PUDNEY, J.: *Bristol Fashion* (Putnam, London 1960)

PUDNEY, J.: *The Seven Skies (B.O.A.C.)* (Putnam, London 1959)

SCOTT, J. D.: *Vickers: A History* (Weidenfeld & Nicholson, London 1962)

Aero-Engines

ANGLE, G. D.: *Airplane Engine Encyclopedia* (Otterbein, Dayton, Ohio 1921)

BURLS, G. A.: *Aero Engines* (Griffin, London 1915)

FEDDEN, SIR R.: *The First 25 Years of the Bristol Engine Department (7th Barnwell Memorial Lecture)*, J. Roy. Aero. Soc., **65** (London, May 1961)

NOCKOLDS, R.: *The Magic of a Name (Rolls-Royce)* (Foulis, London 1950)

OWNER, F. M.: *Bristol Gas Turbines—The First Decade (9th Barnwell Memorial Lecture)*, J. Roy. Aero. Soc. **67** (London, July 1963)

SCHLAIFER, R.: *Development of Aircraft Engines* (Harvard, Boston, Mass. 1950)

WILSON, C. H. & READER, W. J.: *Men and Machines: (D. Napier & Son)* (Weidenfeld & Nicholson, London 1958)

Helicopters

HAFNER, R.: *The Domain of the Helicopter (7th Louis Bleriot Lecture)*, J. Roy. Aero. Soc., **58** (London, October 1954)

HAFNER, R.: *The Helicopter, The First of the VTOL Aircraft* (J. Roy. Aero. Soc., **65** (London, December 1961)

Biographies

BRABAZON OF TARA, LORD: *The Brabazon Story* (Heinemann, London 1956)

BULMAN, G. P.: *Captain F. S. Barnwell (1st Barnwell Memorial Lecture)*, J. Roy. Aero. Soc. **58** (London, June 1954)

CLOUSTON, A. E.: *The Dangerous Skies* (Cassell, London 1954)

EMBRY, Sir B. E.: *Mission Completed* (Methuen, London 1957)

JOUBERT, SIR P.: *The Fated Sky* (Hutchinson, London 1952)

KINGSFORD-SMITH, SIR C.: *My Flying Life* (Melrose, London 1937)

MACMILLAN, N.: *Sir Sefton Brancker* (Heinemann, London 1935)

MACMILLAN, N.: *Freelance Pilot* (Heinemann, London 1937)

MERRIAM, F. W.: *First Through The Clouds* (Batsford, London 1954)

PEGG, A. J. (Bill): *Sent Flying* (Macdonald, London 1959)

SLESSOR, SIR J.: *The Central Blue* (Cassell, London 1956)

TURNER, C. C.: *My Flying Scrap Book* (Sampson Low, London 1940)

WALLACE, G.: *Flying Witness (Harry Harper)* (Putnam, London 1958)

WALLACE, G.: *Claude Grahame-White* (Putnam, London 1960)

WHITTLE, Sir F.: *Jet: The Story of a Pioneer* (Muller, London 1953)

Index—General

(For Aircraft & Engines see pp. 411-415)

Aircraft and Engines